DIVIDING THE CIRCLE
The Development of Critical Angular Measurement
in Astronomy 1500–1850
Second edition

WILEY-PRAXIS SERIES IN ASTRONOMY AND ASTROPHYSICS
Series Editor: JOHN MASON, B.Sc., Ph.D.

Few subjects have been at the centre of such important developments or seen such a wealth of new and exciting, if sometimes controversial, data as modern astronomy, astrophysics and cosmology. This series reflects the very rapid and significant progress being made in current research, as a consequence of new instrumentation and observing techniques, applied right across the electromagnetic spectrum, computer modelling and modern theoretical methods.

The crucial links between observation and theory are emphasised, putting into perspective the latest results from the new generations of astronomical detectors, telescopes and space-borne instruments. Complex topics are logically developed and fully explained and, where mathematics is used, the physical concepts behind the equations are clearly summarised.

These books are written principally for professional astronomers, astrophysicists, cosmologists, physicists and space scientists, together with post-graduate and undergraduate students in these fields. Certain books in the series will appeal to amateur astronomers, high-flying 'A'-level students, and non-scientists with a keen interest in astronomy and astrophysics.

ROBOTIC OBSERVATORIES

Michael F. Bode, Professor of Astrophysics and Assistant Provost for Research, Liverpool John Moores University, UK

THE AURORA: Sun-Earth Interactions

Neil Bone, School of Biological Sciences, University of Sussex, Brighton, UK

PLANETARY VOLCANISM: A Study of Volcanic Activity in the Solar System, Second edition

Peter Cattermole, formerly Lecturer in Geology, Department of Geology, Sheffield University, UK, now Principal Investigator with NASA's Planetary Geology and Geophysics Programme

DIVIDING THE CIRCLE: The Development of Critical Angular Measurement in Astronomy 1500-1850 Second edition

Allan Chapman, Wadham College, University of Oxford, UK

THE DUSTY UNIVERSE

Aneurin Evans, Department of Physics, University of Keele, UK

MARS AND THE DEVELOPMENT OF LIFE

Anders Hansson, Ph.D.

ASTEROIDS: Their Nature and Utilization, Second edition

Charles T. Kowal, Computer Sciences Corp., Space Telescope Science Institute, Baltimore, Maryland, USA

COMET HALLEY - Investigations, Results, Interpretations
Volume 1: Organization, Plasma, Gas
Volume 2: Dust, Nucleus, Evolution

Editor: John Mason, B.Sc., Ph.D.

ELECTRONIC AND COMPUTER-AIDED ASTRONOMY: From Eyes to Electronic Sensors

Ian. S. McLean, Department of Astronomy, University of California at Los Angeles, California, USA

URANUS: The Planet, Rings and Satellites

Ellis D. Miner, Cassini Project Science Manager, NASA Jet Propulsion Laboratory, Pasadena, California, USA

THE PLANET NEPTUNE: An Historical Survey Before Voyager, Second edition

Patrick Moore, CBE, D.Sc.(Hon.)

ACTIVE GALACTIC NUCLEI

Ian Robson, Director, James Clerk Maxwell Telescope, Head Joint Astronomy Centre, Hawaii, USA

ASTRONOMICAL OBSERVATIONS OF ANCIENT EAST ASIA

Richard Stephenson, Department of Physics, University of Durham, UK; Zhentao Xu, Purple Mountain Observatory, Academia Sinica, Nanjing, China; Yaotiao Tiang, Department of Astronomy, Nanjing University, China

THE HIDDEN UNIVERSE

Roger J. Tayler, Astronomy Centre, University of Sussex, Brighton, UK

DIVIDING THE CIRCLE

The Development of Critical Angular Measurement
in Astronomy 1500–1850
Second edition

Allan Chapman, M.A., D.Phil., F.R.A.S.
Wadham College, Oxford, and
Faculty of Modern History, University of Oxford

JOHN WILEY & SONS
Chichester • New York • Brisbane • Toronto • Singapore

PRAXIS

Published in association with
PRAXIS PUBLISHING
Chichester

First published in 1990
This Second Edition published in 1995 by
John Wiley & Sons Ltd in
association with Praxis Publishing Ltd

Wiley Editorial Offices

John Wiley & Sons Ltd, Baffins Lane,
Chichester, West Sussex PO19 1UD, England

John Wiley & Sons, Inc., 605 Third Avenue,
New York, NY 10158-0012, USA

Jacaranda Wiley Ltd, G.P.O. Box 859, Brisbane
Queensland 4001, Australia

John Wiley & Sons (Canada) Ltd, 22 Worcester Road,
Rexdale, Ontario M9W 1L1, Canada

John Wiley & Sons (SEA) Pte Ltd, 37 Jalan Pemimpin 05-04,
Block B, Union Industrial Building, Singapore 2057

A catalogue record for this book is available from the British Library

ISBN 0-471-96169-8

Printed and bound in Great Britain by Hartnolls Ltd, Bodmin

Table of contents

Preface   6

Acknowledgements   7

List of plates   9

1   Instruments and history   11

2   The Tychonic school and its approach to instrumentation   16

3   John Flamsteed and the astronomy of the 'Great Catalogue'   34

4   Dividing as a high art   66

5   The techniques of eighteenth-century positional astronomy   82

6   The achievements of eighteenth-century positional astronomy   98

7   The precision graduation of full circles   108

8   Dividing by machine   123

9   The London scientific instrument-making trade   138

10   The technical frontier; astronomical instruments and the cosmological framework   146

11   The archaeology of the graduated scale   153

Appendix 1: The practical operation of the dividing engine   158

Appendix 2: A Victorian 'Garret Master's' dividing engine?   160

Appendix 3: The Radcliffe Equatorial Sector of 1775: John Bird's last instrument   162

Notes and references   165

Select bibliography   205

Index   207

Preface

The present book is based upon a doctoral thesis that was successfully submitted to the University of Oxford in 1978. It attempts to examine the historical importance of instruments, and the emerging concept of accuracy in the development of astronomy over the period 1500–1850, when the astronomer's foremost task was the measurement of celestial positions.

The quality of evidence produced by astronomers occupied a vital role in man's understanding of the natural world over the period, especially in the explication of such problems as the Earth's motion in space and the acceptance of Newtonianism. The giving of precise numerical values to angular quantities postulated by the theorists was of central importance historically, and depended at all times upon the quality of instruments available.

It is argued that three major technical breakthroughs in instrument making made possible the extension of astronomical knowledge, when the 'frontiers' imposed by an existing technological level were broken through, to provide substantiation for further conclusions in theoretical astronomy.

At all times, the book pays close attention to the details of technical innovation, how instruments were constructed, adjusted and used, but places this discussion within the wider framework of current astronomical theory and the importance of the scientific problems that the improving instruments were called upon to solve.

The book is based upon original research, in a field hitherto almost untouched by modern scholars.

Acknowledgements

In the production of the following book, it has been necessary to seek the advice and assistance of many persons. Foremost amongst them must be Professor Gerald L'E. Turner, of Imperial College, London, whose knowledge of instruments and guidance have been a most valuable asset over the years. I am also indebted to him for suggestions regarding the manuscript of this book and his extensive bibliographical knowledge. Appreciation is also owing to Mr Francis Maddison, former Curator of the Museum of the History of Science, Oxford, along with other members of his staff. I am especially indebted to Tony Simcock of the Museum of the History of Science, however, for his patience, time, and encyclopaedic knowledge of the Museum's collections of objects, books, and manuscripts. It was Tony Simcock who first drew my attention to the parts of the Bird Equatorial Sector, discussed in Appendix 3, and who kindly looked through the text of the second edition of this book.

Also in Oxford my thanks are owed to the staffs of the Bodleian, Radcliffe Science and other libraries, as well as to Mr Francis Petit, of the University Department of Computer Science, for assistance with my researches into the 'archaeology' of the graduated scale.

It would be impossible to thank individually the innumerable people who, over the years, have encouraged me, and clarified and stimulated my ideas, but I must include students, friends, correspondents and colleagues. Especially, I wish to extend thanks to Margaret Gowing, formerly Professor of the History of Science, Oxford, and the Warden and Fellows of Wadham College, who have done so much to provide me with the congenial environment that is essential to all worthwhile activity. Likewise, I thank my wife Rachel, for her assistance with the revised manuscript for this second edition.

Outside Oxford, my first debt is to the staff of the National Maritime Museum, Greenwich, and in particular to Mr Derek Howse, MBE, who for several years has granted me access to the Old Royal Observatory and its collections. I also thank Mr John Dix of the same institution. Likewise, I express my acknowledgements to the Royal Greenwich Observatory, formerly at Herstmonceux, to Dr G. Wilkins and his staff, for generously computing my early micrometer reductions, and to the late

Mr Phillip Laurie, formerly Observatory Archivist. I am also indebted to the late Professor Forbes of Edinburgh, for granting me access to his own work on Flamsteed.

I also owe a great debt of gratitude to the various craftsmen and technicians in Oxford and elsewhere, for their skills and instruction. In particular, I thank Mr Robert Taylor and Mr Brian Busby of the Oxford University Department of Engineering Science workshops, who have always been willing to grant an 'alien' historian access to their domain, not to mention the loan of costly equipment. Similiar thanks go to Mr Ernest Hounslow, the maintenance staff of Wadham College, and numerous other craftsmen who have taught me to work in wood and metal, and thereby learn at first hand the techniques of their callings.

Further, I must extend a general acknowledgement to my friends amongst the amateur astronomers of this country, and especially those of the Salford Astronomical Society, who first taught me how to look at the sky. Last, but by no means least, I thank the craftsmen of the Manchester watchmaking community, from whom I learned so much about practical craftsmanship and the meaning of precision, in the days before 'redevelopment' forced their one-man businessness out of existence.

To my mother and the
memory of my father

List of Plates

Plate no.

1   Elias Allen, fl. 1606–1654.

2   Tycho Brahe's Equatorial Armillary, with one ring.

3   Tycho Brahe's 6-ft sextant.

4   Tycho Brahe's mural quadrant.

5   The 'Nonius' quadrant.

6   Tycho Brahe's 'peg and slit' sights.

7   Tycho Brahe's 'Parallactic Instrument' or Triquetrum.

8 (a)   The cross-staff in use to take lunar angles.

8 (b)   Peter Apian's cross-staff.

9 (a, b, c)   Three early seventeenth century divided scales by (?) Elias Allen.

10   Hevelius' brass sextant.

11   Hevelius' graduated scales.

12   Hevelius' screw-count mechanisms to read off degree fractions.

13   Richard Towneley's micrometer.

14   Suggested geometrical ancestry of the filar micrometer.

15   Interior of the observing chamber in Flamsteed House.

16   Robert Hooke's quadrant and method of screw graduation.

17   Clock-driven equatorial devised by Robert Hooke.

18   Mural quadrant of 10-ft radius, designed for Flamsteed by Hooke, 1676.

19   Seven-foot sextant, built for Flamsteed by Thomas Tompion, 1676.

20   Mural arc, built for Flamsteed by Abraham Sharp, 1688.

21   Screw mechanism of Sharp's mural arc.

22   Detail of the scale and screw mechanism of Flamsteed's sextant.

23   Reconstruction of the diagonal scale of the Sharp/Flamsteed mural arc, 1688.

24   Micrometer and vernier for mural quadrants as perfected by John Bird.

25   Römer's transit instrument, 1675.

26   Transit instrument and fittings, by LaLande.

27   Mural quadrant of 8-ft radius by George Graham, 1725.

28   Vernier scales on Graham's quadrant, 1725.
29   Graduation of Graham's quadrant, 1725.
30   The same scene as Plate 29 artistically re-drawn.
31   John Bird, 1709–1776.
32   The zenith sector in use.
33   The 'Shuckburgh' Equatorial, built by Jesse Ramsden, 1793.
34   Jesse Ramsden's circular dividing engine of c. 1775.
35   The duc du Chaulnes' circular dividing engine of c. 1768.
36   Airy's Transit Circle, 1850, built by Troughton and Simms.
37   Ramsden's five-foot diameter circle for the Palermo Observatory, 1789.
38 (a)   Method for scribing an astrolabe or circle.
38 (b)   Error curves for the four quadrants.
39 (a)   A Victorian 'Garret Master's' dividing engine.
39 (b)   Detail of the graduations on the main wheel.
40   John Bird's Equatorial Sector for the Radcliffe Observatory, Oxford.

Note: Position of Plate Sections

Plates 1 to 12 inclusive appear between pages 30 and 31
Plates 13 to 24 inclusive appear between pages 60 and 61
Plates 25 to 32 inclusive appear between pages 90 and 91
Plates 33 to 40 inclusive appear between pages 120 and 121

1

Instruments and history

The making of accurate angular measurements is one of the fundamental tasks of astronomical research, and from ancient times down to the nineteenth century, the measuring and cataloguing of celestial positions was the astronomer's principal vocation. The accuracy with which it was possible to make such measurements was governed directly by the quality of the instruments, and the reliability of the graduations they carried.

Without improved techniques of 'dividing the circle', celestial mechanics would have been devoid of that foundation of observable data necessary for its growth as an inductive science, while cosmology could never have risen above the level of speculation.

With so much of the Royal Society's achievements based upon the performance of airpumps, clocks and microscopes, it was natural that the best methods of designing and making instruments should assume a leading place amongst their deliberations. The stress on Baconianism, along with the experimental and observational approach to knowledge, emphasized the importance of scientific instruments as the tools which gave precision to the relatively coarse human senses. Instruments came to be seen not only as refinements or aids to human perception, but as the very arbiters in scientific discussion, when the acceptance or otherwise of a theory depended upon the interpretation of observational evidence. The work of Robert Hooke forms a landmark in this respect, for more than any other figure in the early scientific movement, he showed a keen awareness of the instrument as a tool and a limiting factor in research [1].

When one examines the important issues in astronomy between 1500 and 1800, one becomes aware of how the art of dividing the circle prescribed strict barriers to research. This was certainly the case with one of the principal scientific problems of the earlier part of the period, namely, that of the earth's motion in space. Just before 1600, astronomers had agreed that the crucial evidence needed to test the movement or otherwise of the Earth was the detection of stellar parallax. Yet because instruments were incapable of measuring these small quantities until the nineteenth century, the scientific world continued to dispute about what was essentially a piece of observational evidence. It is one of the arguments of this present book that circle dividing established a ceiling of accuracy beyond which astronomical observation could not progress in any one period. Without the ability to accumulate accurate data, theoretical issues could not be settled, so that pressures came to be placed on the craftsmen to produce instruments of yet greater accuracy.

When modern scholars have inquired into the historical importance of astronomical instruments, their attention has usually been directed towards optics, though it might be argued that, until the growth of astrophysics and spectroscopy in the nineteenth century, the optical department of the science remained subservient to the mechanical [2]. It was improved angular measurement, not enhanced visual acuity, that held the key to a whole network of problems from the sixteenth to the early nineteenth centuries, and, with the exception of the discovery of Uranus in 1781, the weight of decisive evidence came from better graduated scales, not better optics.

Though the application of the telescopic sight to angular measurement from the 1660s constituted a major technical breakthrough, the optics involved were simple, conservative in type, and secondary to the engraved divisions. This becomes apparent from the letters, notebooks, and Gresham College lectures of John Flamsteed, the first Astronomer Royal, for while his early decades at Greenwich were beset with instrumental problems, these were almost exclusively of a mechanical nature. The equality of scale degrees, or the regularity of a micrometer screw, claimed more attention than the resolving power of telescope lenses, and nowhere in his extensive writings is more than passing attention paid to optical resolution [3].

Although many innovations in graduation technique took place during the century 1675 to 1775, the optical systems used in the telescopic sights of observatory instruments remained unaltered over the period, and John Bird refused to incorporate achromatic doublets into his instruments, because he considered them to be superfluous [4]. It is true that in the hands of Hadley, Short, Dollond and Herschel the telescope underwent major improvements, yet the fruits of Bird's development, in terms of new discovery, did not occur until after 1780 [5]. To the early Astronomers Royal, the heart of astronomical investigation lay in the stellar parallax, the longitude, and the explication of Newton's laws, and these researches demanded a different system of instrumentation from that required to make a nebula count or study variable stars.

Original accounts of instrument-making techniques, written under the hands of the craftsmen themselves, are scarce [6], and it is true to say that until the late eighteenth century, 'the art of graduation had been carried on in secrecy and silence' in which 'every artist had, or pretended to have, a method of his own' [7]. Not until the Board of Longitude persuaded John Bird to set down his method in print for the benefit of the nation in 1767 did instrument makers begin to consider discussing their methods publicly, and even after Bird had set a precedent, others were loath to follow [8].

This sense of caution in passing on professional secrets in the art of dividing was spelled out by Edward Troughton in a letter to Nevil Maskelyne, the Astronomer Royal, before the presentation of his own method of dividing in a paper to the Royal Society in 1809:

My reputation for the dividing of astronomical and other instruments is by
no means unknown to the world; but the means by which I accomplish it I
have hitherto thought proper to conceal; And if that concealment had been
essential to the advancing of that reputation or the immediate security of my
own interests, it is possible that it might still longer have rested with myself.
[9]

By the time of his writing, Troughton was 56 years old, master of the most
successful instrument firm in London, and feeling, no doubt, that he could afford to
be generous with his experience, especially as it was soon to win him both a
Fellowship of the Royal Society and its coveted Copley Medal.

Whilst the prospect of financial gain from the exercise of a superior secret
technique may seem the obvious reason for reticence, it does not provide an
adequate explanation. The 'secret' of fine graduation could not be embodied in a
brief formula capable of theft, but was obtained from a sense of heightened manual
dexterity, refined by decades of practice, and often performed with hand-held tools.
Improved techniques were best passed on to a diligent apprentice rather than the
readers of *Philosophical Transactions*, with the result that few craftsmen felt any
inclination to publish. In consequence, our knowledge of early workshop practice is
often very deficient, and renders all the more valuable the comments of gentlemen
authors, like Robert Smith and John Smeaton, who visited the workshops and
recorded what they saw.

When sources dealing with workshop techniques do occur, they are invariably
singular, and difficult to substantiate from alternative or supplementary documents.
A simple description of some point of technique will often be repeated by all
subsequent writers, simply through lack of alternative evidence. Thus, Smith's
account of George Graham's dividing technique is repeated almost verbatim by
Edmund Stone, the *Encyclopédie*, and several other histories of dividing [10].
Indeed, the history of workshop practice before the end of the eighteenth century
consists of a small number of detailed studies, with almost no first-hand material to
fill in the gaps or supply commentary.

It was Edward Troughton's assessment of the work of his predecessors in the art
of graduation that made his own paper on dividing so important, for no instrument
maker before him had attempted such a study. By examining the different axioms in
accordance with which various practitioners had worked, and recording workshop
anecdotes, comments on the use of specific tools, and the results of controlled
experiments, Troughton made a great contribution to the historical understanding of
the art of dividing.

It is also important to recognize the extent to which official interest in instrument
making, and especially those branches of the art relating to navigation and astronomy, came to receive official recognition from the middle of the eighteenth century.
With the problem of the longitude still unsolved, a rapid growth in maritime
dominance, and the sense of obligation to complete the 'Newtonian legacy', British
officialdom was rapidly learning the significance of circle dividing to national

prestige. In the 50 years following 1760, the Royal Society and Board of Longitude honoured a number of British instrument makers who made important contributions to the art. John Bird, Jesse Ramsden, and Edward Troughton all enjoyed concrete expressions of approbation, and the last two even received the accolade of Royal Society Fellowship.

Yet the history of circle dividing consists of more than just the accurate construction of instruments; it must also include the development of improved observational techniques by the astronomers themselves. The writings of Dr James Bradley, the mid-eighteenth-century Astronomer Royal, record the degree to which working astronomers felt it incumbent upon themselves to improve their observing procedures so as to do justice to the new instruments placed at their disposal. Taking the lead from Flamsteed, no doubt, Bradley devoted long sections of his *Philosophical Transactions* articles announcing his discoveries of aberration and nutation in 1728 and 1748 to the discussion of instrument problems, while his successor, Maskelyne, did the same when publishing his own Greenwich observations in 1785 [11].

Until recent years, the weight of scholarly attention in the history of science has been directed to its philosophical and methodological branches, with consequent neglect of its more practical aspects. Even when the study of instruments has secured attention, it has often been in connection with their misplaced 'heroic' attributes; eighteenth-century nautical instruments, clocks, watches, and microscopes have long been appreciated for their aesthetic properties, whilst the early history of the telescope was identified in the Victorian historical consciousness with the 'martyrdom' of Galileo.

In many respects, the study of technological procedures was somehow not *real* history, and philosophers could confidently speak of the 'Copernican Revolution' or the 'Newtonian World Picture' without thinking twice about the technological foundations and new standards of accurate measurement that made these reappraisals possible. It is no less remarkable to consider that many undergraduates reading English in the universities can complete their education without properly realizing that Chaucer wrote the first instrument treatise in the English language [12].

When modern scholars have addressed themselves to historical problems concerning instruments, it has all too often been from a taxonomic point of view, where the classification of the instruments has been given priority over their application to specific scientific problems. In spite of a considerable scholarly literature on the astrolabe, our knowledge of the workshop practice which made these common medieval artefacts possible is still rudimentary [13].

The use of pictorial evidence can cast light onto many aspects of the history of technology, though with the exception of a few medieval illuminations, we find little to illustrate the early history of circle dividing. It is unfortunate that instrument making was never discussed in the Bible, for much of our knowledge of the evolution of the tools of the shipbuilder, carpenter, and mason derives from medieval religious paintings depicting the building of Noah's Ark, or the Tower of Babel, where contemporary tools and techniques are often shown [14].

When conventional literary sources fail, it is sometimes possible to cast light on the early history of dividing by the application of archaeological techniques. The discovery of a Greek planetary calculating machine on the seabed off the island of

Antikythera in 1900 has done much to alter opinions about classical precision technology [15], while the author of the present book has attempted to examine the accuracy and reconstruct the graduation techniques of several medieval and later instruments, by the application of modern analytical methods to pieces surviving in museum collections.

The art of 'dividing the circle' thus constitutes an important key to our understanding of the growth of the science of astronomy [16]. Without a knowledge of the context in which scientific instruments are intended to function, and the problems which they are expected to solve, the historian must fail to appreciate many basic issues in early science.

Because research, in so many cases, hinged upon the testing of theories that demanded accurate data, a study of the means by which these pieces of data were gathered forms an essential ingredient in our understanding of how men in previous ages came to formulate ideas about the universe. This means that scientific, and especially astronomical, instruments must be seen as working tools, or more precisely, the physical embodiment of geometrical ideas. It means that the historian must not see instruments as antiquarian or aesthetic objects, but as documentary sources in their own right; as the physical representatives of the ideas and capacities of a given period. In the present book, it is my intention to try to view instruments in this way, for only after having assessed the mensurational capacities of the scientific community for a specific epoch can one hope to write a history which is in itself scientific.

2

The Tychonic school and its approach to instrumentation

TYCHO BRAHE

Of all the astronomers and practitioners discussed in the present book, Tycho Brahe has received by far the greatest attention from historians. This fame is well deserved, but apart from the details of his achievements, it is rare to find a man whose contributions were of such a pre-eminently practical nature the subject of so much attention, for Tycho's stature was never diminished by the reputations of Kepler and Galileo in the way that Newton was to obscure the contributions of Hooke, Flamsteed, Bradley and many others. More than any other figure of the scientific Renaissance, Tycho showed how to address questions to nature and conduct research, and did this through the example of a working technology that was to be more portentous to his successors than even the great legacy of his recorded observations.

It is well known that Tycho's observations provided the factual substantiation for the work of Kepler and the eventual success of Copernicanism, but full appreciation is rarely expressed regarding the technical vocabulary that he likewise bequeathed to science. In the design and use of instruments, he created the model of procedure for the next four generations of positional astronomers, and his influence was very much in evidence when the Greenwich Observatory was equipped with its first set of instruments, over 70 years after his death.

Tycho established a practical tradition that introduced the philosophical community for the first time to the concepts of precision measurement, regularity, and system in the making of observations. Between them, the *Mechanica* and *Progymnasmata* contained a method for the conduct of science that was no less important than Galileo's *New Sciences* or Bacon's *Novum Organum.* By constructing instruments that were ten times more accurate than those of his immediate predecessors, using them consistently for a quarter of a century, and being ever watchful of errors, Tycho was to transform the framework within which astronomy was practised. It was only by conducting research along these lines that clear solutions to the problems of the Earth's rotation, the distance of the stars, and the revision of astronomical tables could eventually be hoped for.

THE PRINCIPLES OF THE TYCHONIC INSTRUMENTS

At the commencement of Tycho's scientific career in the 1560s, there appeared to be only one way of improving instrumental accuracy, and that was by the construction of instruments of such ponderous radii as to permit the drawing of large, easily subdivided degrees onto their limbs. The same principle was also evident in the instruments of both European and Islamic astronomers during the Middle Ages, and was to be embodied in one of Tycho's earliest instruments. This was the Great Quadrant of 14 cubits radius [1], constructed in the garden of his friend Paul Hainzel of Augsburg [2]. Tycho relates that its radius was so great that it was possible to directly subdivide the limb down to 10-second (10″) spaces, although in practical terms it is unlikely to have surpassed the accuracy of 6 minutes (6′) attained by the best of its predecessors [3].

Throughout the fifteenth and sixteenth centuries, mathematicians had been attempting to develop techniques to subdivide degrees by more refined methods, and thus reduce the bulk of observatory instruments. This was the first of the three fundamental breakthroughs in the art of precision mechanics, making possible the construction of instruments that were not only smaller in size, but more accurate. Improved methods of subdividing engraved scales allowed a small instrument to surpass in performance the theoretical accuracy of a common one that was four or five times larger. The other two breakthroughs that allowed more reliable mechanical angular measurements were the micrometer in the seventeenth century, and the circle in the eighteenth, both of which will be discussed presently.

The device employed by Tycho to subdivide his instruments was the diagonal or transversal scale, which underwent relatively little change between his bringing it to fruition at Uraniborg and its passing into obsolescence in the early eighteenth century. Tycho did not invent this scale, and claimed to have first heard of it in 1564 when he acquired an astronomical radius divided with 'transversal points' [4]. He attributed the invention to Homelius and Scultetius, although Robert Hooke was later to claim it for Richard Cantzlar.

The original application of the diagonal scale to circular instruments precedes all of these claims, however, for in the Istituto e Museo di Storia della Scienza, Florence, there is an astrolabe dated 1483, the 360° scale of which is divided to 10′ by means of transversal lines [5]. In 1563, moreover, Peuhler had applied diagonal scales to a circular instrument, though it is unlikely that Tycho was familiar with either of these instruments [6].

Tycho drew his diagonals differently from these earlier practitioners, by using dots instead of lines, and further realized that as the size of the diagonal diminished across the amplitude of the limb, it would introduce errors. He attempted to avoid this problem by making his own instruments of large size, and never extending the diagonals back more than 1/48th of the radius, so as to keep the contraction to a minimum and the calculated error below 3″ [7].

Tycho was one of the first astronomers to recognize the importance of parallax errors, encountered when making an actual sighting with a graduated instrument.

Since classical times the sighting arms, or alidades, of measuring instruments had carried pinnule sights, in which the object under observation was aligned through a pair of fore and aft sighting holes. Tycho realized that the diameters of these holes must correspond to a definite angle, centred in the observer's eye, and that this angle constituted a source of error capable of vitiating the accuracy of the most delicately graduated scale. When he came into possession of a triquetrum that had once belonged to Copernicus, Tycho ascertained that the pinnule sights on the instrument contained an error of up to 7', because of the size of the holes [8].

In an attempt to abolish collimation errors in his own instruments, Tycho developed his 'peg and slit' sight, to replace the crude pinnules (Plate 6). At the fore end of the alidade was placed an accurately-turned cylindrical peg, set facing the observer. At the eye end, a vertical plate was set up carrying two slits, the exact separation between which was the same as the diameter of the foresight peg. To make an observation with this sight, one first aligned a star through the right-hand slit against the right-hand side of the peg. The observation was next repeated on the left-hand side, and when the adjustment was found where the star appeared equally on both the right- and left-hand sides, the alignment was considered to be true. This device came to be fitted onto all the Tychonic instruments, and represented a great improvement on the old pinnule sights, by allowing scales to be read with confidence.

At Uraniborg, Tycho developed his instruments through 'families', comprising the sextants — his earliest instruments — the armillary spheres, and the quadrants. By reading carefully the *Mechanica* in conjunction with the Tychonic observation books printed in the *Opera Omnia,* one can trace distinct sequences of development both within and between these families [9]. Between 1570 and 1590, the sextants became less flimsy, better mounted, and more versatile. Tycho claimed to have invented the astronomical sextant, and one can discern a rapid evolution of the instrument, from the simple vertical piece employed to observe the new star of 1572, to the Sextans Trigonicus of a decade later, when it became a two-man instrument of 6-ft radius, capable of measuring angular separations in any plane, in any part of the sky [10].

Because of its ability to work in any plane, and not just in the vertical or horizontal, the sextant became one of Tycho's most versatile instruments. It was used to measure the angular separations between pairs of stars, so that it afforded the positional data upon which a catalogue could be based. In particular, it was used to determine the place of the vernal equinox, or starting point for all celestial measurements. After computing the Sun's place in the ecliptic, Tycho observed the angular separation between it and Venus, on a day close to the equinox. After sunset, Venus's place was taken from a selected star, thus establishing the star's precise position in relation to the Sun. In this way, he was able to determine exactly the place of α Arietis, and eight other standard stars, the positions of which were noted with great accuracy and could be used as reference points in celestial cartography [11].

Tycho developed several forms of armillary sphere, and at each stage produced an instrument intended to serve a specific astronomical task. Armillaries were used to observe the elements of the great spherical triangles used to build up star catalogues, and could be read in both right ascension and declination coordinates. Tycho's first armillary spheres were heavy, containing a collection of interior rings that should have made them versatile, but succeeded only in making them too heavy, so that their pivots wore and became eccentric. In consequence, his subsequent instruments were simpler and lighter in construction, until the instrument reached its peak in the equatorial armillary. Consisting of a single 8-ft -diameter ring moving within a semicircle set in masonry, the ring being mounted upon a tubular axis with a self-centring bearing, the instrument possessed unprecedented accuracy [12]. By cutting down the number of rings to the minimum required to read right ascension and declination angles, Tycho abolished the problem inherent in earlier armillaries, namely, their tendency to sag under their own weight.

With the quadrants, Tycho evolved the idea of setting up a fixed point of reference in the sky, by constructing a mural arc that was secured to a meridian wall [13]. His observing techniques were then developed so that the movable instruments, such as the voluble, or rotating quadrants, reading latitude and longitude coordinates in any part of the sky, could always be checked against the stable mural arc. Tycho, it seems, attempted to devise a 'web' of cross-checks so that instruments working on different mechanical principles, such as the quadrant armillaries and sextants, could be checked against each other until reliable congruity was obtained.

It has been suggested that the reason why Tycho built so many instruments was in an attempt to evolve reliable prototypes, and one recent scholar has shown how, from a study of Tycho's printed observation books, one can date when specific instruments in the *Mechanica* were introduced, superseded or phased out [14].

Several scholars have also made reductions of the Tychonic observations in attempts to discover the true working accuracies of the instruments. Working from the observations of the 1585 comet, C. A. F. Peters calculated that the Equatorial Armillary was accurate in declination to ±49″, and in right ascension to ±81″, and that a single sighting with the sextant was probably true to ±45″ [15]. Similarly, Dreyer calculated that the position of Tycho's Eqinox Star, α Ariets, was accurate to within an incredible ±6″.

Upon comparing the mural quadrant observations with Le Verrier's tables, Tupman detected a progressive improvement in the quality of the resulting observations, so that between 1582 and 1590, the error fell from 47″ down to 21″. Indeed, Tycho's lifting of the instrumental 'ceiling' was to be of crucial importance to the conclusions of Kepler and subsequent astronomers, as will be discussed later in the book [16].

The most recent attempt to establish the accuracy of the Tychonic instruments by reductions is that of W. Wesley, who has devised a computer program to make comparisons between Tycho's observing books and the calculated disposition of the heavens when the original observations were made. By this means, it appears that the eight instruments investigated by Wesley had a remarkably uniform error distribution, being accurate to within 30″ to 50″ [17].

Though a set of 'Tychonic-type' instruments built under the supervision of the seventeenth-century Jesuit missionary, Ferdinand Verbiest, still exists in China, it is unfortunate that none of Tycho's original principal instruments survive. Verbiest's *Astronomia Europaea* is most illuminating, however, as it contains construction plates showing how 6-ft armillary rings, for a duplicate of the instrument in Tycho's *Mechanica*, were cast, polished and graduated [18].

Tycho's influence on the seventeenth century was profound, and extended across both the practical and theoretical departments of astronomy. By lifting the 'ceiling of accuracy' of Renaissance astronomy, Tycho's observations were eventually to resolve the deadlock into which cosmology had fallen by 1600, upon the problem of the Earth's motion in space.

Although modern scholars have investigated this aspect of scientific history with far greater assiduity than the instrumental background upon which its evidence rests, it is necessary to allude to Tycho's unconscious contributions to Copernicanism, to illustrate the wider significance of his instruments.

His inability to detect a parallax for the new star of 1572, although many of his colleagues across Europe were producing fantastic values for the same, provided a demonstration that change did take place within the greater heaven, contrary to the accepted canons of physics. The motions of the bright comet of 1577, which he observed with the steel sextant, likewise convinced him of the mutability of the supra-lunary realm, and the implausibility of the doctrine of the crystalline spheres. Although these observations convinced Tycho against the plausibility of the Ptolemaic system, they did not encourage him to become a Copernican, but rather to perfect his own Earth-centred system [19]. In an age that was first learning to weigh observational evidence in the construction of scientific hypotheses, Tycho's demonstration of change in the greater heaven, and of the comets' likelihood of colliding with the crystalline spheres, was of great cogency in the cosmological debate.

Tycho's observations achieved great posthumous importance in the hands of Kepler, and it is well known how the latter deduced his first law from the observations of Mars [20]. But what was significant in relationship to Tycho's instruments was Kepler's concern for a discrepancy of a mere 8' between the predicted place of the planet according to conventional spherical orbits, and the *observed* place as obtained by the instruments. For any observer before Tycho, 8' would have fallen well within the margin of instrumental error and, hence, would have been ignored.

Kepler wrote:

> Ptolemy did not claim to reach down beyond a limit of accuracy of 1/6° or 10' . . . [which] behoves us [what] a very careful observer Tycho Brahe was . . . in whose observations an error of 8' . . . could be disclosed. Thus, these single eight minutes indicate to us the road towards the renovation of the entire astronomy. [21]

Only after Tycho had made a minute of arc a sensible quantity in astronomical measurement could such orbital discrepancies command attention [22]. The achievements in theoretical astronomy which followed as a consequence of Tycho's work stress the dramatic elevation of the accuracy-ceiling which he brought about in practical astronomy. This he accomplished in two ways: firstly by the construction of a set of instruments of unprecedented accuracy, and secondly, by the use of these instruments in accord with a technique of scrupulous cross-checking and systematic, regular observation. Tycho's realization that observations must be not only accurate, but plentiful in number and made in accordance with a regular pattern, was a legacy to posterity no less significant than the more obvious details of his instrument technology. Without a large corpus of accurate observations at his disposal, made regularly over a period of many years, it is unlikely that Kepler would have produced a solution of such originality to the problem of Mars.

In conclusion, it must be said that little is known about the makers of Tycho's instruments, or the workshop techniques by which they were constructed. With the exception of the cross-staff, made by Walter Arsenius, he was largely silent regarding the craftsmen he employed. Most of the instruments were probably built by Tycho's team of artisans at Uraniborg, and may have received their actual divisions under Tycho's own hand.

Jost Bürgi, mathematician to the Landgrave of Kassell, was familiar with Tycho's method of drawing diagonals, having learned of them from Paul Wittich in 1584 [23]. He equipped several of the Landgrave's instruments with modified diagonal scales, where he replaced the rows of dots with parallel circles, although there is no record of him having made instruments for Tycho.

In his *Historia Coelestis,* Tycho described a form of quadrant with a denticulated limb that was traversed by a screw or gear pinion set into the end of the alidade, so that by turning the screw, the alidade was advanced through a number of degrees [24]. The screw would have acted as a delicate adjustment in sighting the alidade, although at the time it was impossible to cut screw and gear teeth with the necessary degree of accuracy to measure angles reliably by counting the revolutions of the screw.

Still extant in the Prague National Museum is a screw-edged sextant bearing the inscription 'Pragae Fecit Erasmus habermel 1600' that is similar in many ways to that described in *Historia Coelestis.* After leaving Uraniborg, Tycho spent the last months of his life in Prague, and though the date of the sextant makes it too late to have contributed to Tycho's mature work, it is possible that he may have used the instrument when resident in that city [25]. If this is in fact correct, it remains one of the few surviving scientific artefacts from the first man to make significant advances in practical astronomy since antiquity.

CIRCULAR SCALE DIVISION

Circular division in the sixteenth century was concerned with two problems: the production of 90 accurately drawn degrees, and their subdivision into minutes and seconds. Most early writers on astrolabes and similar instruments seem to assume a familiarity amongst their readers with the art of dividing, and pass over the construction of scales with a brief remark similar to the recommendation ascribed to Chaucer, to 'Devyde it into sixty parties equals' [26]. One of the earliest accounts of dividing, however, comes from a work on dialling by Thomas Fale, and as this constitutes the literary point of commencement, the passage is worth citing in full.

> First divide eche of them [the quadrants] into three equall partes, and every one of these into three other partes, so that you shall have nine divisions in either quadrant, where every one shal represent ten degrees. Againe, part evry one of these into two, and eche of those into five (if you can) and so is eche quadrant divided into 90 degrees. [27]

The only mention of subdivision in this account refers to breaking each degree into three parts, if the limb be large enough.

Fale's technique was the same in outline as that developed by George Graham in the early eighteenth century, and embodied the time-honoured method of using the radius of the quadrant to divide the limb into three parts, and draw the smaller fractions using bisections, trisections and quinquesections of the angle to obtain single degrees. It derived from Euclid's use of the radius to produce the six angles of a hexagon [28].

On the small scales of the astrolabes Renaissance craftsmen achieved good results with dividing methods similar to the one just cited. But no attempts were made by Western practitioners to divide these scales down to subdivisions until Pedro Nunez's method, as described in *De Crepulis* in 1542 [19].

Although never successful in practice, Nunez's (or Nonius's) method of subdividing embodied a principle which was eventually to lead to the vernier scale, after passing through a sequence of intermediary developments [30].

Nonius' quadrant consisted of a flat plate of brass upon which were scribed 45 quadrantal arches, one inside the other. The outermost of their number was divided into 90 ordinary degrees, but the second into only 89°, the third into 88°, and so on, until the last carried only 46 parts. Between them, the 45 arcs constituted a table of proportion, so that after making an observation, one noted which division on which arc came into exact contact with the edge of the alidade, thus providing a proportion from which the angle could be derived arithmetically. Thus, if the alidade rested on the 32nd division of the arc containing 50 equal parts, the following proportions would ensue $32:50=x:90$. As 1/50th of 90° is 1° 48′, it was only necessary to multiply 1° 48′ by 32 to obtain the angle 57° 36′.

Ingenious as the Nonius method appeared in theory, its accurate construction would have been impossible before the invention of the dividing engine in the eighteenth century. Tycho Brahe was the only astronomer to attempt to observe with a quadrant divided in this way, and he soon abandoned the 'Nonian method [which]...is insufficient in practice, and experience will show that the promised accuracy is not in fact obtained by it.' [31]

Yet leaving aside the constructional difficulties of the instrument, the Nonian method of graduation introduced the mathematical community to the principle of delineating subdivisions by the coincidence of lines on a proportional scale. This came to be developed by the mathematicians Clavius and Curtius, whose ideas provided the necessary ingredients of what was to become the vernier scale. They attempted to simplify the Nonius quadrant both by reducing the number of concentric arcs required to read an angle, and by dividing them up into sequences of equal parts that could be arrived at by continuous bisection, such as the number 128 [32]. It was Clavius who suggested drawing the proportional scale on an auxiliary quadrant possessing the same radius as the principal one, so that the amplitude of 61 natural degrees was divided into 60 equal parts, the residual minutes being read off with dividers, by stepping off the interval on the auxillary scale [33]. Pierre Vernier made the final development in the scales of proportion in 1631, by attaching Clavius's auxiliary scale to the moving alidade of a quadrant, so that the two scales could be .read directly against each other [34].

Only after Vernier had achieved this mechanical simplification could the scale of proportion become of practical benefit to astronomers, and even then its adoption was slow. This was occasioned partly by the popularity of the diagonal scale, which was already well established by 1630, in addition to which the construction of really accurate verniers, where a given set of main-scale degrees formed a perfect proportion against the auxiliary degrees, was extremely difficult from a practical point of view.

Hevelius was the first major astronomer to make extensive use of the vernier, although it was not until the second quarter of the eighteenth century that technical proficiency was advanced sufficiently to establish it in the instrument-making repertoire [35]. Even then, it was considered difficult to make a really accurate vernier [36], and by 1786, John Smeaton was advocating the abandonment of the scale for all precision work, and its replacement by the micrometer: an exhortation which had taken effect by 1800.

THE MEASUREMENT OF ANGLES BY INSTRUMENTS FITTED WITH STRAIGHT SCALES

Dividing a curved scale into an equal number of degrees was a process of great complexity. Ninety is not an easily divisible number, and the striking of chords with a beam compass leads to inevitable discrepancies between the part-circles and straight lines used to construct a scale of degrees.

One way of eliminating these problems and simplifying the construction of divided instruments lay in utilizing the properties of right-angled and isosceles triangles, the proportions of which correspond to parts of a circle from which the internal angles could be computed, once the lengths of the sides were known. They depended on the relation between the radius, chord and tangent of a circle, and as these were already understood and tabulated by the sixteenth century, a method existed whereby it was possible to make angular measurements without recourse to circular scales. During the sixteenth century, much attention was paid to the development of two instruments embodying these principles of graduation: the triquetrum and the cross-staff or astronomical radius. Whilst neither of these devices was of direct consequence to the development of observatory instruments, they enjoyed considerable contemporary importance, and proved invaluable to the surveyor and navigator.

A third class of instruments also existed in which a linear scale was used to measure celestial angles in the geometrical square, although it was not a major influence in the art of graduation [37].

The triquetrum

Though deriving from antiquity, the triquetrum entered scientific currency in the West when Regiomontanus began to observe 'per regulas Ptolemae' around 1462. His 'rulers' carried equal divisions and a description survives of how they were used to make observations in 1475 [38].

Copernicus also possessed a triquetrum, and in 1584 it entered the collection of Tycho Brahe, who described it in the *Mechanica*. It worked on the principle that when two radii are drawn from the centre of a circle, it is possible to discover the angle subtended between them by the length of the resulting chord produced at the circumference. The rules DF and DE acted as radii to the circle, the centre of which was the pivot D, being rectified to the zenith with a plumb line at DF. The radial arm DE was fitted with pinnule sights for the location of stars, and as it rotated about the centre, away from DF, it formed an isosceles triangle with EF, which acted both as a base to the triangle, and a chord to the circle centred at D. Knowing the length of the radial arms — four cubits — and the length of a chord for a given observation, it was possible to obtain the angle subtended at D [Plate 7]. This could be accomplished either by engraving a line of chords on to the ruler EF, so that angles could be read directly, or by drawing equal divisions of length and obtaining the angle by computation. The first method is simpler in operation, allowing angles to be read directly, but unreliable where great accuracy is desired, for as its scale is but a copy of an existing line of chords, it is twice removed in accuracy from the perfect computed chord. It was almost certainly for this reason that Copernicus fitted his triquetrum with equal divisions, which required calculation but permitted greater accuracy [39].

Tycho found the pinnule sights of the Copernician triquetrum to be unsatisfactory, consisting as they did of holes drilled through the back and fore sighting plates. To facilitate the easier location of a star, the hole in the front sight was made quite large and Tycho discovered that its aperture was so great as to correspond to 8′ or 10′ in the sky. As there was no way of telling whether a sighted star occupied the centre or periphery of this hole, it immediately introduced an error factor of 8′ or 10′ into each observation.

The chief advantage of the triquetrum lay in its simple construction, which required only a set of equidistant divisions along a straight rod, though Tycho found its accuracy to be substantially inferior to that of the Uraniborg quadrants.

After examining this Copernican instrument, Tycho set about the construction of a second triquetrum, in brass, to an improved design [40]. The improved sights and stable mounting of the second triquetrum were found to work to Tycho's satisfaction, making it 'possible to determine both the altitude and azimuth without sensible error, as well with this instrument as with the largest quadrants'. By this time, however, Tycho possessed instruments of much higher efficiency than the triquetrum, and his observation books do not suggest that it was much employed in serious work [41].

The cross-staff

Though originally ascribed to Levi Ben Gerson, the cross-staff underwent considerable development in the hands of sixteenth-century European practical mathematicians, as a measuring instrument that did not require a circular graduated scale. Whilst the disposition of its parts was different from that of the triquetrum, it was an instrument of the same family in its use of linear graduations and tangents in place of circular scales. Like the triquetrum, its divisions could either be equally or unequally spaced. The former were of value to the astronomer, the latter to navigators as a direct reading instrument. Most of the subsequent history of the staff is concerned with the direct reading variety, through Horrox (see p. 26) used equal graduations.

Two methods were available by which it was possible to obtain the places of the unequal divisions for the direct reading cross-staff [42]. One could either obtain them from trigonometrical tables using sines and tangents, or else they could be constructed graphically. Both methods were widely used, although for directness and simplicity of construction, the graphical method was the more significant.

The basic geometrical method of cross-staff division was demonstrated by Petrus Apian in 1524 [43]. A semicircle was drawn on a large flat surface, the radius of which corresponded exactly to the radius of the intended cross-staff. The two quadrants of the semicircle were each divided into 90° with beam compasses, and each point connected to the centre of the arc with a radial line to be projected onto the staff FB. Once the radial line had been graduated in this way, any number of copies could be made from it, by scribing with a set square (Plate 8 (a) and (b)).

For the graduation of the main staff itself, Apian's method remained unchanged in principle, although geometrical improvements were later introduced by Cortes and Waghenaer for the purpose of increasing the spacing between the larger angles, and thus facilitating greater certainty of observation [44].

It was at sea that the staff assumed its true importance, being employed to take the height of the Sun and Pole Star, and in this capacity it received considerable attention from navigational writers over the course of the following century. Smoked glasses were attached to the tips of the cross-pieces to reduce the solar glare, and a technique was devised whereby it was possible to observe the Sun by making the shadow of the cross-piece fall upon the scale, thus avoiding the problem of observing the Sun directly [45]. The instrument reached its final form in the Davis, or back-staff, which also incorporated conventional circular degree scales [46]. But as these subsequent developments were aimed at improving the nautical rather than the astronomical capabilities of the instrument, their further treatment would be out of place in the present context [47].

Several scientific men attempted to obtain consistent results with the cross-staff, one of whom was Bernard Walther of Nuremberg. Using a six-cubit staff, or radius, divided into 1300 equal parts, he succeeded in deriving the angle 14° 35' as the separation between Mars and Saturn on the night of October 17th 1475. He also used the instrument to observe a comet. Cross-staffs carrying equal divisions were also being used in Germany in the late fifteenth century by Regiomontanus and Purbach. Nearly a century later, a form of cross-staff was used by John Dee and Thomas Digges to observe the new star of 1572, proving to the eventual satisfaction of both men that the star showed no apparent parallax [48].

It was Tycho's perceptive analysis that provided the best assessment of the instrument's limitations in scientific research. Tycho considered that the chief advantage of the staff resided in its simplicity and portability, but these were outweighed by its unsuitability for critical work, as he discussed in the *Mechanica* [49]. With Apian's graduation technique, however, accuracy was only placed one step further back, for his description of a circle projected onto a straight stick did not dispense with the need for circles during division itself, and hence did not provide an entirely independent method. Because the division of the semicircle into 180° remained an essential pre-requisite of the method the staff's eventual reliability was naturally prey to the accuracy of the original divisions, no matter how flawless the subsequent method of projection. At best, it could only be considered a copy once removed of an arc of unproven quality, and once the division of this 'master radius' had been transferred onto a blank wooden rod of the cross-staff, the instrument itself became a third-hand copy. Even if one succeeded in graduating a perfect staff, the radial cross-piece — fitted either with plain sights, or the adjustable *pinnacidia* of Petrus Apian or Gemma Frisius — was subject to too many optical and mechanical eccentricities to permit critical alignments [50].

While it is true that for purposes of astronomical research, as opposed to navigation, the cross-staff was really a substitute for a good quadrant, some fine original instruments do survive. The brass staff of 1563 by Walter Arsenius, now preserved in Madrid, is one of the finest [51].

JEREMIAH HORROX (1619–1641)

It is not an exaggeration to say that Jeremiah Horrox possessed one of the most original scientific minds of the seventeenth century. A follower of Tycho, Horrox combined a gift for instrumentation with a theoretical genius that later won the acclaim of Hevelius and Flamsteed. His contributions to the lunar theory were the first significant advances on the subject since antiquity, and earned the praise of Newton himself in the pages of *Principia* [52].

In his correspondence with William Crabtree (1610–1644), Horrox spoke of using a variety of linear measuring instruments, referred to as *astronomical radii,* which worked by triangulation. They belonged to the same family as the instruments discussed above, but Horrox developed the techniques of construction and use so as to make them capable of providing the accurate observational evidence upon which his more illustrious theoretical contributions came to be founded.

It was probably poverty that first turned Horrox's attention towards the cross-staff, being as it was the simplest of all divided instruments, though later evidence suggests that he was a skilled circle divider in his own right, and quite capable of making a quadrant [53]. Horrox invented no new method of division, but achieved his results by a combination of painstaking care, great manual dexterity and the confinement of most of his measurements to small angles. In Horrox's writings, it is possible to trace his application of triangulation techniques through a variety of forms from the astronomical radius, to the camera obscura (for measuring the solar diameter), and eventually the telescope itself.

One of Horrox's earliest instruments was a staff of 3 ft, the length of which represented 10 000 equal divisions. Along the main staff ran a cross-piece, or vane, 1 ft long, divided so that it read degrees and minutes directly, by means of a tangent scale. The places of the graduations were derived from Pitiscus's Canon of Tangents and were 'non in partes aequales'. From a table of corrections that Horrox compiled for the instrument, it appears that its cross-piece, or transversal, encompassed 16° [54], although this angle could have been increased by moving the cross-piece closer to the observer's eye and noting which of the cross-piece divisions it occupied. Upon the cross-piece were mounted two 'pinnacidia', between which Horrox 'enclosed' the objects under observation, after the method illustrated by Gemma Frisius.

It is clear from his surviving observations, however, that Horrox also possessed a cross-staff on which the angles were not read directly in degrees, but were computed from the proportions of a tangent scale that was drawn onto a fixed cross-piece that formed a 'T' with the radial rod. It was probably based on prototypes described by

Peter Apian and Gemma Frisius. Though the radial rod was always spoken of as containing 10 000 equal divisions, one must remember that in reality the divisions were never drawn, and the rod was left blank. The 10 000 divisions represented the 10 000 units of a table of Natural Tangents, in which the 100 and 1000 parts were used to derive the linear divisions drawn onto the 'T' cross-piece. If, therefore, one had a radial rod 36 inches long, the 100th divisions drawn onto the cross-piece and against which the pinnacidia were adjusted to the stars, were 0.36 inches in extent. A well-drawn set of transversal lines, furthermore, could sub-divide down to 1000ths or less.

Close attention was paid by Horrox to the errors of his instruments, and in November 1637, he wrote to Crabtree of his recent observation of the angle subtended between Saturn and Venus. The staff gave a direct reading of 10° 29′, but remembering Edward Wright's discussion of the eccentricity of the eye in his *Certain Errors of Navigation* [55] Horrox set about re-determining the error value. Allusion has already been made to the difficulty of placing the observer's eye at the precise optical centre of the staff, and Horrox solved the problem by placing a pin at this point, to guide the eye. Shifting his eye to different sides of the point, he found it to result in observed values that were 7′ too large, when worked out against the staff's linear divisions. A correction for this amount was applied to all past and future observations made with the instrument [56].

By December 1636, Horrox had brought a second 'radius' into operation, which was 11 ft long and seems to have been designed for the special task of measuring the solar diameter. The close attention paid to detecting suspected variations in the diameter may have been occasioned by his own conviction of the truth of Kepler's first law, together with his interest in the solar parallax [57].

Two upright metal sights set at the instrument's far end were carefully adjusted until they 'enclosed' the Sun, forming a long, narrow triangle with the observer's eye, from which it was possible to calculate the diameter trigonometrically. To eliminate errors caused by the sights of the new radius, he adopted the practice of using the internal edge of one sight and the external edge of the other, to obtain mean values [58].

Crabtree used a similar technique, by setting one star to the inner, and the other to the outer edge of the *pinnacidium,* when observing with his cross-staff. He sometimes observed bright stars by replacing one of the *pinnacidia* with an 'iron stylos', which could be adjusted to bisect the star [59]. It is amongst Crabtree's letters to Gascoigne that one finds the most explicit description of the technique used to measure variations in the solar diameter by radial instruments.

Instead of having fixed and movable sights, as on the common radius, two needles were erected vertically on a small beam. Crabtree then moved his eyes away from them, until the inner and outer edges of the respective wires touched the sun, at which point he read the appropriate graduation. Viewing the sun through thin clouds on April 6th, 1641, he discovered that it was exactly 'enclosed' by two wires 19.75 units apart, when they were placed 2011 units from the eye, from which he computed a diameter of 32′ 03″, an extraordinarily accurate value [60].

A remarkably high degree of accuracy was obtained by Horrox and Crabtree in their solar measurements. As the orbital variations in the solar diameter can be considered regular over a period of 350 years, it is possible to check their original observations against a modern ephemeris, after applying a ten-day calendar correction. A selection of their observations are cited below, for the solar semi-diameter [61].

		Observed	*Modern*
Crabtree	6th April 1641	16′ 01½″	15′ 58″
Horrox	10th April 1637	15′ 35″	15′ 57″
	29th April 1637	15′ 30″	15′ 52″
	29th April 1637	15′ 05″	15′ 52″

From his observations, Horrox 'Concludendum itaque hinc videtur, solis diametrum in Apogaeo 30½′ in Perigaeo 31½′ in media distantia, 31′ [62]. These values are slightly smaller than the ones later decided upon by his friend Gascoigne in 1641, who had observed the Sun to vary between 31′ 40″ and 33′; but it is possible that his solar diameter measures had been made with an optical micrometer [63].

Horrox noted that his measures of the solar diameter, made with the mounted wires, tended to be excessive when compared alongside identical observations made with a 'foramen', or pinhole camera technique [64]. With the foramen, knowledge of which he probably obtained from Tycho and Kepler, he admitted the direct light of the sun in a darkened chamber through a pinhole, and intercepted it on a screen. Its geometry was identical with that of the radius, but its chief advantage lay in dispensing with the delicate manipulation of upright wires, and the errors arising from the eccentricity of the eye. Passing sunlight through a hole 5 units in diameter, he found that at a projection distance of 4100 units, the sun formed an image 42½ units across, from which he computed its angular diameter to be 31′ 26″.

Comparisons with modern values for his semi-diameters made with the foramen are listed below [65].

	Observed	*Modern*
December 2nd, 1636	15′ 43″	16′ 16″
November 15th, 1636 (mean)	15′ 47″	16′ 14″

Horrox's final value for the solar diameter as it approached winter perigee, which one assumes was an average derived from all his best observations made by all methods, was 15′ 45″. He adopted this value 'because I found it from my own repeated observations to be very close to the truth', and he was to use it as the basis for his crucial derivation of the solar parallax from the 1639 transit of Venus [66].

Until the invention of the filar micrometer no adequate instruments existed for the measurement of *very* small angles, and Horrox and his friends devised several other naked-eye techniques that depended upon the properties of tangents, radii and triangles. Considerable speculation existed in the early seventeenth century about whether the stars appeared from the Earth as mere points of light, as the infinite universe of Thomas Digges and the more daring Copernicans implied they should [67], or whether they had clearly measurable diameters. Kepler considered the fixed stars subtended 2', and Galileo 5". Horrox was convinced that they appeared as no more than point sources, and demonstrated the same by using a telescope to observe an occultation of the Pleiades cluster by the dark edge of the Moon. Each of the stars vanished instantly, as the Moon covered it, whereas had they shown measurable diameters, each would have faded gradually as the Moon moved through 2' [68].

Horrox carried the principle of triangulation down to the limits of naked eye resolution in his attempts to measure planetary diameters. A hole was made in a card, with a needle of known diameter, through which he sighted the desired planet. Once located at the centre of the hole, he moved the card away from his eye, until the point was reached at which the planet exactly filled the hole. Careful measurement was made of the exact distance between his eye and the card, and as the diameter of the hole was already known, the dimensions of a long radial triangle were thus obtained, from which it was possible to calculate the angle subtended by the planet. Using this method, Venus was found to have a diameter of 27" in January 1640 as it moved to eastern elongation [69]. This same technique was applied to the fixed stars themselves, but Horrox found that no matter how far he moved the hole away from his eye, a star never filled it, which confirmed his opinion that they did not show angular diameters.

Although one is compelled to admire Horrox's originality in applying techniques of linear graduation to so many types of measurement, he clearly could not depend upon them to obtain the critical accuracies he desired. A small error committed in positioning the eye, when laying down the base line or striking off the length of one of his long narrow triangles, could have caused wild discrepancies in the eventual results. But what appears remarkable are the consistently high accuracies of his measurements, when compared alongside modern values, which pays high tribute to his genius as a practical geometer.

Horrox's most famous single achievement was his prediction and observation of the Venus transit of 1639. Though his own observations of the motions of Venus made with the cross-staff may have assisted him in the original prediction of the transit, his chief indication of the impending event came from the errors in current astronomical tables [70]. Combining the results of the tables with his own knowledge of Venus's motion, he computed that the planet would cross the Sun's disk on November 24th 1639 (Old Style), and informed Crabtree accordingly. This observation, from which Horrox derived such a wealth of fundamental information, was made by projecting the image of the Sun with a telescope into a circle drawn on a sheet of paper. Before commencing the observation, he had divided the 6-in circle into 360° with an accuracy, so he boasted, that exceeded that of a 50-ft quadrant, although he says nothing of his graduation technique. The diameter was divided into 30 parts, so that they could be adjusted to minutes of arc of the solar image, when projected in to fill the circle. Once Venus began to move across the Sun's disk, the divisions gave him the exact point of ingress, and the planet's path with relation to the Sun's centre, from which its physical and orbital characteristics could be deduced. Though Gassendi had used projection to observe the Mercury transit of 1630 [71], Horrox's work provides the first example of the telescope being used as a measuring instrument to yield really significant results. Gassendi had been surprised by the smallness of Mercury when seen in transit, and Horrox took careful measurements of Venus when it appeared likewise. The currently accepted values for the planet's conjunction diameter varied between 3' and 11' [72], but when it was deprived of its brilliance during transit, Horrox found that the black image observed only occupied 1' 12" on the 30-part scale into which he had divided the diameter of his projection circle [73]. Upon correcting these proportions in accordance with a perigean value for the solar diameter of 31' 30", he obtained a value of 1' 16" for the apparent diameter of Venus seen in conjunction. Using the same technique, Crabtree also compared the projected image of Venus with the solar diameter, and estimated that it occupied 7/200ths of the same, from which a value of 1' 3" was derived for the planet's apparent diameter. This agrees extraordinarily well with the modern *Nautical Almanac* value of 1' to 1' 34" for the mean conjunction diameter of Venus, but Crabtree's results contained an element of luck, for upon first seeing the planet, he was seized with a fit of aesthetic ecstasy that can hardly have conduced to methodical observation [74]. From observations of the apparent size and motion of Venus across the Sun's disk, Horrox was able to derive a value of 14" for the solar parallax, which was a fourfold improvement on Kepler's 59", and a tolerable approximation to the modern figure of 8.79" [75]. As the solar parallax was the basis upon which estimates of the Sun's distance were founded, such a revision was not without significance in the comprehension of the size of the solar system. The transit was also invaluable in enabling Horrox to make the first really accurate evaluation of the node of Venus' orbit, the position of which was a key towards a fuller understanding of the planet's motion.

All the instruments and techniques discussed above depended upon the linear properties of the radius, tangent and lines of proportion, as an alternative to divided arcs, in the measurement of angles. They helped provide a basis from which Horrox could make original contributions to celestial mechanics and provide the first satisfactory theory of the Moon's orbital motions. His contributions to the 'three-bodies problem' placed him at a mid-point between Kepler and Newton, for Horrox provided the first *physical* demonstration of the Sun–Earth–Moon system [76], which eventually led Newton to his *mathematical* model upon which the theory of universal gravitation came to be founded.

Horrox and his circle were assiduous observers, and their approach to the use of instruments was largely formulated from their dismay with most of the astronomical tables then in current usage. The contradictions between the various tables concerning the conjunction of Venus were only one instance of their unreliability. The Rudolphine Tables of that 'sublime and enviably happy genius', Kepler, were considered to approximate closest to the truth, after which the others descended through Longomontanus and Reinhold down to Lansberg the 'Belgian astronomer . . . so often deceived by his pretensions of Universal accuracy'. Horrox thus set about making his own instruments and addressing his questions to Nature direct for 'no one who has eyes and who diligently avails himself of his opportunities can be said to be destitute of astronomical instruments' [77].

Jeremiah Horrox was the last practising astronomer to pay serious attention to the use of instruments carrying linear scales, and it is not unfitting to consider that he developed the necessary techniques as far as they could reliably go. It is my opinion,

Plate 1 — Elias Allen, fl. 1606–1654. One of the leading instrument makers of the Jacobean period, shown with a collection of tools and instruments. Allen is holding a pair of dividers, while on the bench before him is a horizontal sundial, and an eqninoctial ring dial ring, along with a circumferator. Hanging on the wall are a sector and a quadrant. He enjoyed a considerable reputation as a scale divider, and a quadrant of 6-ft ring radius, signed and dated 1637, is preserved in the Museum of the History of Science, Oxford. [See Plate No. 9.] Science Museum, Neg. No. 457].

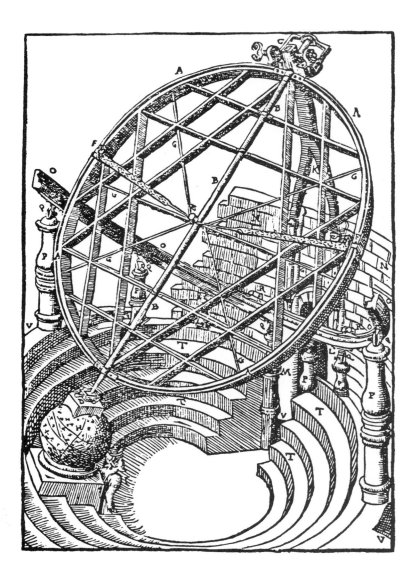

Plate 2 — Tycho Brahe's Equatorial Armillary, with one ring. One 9-ft diameter ring rotates around the Polar Axis, to read declinations by the alidades marked F–E, against the central peg. Right Ascensions are taken against the semi-circular arc 'o-o-o', set in the Equatorial plane. Tycho Brahe, *Astronomiae Instauratae Mechanica* (Wandesburgi, 1598) Sig. C₃v.

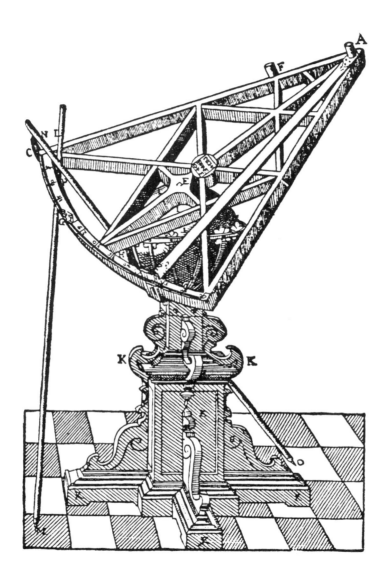

Plate 3 — Tycho Brahe's 6-ft sextant. Two observers take angular separations across the centre peg 'A' to read horizontal angles for the reduction of right ascensions. This instrument acted as a prototype for the sextants of Hevelius (see Plate 10), and Flamsteed (Plate 19). Tycho Brahe, *Astronomia Instaurate Mechanica* (Wandesburgi, 1598) Sig. Dv.

Plate 4 — Tycho Brahe's mural quadrant. This instrument, of 6-ft radius, was the prototype of many subsequent mural quadrants over the next two centuries. The idea of having a large graduated arc in the plane of the meridian has been one of the most important inventions in instrument technology. It was a direct influence on Flamsteed, passing from him into the mainstream of instrument design. Tycho Brahe, *Astronomia Instaurate Mechanica* (Wandesburgi, 1598) Sig. A₄v.

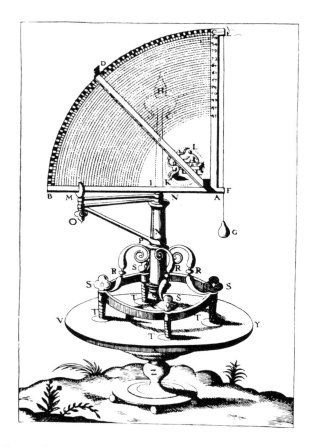

Plate 5 — The 'Nonius' quadrant. Tycho Brahe, *Astronomia Instaurate Mechanica* (Wandesburgi, 1598) Sig. Av.

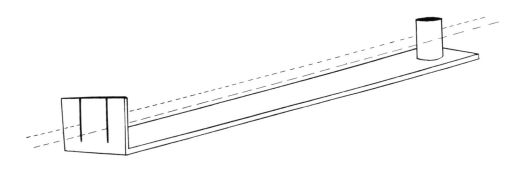

Plate 6 — Tycho Brahe's 'peg and slit' sights. The peg is placed at the centre of the instrument, and the two slits on the alidade. Because the separation between the slits is exactly the same as the diameter of the peg, error-free collimation alignments were possible by sighting a star first on one, then on the other side of the peg. Allan Chapman.

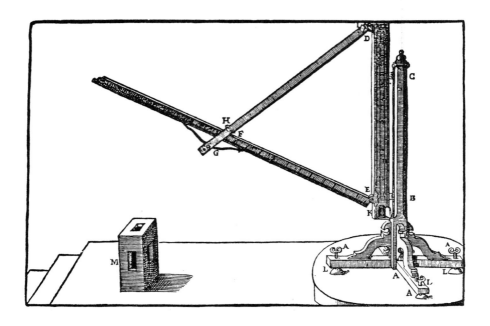

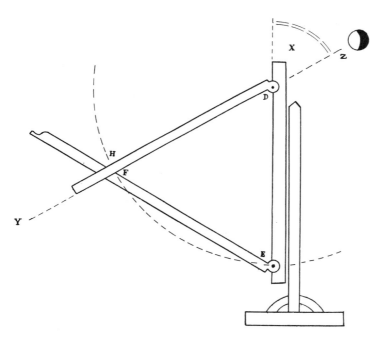

Plate 7 — Tycho Brahe's 'Parallatic Instrument', or Triquetrum. Tycho Brahe, *Astronomiae Instauratae Mechanica* (Wandesburgi, 1598) (upper illustration). Sig. B₂v. The upper illustration depicts a triquetrum (sometimes called Ptolemy's rulers), possessed by Tycho Brahe. The lower is the author's own drawing of its geometrical function. The point 'D' acts as the centre of the circle out of which the angles are measured. 'D–F' and 'D–E' act as radii to the circle, while 'H–E' forms a chord. An observer sights the moon in the position 'Y–Z'. By knowing the lengths of the two radii 'D–F' and 'D–E', and the length of the chord 'H–E', he can calculate the angle 'X'.

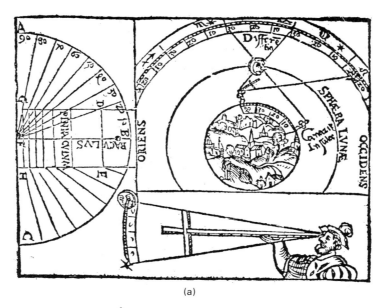

(a)

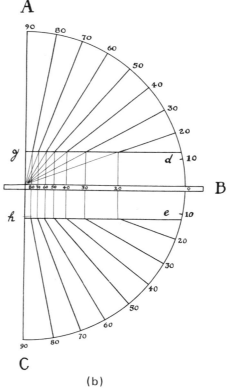

(b)

Plate 8 — (a) The cross-staff in use to take lunar angles. The method of projecting circular angles onto a straight staff is shown in the inset. Peter Apian *Cosmographicus* (Landshut, 1524) Diagram f. 32. (b) Peter Apian's cross-staff: detail reconstruction, depicting circular projections onto a straight staff. Allan Chapman.

Plate 9 — Three early seventeenth-century divided scales by (?) Elias Allen, in the collection of the ▶
Oxford Savilian Professors, now in the Museum of the History of Science, Oxford. From original photographs taken by R. T. Gunther. (a) Six-feet-radius quadrant, signed 'Elias Allen Fiecit Londini, 1637'. The
limb is divided directly down to 2-minute intervals, and to 12 seconds by diagonals. This is a beautifully
engraved but not especially accurate scale. See Chapman below. (b) Unsigned 24-inch-radius quadrant,
formerly used by Prof. John Greaves *c.* 1637. The scale divisions were built up from the central row of
original dots 10 minutes apart. It read down to 1 minute by diagonals. See Chapman below. (c) Unsigned
six-feet-radius sextant, *c.* 1637. It was less finely executed than the two quadrants above, and in spite of its
expansive limb, only read to a single minute of arc. This probably says something about the relative low
priority given to Right Ascension angles (which the sextant measured) as opposed to Declination ones
(measured by quadrants) by early seventeenth-century observers. See, R.T. Gunther, 'The first Observatory Instruments of the Savilian Professors at Oxford', *The Observatory*, **60** (July, 1937) 189–197. Also,
A. Chapman, 'The design and accuracy of some observatory instruments of the seventeenth century',
Annals of Science, **48** (1983) 457–471.

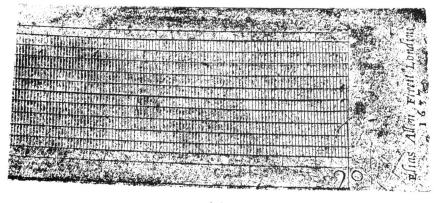

(a)

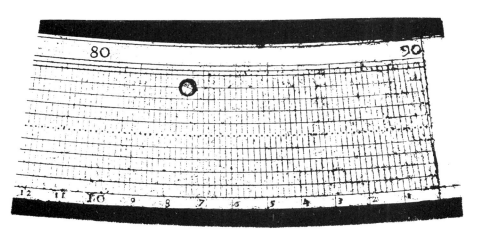

(b)

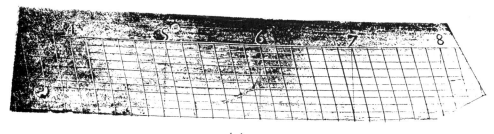

(c)

Plate 10 — Hevelius' brass sextant. J. Hevelius, *Machina Coelestis* I, (Dantzig, 1674) Plate N.

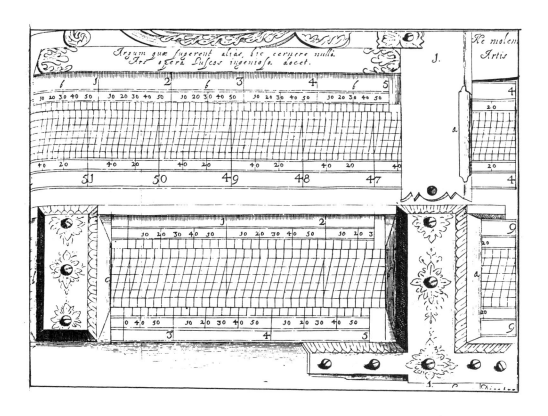

Plate 11 — Hevelius' graduated scales. The diagonal scale reads off the angle 45° 36′ 20″ against the alidade 'a'. Hevelius, *Machina Coelestis* I, (Dantzig, 1674) Plate T, inset.

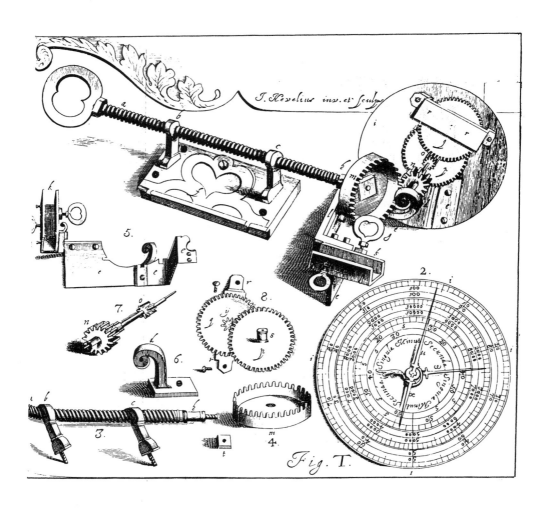

Plate 12 — Hevelius' screw-count mechanisms to read off degree fractions. *Machina Coelestis* I, (Dantzig, 1674) Plate T, inset.

however, that a sequence of ideas may be discerned that started with the cross-staff, and eventually formed the basis of the filar micrometer, once practitioners learned to equate the length of a radius (staff) with the focal length of a lens, and the distance between its cross-piece sights to the wires in a micrometer eyepiece. It was not for nothing that the first effective filar micrometer was the brainchild of Horrox's associate William Gascoigne, who must have been acquainted with his friend's attempts to measure the diameter of the Sun with two needles in the end of an 11-ft stick [78]. The suggested course of this development will be examined more closely in Chapter 3.

JOHANNES HEVELIUS (1611–1687)

In his approach to the instruments of angular measurement, Hevelius is frequently seen as the grand anachronism of seventeenth-century astronomy. His observations were undoubtedly the most accurate and comprehensive to be made public during the century, but by the time they came from the press, between 1673 and 1679, the instruments used to make them had been rendered obsolete by the newly-invented telescopic sight. Hevelius was the last, and most advanced, astronomer of the Tychonic school.

Although he used telescopes, pendulum clocks, and slow motion adjusting screws to make special kinds of observations, the principles upon which his positional instruments—his sextants and quadrants—depended were essentially the same as those of Tycho. The instruments were of Tychonic proportions, carrying the familiar arrangements of peg and slit sights, for mapping the sky by interlocking triangles. Whilst in the early part of his career Flamsteed was to use Tycho's 'triangulation' method of stellar cartography, he abandoned it after a few years, thus leaving Hevelius as the last Tychonican *ad finem*.

Following the procedure in Tycho's *Mechanica,* Hevelius confined the treatment of his instrument graduations to description, without revealing how the divisions had been drawn. Even the chapter in *Machina Coelestis* that is devoted to the scales on the Hevelian instruments says scarcely anything about the techniques of construction. But if the copper plate 'T' that depicts them is any indication as to their quality, they must have been superlative [79].

Hevelius's scales were doubly significant since they also provide the earliest example of a vernier scale being used upon an instrument intended for astronomical research. Hevelius divided each degree space into 5′ intervals, and the disposition of his diagonals and vernier can be ascertained from Plate 11. After making an observation and reading the main scale diagonals to find the nearest minute, resort was made to the vernier, where the individual seconds were shown. On Plate 11, the angle indicated contains 45° 36′ 20″ [80].

Hevelius was the first astronomer to equip his instruments with fine adjustments upon the alidade. Whereas Tycho had simply relied upon the balance of his alidades to align them onto a desired star, Hevelius invented a fine-pitch screw, one end of which engaged the alidade, the other end residing within a bracket that could be locked to any part of the limb with a thumb screw. Having found the approximate vicinity of a star, the alidade could be brought into critical alignment using the screw.

Some of Hevelius's adjusting screws were made to operate in conjunction with geared count-mechanisms, whereby the turns were registered upon a dial. Ideally, such devices would provide useful cross-checks upon the subdivisions, although from the engravings they appear altogether too complicated to have worked properly at a time when it was impossible to make a train of six small gear wheels that was not subject to considerable backlash (Plate 12). Teeth had to be hand-filed, and though this may have been adequate for watchwork, it was not enough to measure seconds of arc. Some of Hevelius's count mechanisms contained over half a dozen gears, pinions, and crown wheels that must inevitably have been inferior in operation to his graduated scales. John Flamsteed was to leave the most forceful contemporary account of the impossibility of making contemporary gears work in accordance with graduated scales, when he described his screw-edged Greenwich sextant.

After the destruction of Hevelius's observatory by the fire of 1679 [81], his detachable screw-set adjusters do not seem to have been used elsewhere until George Graham applied a similar device to the quadrant built for Halley in 1725. As Graham left no account of the instrument under his own hand, there is no indication of where he may have encountered it originally. Though the later device — simplified and shorn of its gear trains — could have been Graham's own invention, it must be remembered that Hevelius's work was well known in the Royal Society circles in which Graham moved. Instrument makers were notoriously reluctant to commit their secrets to paper, and the historian often encounters apparent connections between the works of different makers for which no written evidence can be adduced.

The mounting of Hevelius's quadrants was basically the same as those of Tycho. His largest quadrant was a voluble instrument, rotating upon an axis, the whole arrangement of which is strongly reminiscent of Tycho's voluble quadrant [82].

With his sextants, however, Hevelius provided a valuable addition seen on none of the Tychonic instruments — a slow-motion tracking screw designed to follow the desired pair of stars across the sky, whilst their separation was measured. It is best depicted in the 'Sextante Magno Orichalcico' [83] (Plate 10), where the second observer, working on the 'fixed' sight at Hevelius's left hand, actuates a long screw that joins the edge of the sextant to an anchor support in the wall of the building. By slowly turning this screw, a practised observer would be capable of compensating for the 'movement' of the sky, whilst Hevelius made the necessary measurements on the alidade. These instruments were the first ever to utilize mechanical aids in the tracking of objects across the sky, and their presence indicates a new level of appreciation in the concept of precision that had been absent in Tycho [84].

The sights on the Hevelian instruments were, once again, very similar to those on the Tychonic originals, although to ensure optimum accuracy, Hevelius made the apertures of the back sight slits adjustable with fine screws. This enabled him to 'catch' a star with the slit wide open, then close it gradually to make alignment with the fore sight.

The results obtained by Hevelius equalled — and in many cases, surpassed — the uppermost limit of accuracy attainable by naked eye instruments. His observations, accurate to about 15"–20" [85], could compete easily with any of the early telescopic observations, and were not seriously rivalled until Flamsteed and Römer had developed their own observing techniques after Hevelius's death.

The reason for Hevelius's success was twofold. Firstly, his instruments were not experimental models (as were so many of their over-vaunted telescopic competitors), but exquisitely fashioned, mature specimens that had been brought to perfection by the joint experiences of two of astronomy's most scrupulous and exacting practitioners. Secondly, Hevelius possessed eyesight of an uncommonly high acuity and resolving power. It continued, undiminished, into his old age, to be attested by Halley when he was sent to Dantzig by the Royal Society to adjudicate in the telescopic sights controversy in 1678.

Hooke's argument in favour of telescopic sights, which he ranged against Hevelius, remained grounded in his demonstration that as the unaided human eye could not reliably resolve angles smaller than 1', Hevelius's observations could not have surpassed Tycho's, irrespective of the quality of his instruments [86]. But the possibility of Hevelius possessing unusually acute eyesight does not seem to have been a contingency that Hooke fully appreciated.

By the time of Halley's visit to Dantzig, Hevelius was in the midst of a rearguard defence of a system of instrumentation that had become obsolete. Whilst the Hevelian instruments were still in themselves the finest pieces extant, and found by Halley to be every bit as fine as their owner made out, they could only perform *really* well when used in conjunction with the eyes of Hevelius himself. Their potential for further development had been exhausted. The telescopic sight, conversely, was rich with both optical and mechanical possibilities, which required only the craftsmanship of Abraham Sharp and George Graham to transform into physical realities.

Hevelius is rich in the contrasts that characterize the transitional figure. In the realm of visual astronomy he pioneered the use of long-focus telescopes, performed original works in cartography and cometography, and was one of the first men to map the moon with reasonable accuracy [87]. Like Tycho's, his lifework was executed as a great private enterprise with observatory, library, workshop, and printing presses that derived from his own patrimony and owed nothing to the state. It is this aspect of personal *virtú* that makes Hevelius so much a figure of the Northern Renaissance, for he was destined to be the last important researcher to address himself to the wholesale revision of astronomy at his own expense. With the founding of English and French national observatories in the 1670s, and the recognition of the value of scientific navigation to the nascent seaborne empires of the North, the patronage of astronomy was soon to assume a different complexion. It is within this context of technical and organizational transition that one must evaluate Hevelius. Though he made use of such modern inventions as the pendulum clock and simple micrometers, he saw them as *adjuncts* to the great quadrants and sextants of what was really a sixteenth-century system of instrumentation. In this sense, Hevelius marks both the high-water mark and swan song of the Tychonic school of astronomy [88].

3

John Flamsteed and the astronomy of the 'Great Catalogue'

... Yet however skillfull any person be except hee be accomodated with convenient and fitting instruments, he cannot put knowledge into practice

John Flamsteed, 1681 [1]

During the seventeenth century, the theory and practice of astronomy underwent profound revision, producing a new appreciation of nature, and man's relationship to it. The dimensions of the Solar System came to be known with considerable accuracy, the physical characteristics of the Sun, Moon and planets were ascertained, and the approximate velocity of light established. Galileo and Newton produced enduring intellectual monuments, but it must at all times be remembered that these achievements, and those of their contemporaries, were eventually brought to fruition by major developments in practical astronomy and the use of instruments.

Although it is well known that Galileo and Newton either used or were in some way dependent upon discoveries made with instruments, one may venture to say that it was not from these men that the century's most fundamental astronomical innovations sprang. The seventeenth century's noblest legacy to science was the realization of the concept of precision, and how future intellectual achievement must square with increasingly exact observations of nature. It was the first age in which men learned to measure in the scientific sense, and nature took on a quantitative aspect, especially as the significance of the Tychonic observations penetrated the consciousness of the philosophical community.

The century witnessed an unprecedented interest in mechanical innovation, and several instruments appeared that indicated the way in which future developments were likely to move. It was through the perfecting of these instruments during the following century — made possible by improved knowledge of materials and workshop techniques — that astronomy was to mature into a truly exact science.

If any invention was basic to seventeenth-century astronomy, it was the telescope. As a purely visual instrument, it opened what were quite literally new worlds to human scrutiny, and allowed for the first time a *physical* study of the planets. But the decisive arguments of the age could not be resolved by mere looking. It was more important to *measure*, and the telescope realized its true value in combination with other instruments which enabled it to become a tool of measurement; in particular, its adaptation to the telescopic sight on graduated instruments, the micrometer, and the pendulum clock.

THE TELESCOPIC SIGHT

Only a few years elapsed between the public announcement of the invention of the telescope in 1609 and the realization that it could greatly improve the performance of graduated instruments if used as a sight, by making the object under observation appear clearer and easier to locate than if viewed through conventional pinnules. Several astronomers had attempted to adapt the telescope to measuring purposes by attaching it to the alidade of a quadrant, but without success [2]. Their failure was occasioned by their use of the Galilean telescope, the optical system of which did not permit the postioning of a reticule in the instrument's field. Without a reticule one could only guess when the telescope was centred upon a star, and this allowed so large a margin of error as to defeat the purpose of using a telescope at all. In the early experiments with telescopic sights, their only real utility came when used to observe the Sun by projection. Scheiner's helioscope of 1624 worked in this way, projecting the solar disk on to a centred piece of paper, but as its primary purpose was to observe sunspots, it cannot be considered a true telescope sight [3].

Morin, in 1634, came closest to achieving success in the adaptation of the Galilean telescope to sighting purposes. Wishing to take advantage of the bright image afforded by a telescope, he secured one to the alidade of his quadrant. When observing, he brought the star to the centre of the field by the aid of a slip of metal into which a groove had been cut, that covered the object glass. It was thereby possible to locate a star in the open part of the field and guide it to the centre, or line of collimation, by bringing it down to the bottom of the groove [4]. Ingenious as the device may have been, it had little scientific potential. By deliberately obscuring half of his small-aperture object glass, Morin greatly reduced the efficiency of his telescope, and as the slit into which he brought the star had a definite width — thus subtending an angle — it was impossible to obtain *point* centring. Success would have been further impeded by the fact that when any obscuring medium is placed across any lens surface, its image always appears blurred, as it is not located at the point of common focus. Morin's attempts to centre the star within a badly blurred slit could not have been conducive to accurate collimation or worthwhile results.

It never seems to have occurred to Morin to place a marker to designate the line of collimation at the instrument's common focus, although this would have been difficult with a Galilean optical system.

Little is known regarding the precise optical characteristics of these early telescopes, for it is rare to find details that are sufficiently precise to allow reconstruction. But in an undated letter of *c.* 1641, sent by William Gascoigne to Oughtred, sufficient details were given to enable Gaythorpe to derive the characteristics of Gascoigne's instrument [5]. The letter referred to a Galilean telescope with an object glass of 1.20-in diameter and a focal length of 44.8 in. Its lenses were of the 'light' type of glass common before 1670, and produced a magnification of 11.2

diameters and a field of 25' [6]. Indeed, it would have been scarcely superior to Galileo's original instrument, and whilst this clearly could not have been the telescope used by Gascoigne in his optical researches, it would, nonetheless, have been a characteristic refractor of the period.

The practical development of the telescopic sight could not be commenced until the advantages of the Keplerian optical system were properly understood. By replacing the concave eyepiece with a convex or positive eyepiece, it was possible to establish a common point of focus for the instrument that fell within the tube, between the object and eye lenses. If a marker were placed at this point, it would stand out, sharply defined in the field of view, and could designate either the centre or fractional parts of the telescope's field. This *reticule* constituted the starting point of the true telescopic sight and filar micrometer.

The initial discovery was made by the Yorkshire mathematician William Gascoigne (1612–1644), who, upon observing the Sun with a Keplerian telescope, noticed that a spider's web which had fortunately become interposed between the two lenses stood out in sharp relief [7]. Gascoigne developed the invention considerably for his own use and that of his scientific friends in the North of England, but failed to publish anything to the world at large. His correspondence with William Crabtree illuminates the extent to which the development had proceeded by 1641. Gascoigne wrote: 'If here [at the focal point] an Hair be set, that it appear perfectly through the Glass, — you may use it on a Quadrant, for the finding of the Altitude of the least Star visible by the perspective wherein it is.' He further recommends that if the night be so dark that the hair is not visible, one could 'place a candle in a lanthorn, so as it cast light sufficient into the glass' [8] to illuminate the cross-hairs. This was to remain standard observing practice for over two centuries.

Gascoigne quickly recognized the great improvement in observational accuracy that would be possible as the consequence of an efficient telescopic sight. He was acquainted with the Liverpool astronomer Jeremiah Horrox, whose contributions to the lunar theory were acknowledged by Newton. It was Gascoigne's intention to examine Horrox's lunar theory observationally with the aid of telescopic instruments, for he told Crabtree 'I am fitting my sextant for all manner of observations by fitting two perspecills with threads', so that 'Mr. Horrox, his Theory of the Moon, I shall shortly be furnished to try' [9]. The sextant he used was probably similar in form to Tycho's but with telescopic rather than plain sights.

When Horrox himself first heard of the invention, Crabtree relates, it 'ravished his mind quite from itself and left him in an extasie between admiration and amazement'. Such was the power of the experimental philosophy to the men of 1640 [10].

Prior, no doubt, to his invention of the reticule telescopic sight, Gascoigne had been experimenting with lenses as a means of making the rays of the sun fall on to one spot on the quadrant, as a way of taking his altitude. Writing to William Oughtred in the undated letter cited above, he described his observation of a solar eclipse made with 'one glass' that projected the image along 'an iron ruler, moveable on the centre of a sextant of four feet' [11]. This may have been the instrument later described by Crabtree as 'your other device of a glass in a cane on the moveable ruler of your sextant' [12]. Nothing is known of the precise number of instruments with telescopic sights that Gascoigne caused to be built, but when Crabtree visited him in 1640, he was 'transported' by the number of 'selected dainties' that were shown to him.

In addition to the instruments already mentioned, Gascoigne spoke of ordering an 'iron quadrant of five foot' along the 'cursors of iron, with glasses in them and a thread for my sextant' [13]. This may well have been part of the same 'Iron Carkasse of a Sextant wch Mr. Towneley told me was Mr. Gascoigne's', seen by Flamsteed at Towneley Hall, and later described to Molyneux in 1690 [14].

It was the opinion of William Derham, when he published part of the abovementioned correspondence in 1717, that it was 'sufficient to shew that Mr. Gascoigne as early as 1640, made use of telescopes on quadrants and sextants' [15]. His reticule was simple to construct, easy to use and, unlike Morin's finder, did not reduce the telescope's light grasp by obscuring part of the field. But Gascoigne's work on the telescopic sight fell into neglect after the inventor's death in the Civil Wars in 1644, and it was not until the Restoration that the subject aroused attention once again.

As early as 1649, however, the Italian astronomer Divini was alleged to have constructed a telescope with crossed hairs near the eye-lens, although this claim was not made in writing until 1663, after the publication of Huygen's *Systema Saturni* [16]. Whether Divini's 'trellis' constitutes a true reticule is hard to establish, for his text is not clear as to its precise location in relation to the eye-lens; McKeon discusses the possibilities involved in his article on the reticule [17]. To Divini is also attributed the early application of telescopes to surveying instruments [18].

Huygen's discusses the use of the telescope as a measuring instrument in *Systema Saturni* (1659), and his work will be treated more fully below. Robert Moray was corresponding with him on the subject in December 1664 [19], and Moray's work, along with that of Hooke and Wren, indicates that by 1665 several English practitioners were conducting experiments with telescopic sights. In his *Animadversions* (1674), Hooke claimed to have examined the motions of the 1665 comet with a telescopic measuring instrument [20]. Because of the plague then raging in London, Wren travelled to Paris in the autumn of 1665, was 'well received' by the French astronomers, and probably discussed with them his work on telescopic sights [21].

How, precisely, the reticule re-entered scientific currency after a lapse of over 20 years is difficult to establish, but of greater importance than national priority was the eagerness with which the scientific world made use of the invention. The re-discovery seems to have been made quite independently, without any knowledge of the work of Gascoigne, and this applies equally to the English astronomers as to Huygens and Divini on the Continent. But as astronomical telescopes were regularly fitted with positive, convex eyepieces by 1660, one might consider the re-discovery of the reticule simply a matter of time.

Following the deaths of Crabtree and Gascoigne in the 1640s, their papers came into the possession of the Towneley family [22], and whilst they were subsequently invaluable to Richard Towneley in the invention of the micrometer, and to Flamsteed for his grounding in optics [23], their implications still lay concealed in 1665.

The French astronomers, though having little claim to the invention of telescopic sights, were quick to utilize them, and by 1667 the Académie had set up an experimental quadrant. It was noted by Olmstead that the French developed their telescopic sights in stages, sometimes using a single lens, then an optical system, with one or two wires, and finally mounting a complete telescope, with reticules, on to a graduated limb [24]. By the time of Jean Picard's observations to measure the length of a meridional degree in 1669, he was using instruments with fully developed telescopic sights with reticules, fitted respectively to a 38-in quadrant and a 10-ft zenith sector [25]. In the same year, Robert Hooke installed at Gresham College a telescopic zenith sector with a complicated system of reticule wires, for use in his attempts to measure the stellar parallax [26].

The first phase in the history of the telescopic sight as a continuing tool of scientific research took place between 1663 and 1669. But it is not without irony to reflect that the combined work of the French Academicians, Gresham College, and the learned world in general succeeded in producing by 1669 an instrument that was not substantially superior to the product of William Gascoigne's single-handed researchers, completed 30 years before.

Hooke became the staunchest advocate of the use of telescopic sights, and took it as a personal insult when Hevelius disdained to use them. After an increasingly bitter exchange between the two men, Hevelius clearly stated his case against the use of telescopic sights in *Machina Coelestis* (1673). As the reticule of such a sight could be removed not more than a few inches from the observer's eye, it was a less effective sight than one of his 'open sight' pinnules situated 6 or 8 ft from the eye. Hevelius granted that telescopic sights made the images clearer and more distinct than they appeared to the naked eye, but this was of no advantage if it was not possible to ensure an accurate line of collimation because of the reticule's proximity to the eye [27]. Hooke chose to deal with the properties of telescopic sights as part of his Cutlerian Lecture for 1674, framing his reply in *Some Animadversions . . . on the 'Machina Coelestis' of Hevelius*, where he argued that, as Hevelius's instruments worked upon the same principles as those of Tycho, the observations made with them could not be considered in any way an advance [28]. Hooke argued that Hevelius could have improved the accuracy of his observations 40-fold by using telescopic sights, and that as the human eye was incapable of resolving angles smaller than 1′, it was impossible to measure beyond it, irrespective of the quality of the instrument's graduations.

The subject of telescope sights launched Hooke into a series of original experiments to discover the angular resolution of the human eye. He drew a series of measured squares on a board, and moving away from them, took note of the exact point at which it was no longer possible to discern them individually. By comparing this distance with the size of the squares, he computed that at vanishing point, each square subtended an angle of 1′ at the observer's eye [29].

Enquiry was then made to discover whether this resolution varied when the observer was attempting to distinguish between light and dark objects. He found that it was possible to perceive an angular separation of less than 1′ when looking at two dark objects with light shining between them, but when one looked at two bright objects (such as stars) that were closer than a minute 'they coaless and appear one' [30]. Hooke's original value for average visual acuity comes remarkably close to that accepted today. Even allowing for Hevelius's uncommonly acute eyesight and wealth of experience, it is impossible to deny the force of Hooke's argument [31].

Hooke's advocacy of telescopic sights engendered considerable controversy with

Hevelius, who adamantly refused to countenance them, and, in an attempt to make an independent adjudication on the matter, Halley travelled to Danzig in the summer of 1678. Upon examining the Hevelian instruments, he was greatly impressed by their quality, and wrote to Flamsteed that Hevelius and himself were capable of obtaining consistent readings to an accuracy of 10″, and sometimes to half that amount [32].

Yet much of the anger stemmed not so much from Hooke's scientific claims as from the manner in which he pursued them against the revered German astronomer who was 30 years his senior. His snide references to Hevelius, the sarcastic tone of his Cutlerian Lecture, and his other 'unmannerly railings', served only to anger Hooke's English colleagues and intensify the sense of persecution felt by the Curator of Experiments [33].

Flamsteed's letters make it abundantly obvious that he had little personal regard for Hooke, but even he was unequivocal as to the advantages of telescopic sights, and it was a comment of Flamsteed's in *Philosophical Transactions* of 1672 that first sparked off Hevelius's defensive wrath [34]. After assuring Oldenburg that 'no such familiarity' existed between Hooke and himself, Flamsteed stated that 'I am of the opinion that Glasses excell plain sights for observations' to such an extent that 'tis easier to mistake four inches when measuring a foot' than to mistake half a minute with telescopic sights. Needless to say, all the Greenwich instruments carried such sights [35].

In spite of the advantages of telescopic sights, however, Flamsteed was aware that no systematic study had been made of them, and little was available in print. He endeavoured to correct this deficiency in his Gresham College lectures in 1681, where lectures five and six dealt at considerable length with telescopic optics, reticules, and instrument rectification. In his sixth lecture, Flamsteed endeavoured to restore the somewhat eclipsed Gascoigne to his true place in the history of the reticule. But as Professor Forbes remarks, the attendance figures at Flamsteed's lectures were so low that their effect on instrumentation must have been negligible [36].

Considering the state of technology in 1675, Hevelius was quite correct in asserting the superiority of his instruments, but the crucial fact that eluded Hevelius was the developmental possibilities inherent in the telescopic sight that had become exhausted in his own instruments. Once instrument makers had mastered the methods of collimating telescopic sights, so that their reticules always read true both to the optical axis and the centre of the instrument's divisions (thus negating Hevelius' criticisms), they became part of the necessary equipment of astronomical research.

Although this was not obvious to any astronomer of the age before 1675 — with the possible exception of Hooke — the telescopic sight provided a decisive technical breakthrough, without which practical astronomy would have been incapable of progressing. To most seventeenth-century astronomers, improved accuracy meant better dividing of graduated scales, and by the mid-century this art had become highly developed, though ill-documented. The arcs of Tycho, and certainly those of Hevelius, carried divisions the uniformity and regularity of which exceeded 1′. Hevelius's instruments, complete with transversals, verniers, and screw-sets, were probably reliable to 15″ in actual division [37]. But further development in the craft of scale-dividing would have been futile had the astronomers who were to use the instruments been incapable of resolving angles beyond 1′.

The physical limitations of the human eye represented a ceiling to all future astronomical endeavour, until the invention of telescopic sights allowed the visual acuity of observers to catch up with standards of dividing. By 1680, this balance had not only been redressed, but tipped over to the opposite extreme, as a return was made to the former situation, where the hand of the engraver had been unable to match up to the eye of the observer. This, in turn, called forth new levels of skill from the instrument maker.

THE MICROMETER

In astronomical connotations, the word 'micrometer' came at an early stage to be attached to two quite separate instruments. One was a device, be it a pair of reticule wires or a measuring plate, placed at the point of common focus of a telescope which would serve to deduce the angular extent of the field of view. The other referred to a precision screw, the whole and part turns of which could be used to measure accurately quantities too small to be reckoned by conventional linear methods. In practice, both ideas — reticule and screw — came to be embodied in one instrument, the filar micrometer, in which two reticular wires were mounted in the field of view, and moved towards and away from each other with a screw, the counts of which designated the angle subtended. One may see in the early filar micrometer a distinct development from the telescopic sight. Once it had become feasible to place reticules in the telescope where the size of the field of view was known, it followed that any two or more reticules must contain between them an angle that corresponded to a fraction of the whole field. This would constitute the simplest form of fixed aperture micrometer. When one of these wires came later to be mounted on to a separate frame, so as to be movable across the field of view, it then became possible to read off any angular quantity that was less than the overall field of the telescope by simply 'enclosing' the extremities of the object between the fixed and movable wires. William Gascoigne, who invented the telescopic sight, was also the first astronomer to mount a moving reticule in the manner outlined above to make a filar micrometer.

It may be argued, however, that the ideas present in the early micrometer did not stem directly from the invention of the reticule, but rather were given a new degree of precision by it. Gascoigne's micrometer measured the diameter of astronomical bodies by triangulation, using a technique that was identical in principle to that embodied in the astronomical radius and camera obscura.

Mention has already been made of the astronomical radius and how it measured angles by delineating tangents of an arc upon a radial cross-piece. Horrox had used a form of radius to measure the Sun's diameter, by placing two pins, or mounted hairs, close together at the end of long rod so that they 'enclosed' the Sun. Such a device embodied all the geometrical properties of the micrometer, utilising two pointers to form a long narrow triangle, the acute angle of which terminated with the observer's eye. The same geometrical principle was further refined in operation by the 'foramen' or camera obscura technique, where the direction of the triangle was reversed, so that a pinhole replaced the observer's eye at its apex. By admitting light through a pinhole into a darkened chamber, an image of the Sun was cast on to a screen. The extremities of this image, as measured with dividers, had a relationship to its distance from the projecting pinhole that was in the same ratio as the triangles of the astronomical radius. Realizing that the same principle applied with lenses, whereby the extremities of the projected image corresponded in amplitude to the extremities of the *object* being projected, Gascoigne made the crucial step of replacing the pinhole with a lens [38] and making the image fall inside the tube of a telescope. In the filar micrometer, the pinhole became an object glass, and the screen on which the image fell became the common focal point of the objective and eye lenses. Instead of striking off the size of the image with a pair of dividers, one 'enclosed' it with the reticule wires (Plate 14).

While it is not being argued that Gascoigne consciously proceeded through each of these stages, from radius to foramen, as preliminaries to the invention of the micrometer, it must be understood that these techniques were already in current use among practical astronomers, and a knowledge of them must at least have coloured his thinking. The development of the micrometer became possible after the invention of the reticule, and through Gascoigne's realization that cumbersome triangulations with camera obscura could be made more simply and advantageously inside the tube of a telescope.

What elevated Gascoigne's instrument from an ingenious form of telescopic sight to an instrument of independent scientific potential was his invention of a mechanism by which the reticule wires could be advanced across the field of view. To achieve this end, he mounted each reticule on to an accurately made screw, so that when the screws were turned, the reticules either advanced or receded in relationship to the centre of the field, thus making it possible to 'enclose' the object with them. The screws were of a known pitch, so that one revolution advanced the reticule through an exactly determined part of the field of view. It was thus possible to find the telescope's overall angular field of view by simple computation, and then divide it into fractions by counting the screw turns. As the end of the screw carried a divided plate, it was possible to measure off fractions of a turn, and thus relate them to angular openings between the reticules.

The principle of using screw turns to measure small distances constituted an invention in its own right, quite independent of the telescopic sight. It is this part of the filar micrometer that comprised the 'micrometer' proper, and was to be invaluable to the subsequent development of astronomy, mechanics, and engineering.

Gascoigne neither published a description of his micrometer nor left a surviving account of it. Knowledge of the instrument, along with Gascoigne's other works, was preserved by Richard Towneley, who salvaged the original micrometer with the inventor's papers in the 1640s [39]. Several Gascoigne letters passed into the hands of William Derham in the early eighteenth century, some of which he published. Amongst them was a letter sent by the inventor to Crabtree dated Christmas Eve 1641, 'wherein he describes the wheel-work of his micrometer' [40], though unfortunately this was not a part of the letter he published. All that now remain of Gascoigne's papers are the fragments on telescopic sights, printed in *Philosophical Transcriptions* along with those reprinted by Flamsteed and Rigaud.

No indication exists of the trade or identity of the craftsman who made

Gascoigne's micrometer. In building the framework of his quadrant, Gascoigne spoke of employing 'a country joiner', and other workmen, perhaps including a blacksmith. It is unlikely that such men could have undertaken the construction of a micrometer [41].

When Richard Towneley exhibited his own improved instrument to the Royal Society in 1667, he employed 'an exact and ingenious watchmaker of these parts' to construct it, and as the Gascoigne and Towneley estates lay within a few miles of each other, it may be surmised that the original inventor engaged a man of similar calling [42] (Plate 13).

In May 1672, Flamsteed visited Towneley Hall, made transcripts of the Crabtree and Gascoigne manuscripts, and probably saw the original micrometer [43]. From his account of the instrument in *Historia Coelestis*, we know that Gascoigne's micrometer possessed two screws, and that Towneley later simplified their function to be performed by one [44]. This was accomplished by cutting two separate threads, left- and right-handed, into the same cylindrical rod, so that when the rod was rotated, two distinct motions were communicated to those parts of the instrument that controlled the sights [45]. Flamsteed also printed several tables of micrometer observations made by Gascoigne with his original instrument to compare with his own, and these have proved to be of considerable value in assessing the instrument's performance [45].

In an attempt to determine the working accuracy of this micrometer, the present author has caused a selection of these figures to be computed so that the values obtained by Gascoigne could be compared with co-ordinates for the same objects, reduced in accordance with modern celestial mechanics to the dates of the original observations. Celestial mechanics has now reached a state of exactitude whereby it is possible to state exactly the place a planet occupied, or what diameter the moon subtended, for almost any hour in the sixteenth or seventeenth centuries. The Royal Greenwich Observatory at Herstmonceux kindly undertook the computation, and, for every Gascoigne observation, supplied its correct computed value, thus creating a standard against which to check the original instrument.

Reduction was made for three different sets of observations, comparing 80 measures of the lunar diameter, made between 1640 and 1642, six observations of the stars of the Pleiades cluster, and four planetary diameters. Among the observations made of the lunar and planetary diameters, it is immediately noticed that Gascoigne's measures tend to be bigger than the computed values. Of the 80 lunar diameters, 66 are too large, along with four of the planetary diameters. This is not uncommon in micrometric work, for it is difficult to enclose the micrometer wires exactly to the limb of a bright circular disk, and most inexperienced observers produce excessive values. Optical irradiation sometimes makes it confusing to establish precisely where the bright halo surrounding the object ends and the disk begins. Even using modern instruments, a great deal of practice is required before an observer can make accurate measurements.

Like all other telescopes of its day, Gascoigne's instrument would have been afflicted with chromatic and spherical aberrations, causing the resulting images to be surrounded by a blurred haze of colours to the depth of several seconds. When making a measurement of an object, it would have been almost impossible for Gascoigne to determine precisely where the Moon's edge lay in the field of view, and where the 'circle of confusion' surrounding it began. In all probability, therefore, he would have produced excessive values, as he measured not only the size of the Moon, but part of her blurred halo as well. Though it is true that astronomers such as Hevelius and Huygens eliminated chromatic aberration by focusing the yellow light, these astronomers invariably used 'ariel' telescopes, which produced a large spectral band, whereas Gascoigne worked with instruments of short focal length, where colour selection would have been almost impossible.

Although Gascoigne does not discuss the mounting of the telescopes, he probably used a simple altazimuth, similar to that of Towneley. In 1667, Towneley remarked that one could always obtain more consistent measurements on land-angles than in the sky because of the 'swift motion of the planets' [47]. Furthermore, Gascoigne says nothing about the altitude of the Moon, refraction or weather conditions at the time of making each observation, and these factors could have affected the observations substantially.

The 80 lunar observations [48] are spread between error extremes of $+150''$ and $-34''$, with a root mean square of $+35''$, and a mean for the entire sequence of $+20''$. Fifty-four of the 80 observations fall between the error range $0''$ and $+40''$, and only 11 between $+40''$ and $+90''$, in gradually descending order. Fourteen observations fall between $0''$ and $-40''$, again in descending sequence. One observation lies well off the sequence with an error of $+150''$. Reckoning the mean lunar diameter to be $1865.50''$ [49], the $20''$ mean error indicates that Gascoigne was capable of making this observation to 1.07% accuracy.

The planetary observations are not sufficient in number to permit a distribution analysis, though what emerges very clearly is the rapid increase in error that occurred when Gascoigne attempted to measure the very small angular quantities, as subtended by the planets [50]. From four observations (see Table 3.1) made in 1640, the

Table 3.1

		Observed	Computed	Difference
Jupiter	August 25th	51″	41″	+10″
Mars	August 25th	38″	24″	+14″
Mars	December 24th	25″	8″	+17″
Venus	December 24th	25″	12″	+13″

errors run as follows, adding ten days to the original date, to compensate for the change from the Julian to the Gregorian calendar. Jupiter, the largest planet, produces the smallest error at $10''$ or 25%, whereas the second Mars observation gives a value that is in excess by 200%.

Gascoigne also left six micrometer measurements for the stars in the Pleiades cluster [51]. No doubt because he was not 'enclosing' a disk, but cutting a point of starlight, these observations do not tend uniformly to excess quantities. Of the six observations, only two are bigger than the computed angular separations, and four smaller. The root mean square is $32''$, and the mean $- 15''$.

In addition to these values, Towneley stated that Gascoigne made many other observations of various objects 'to gather the many certainties in the Heavens'. In particular, he mentioned 'The finding [of] the Moon's distance from two observations of her horizontal and meridional diameters', in order to establish Gascoigne's priority against the Parisian Auzout, who had recently made the *same* observations with a micrometer of his own devising. Towneley considered he would be 'A great wronger of our Nation' if he did not vindicate Gascoigne's invention and research, against the claims of the French [52].

It is evident from Gascoigne's work that, even in its rudimentary stages, the filar micrometer had made possible the measurement of angles to a hitherto unprecedented degree of accuracy. As with the telescopic sight, however, the instrument fell into neglect until the 1660s. Richard Towneley improved upon Gascoigne's original, producing an instrument about 'the bigness of a pocket watch', which he eventually demonstrated to the Royal Society in 1667 [53]. His instrument had only one screw that controlled the motion of a single pointer, the other being fixed. A device that was governed by the micrometer screw maintained the place of the pointer in the line of collimation and prevented their alignment from altering as the screw was turned. Robert Hooke provided an excellent set of plates for the instrument, showing how the micrometer was fitted on to a telescope, along with its 'slow motion' mechanism, which facilitated the tracking of objects across the sky. The end of the micrometer screw carried a circular brass dial, of 3-in. diameter and divided into 100 equal parts, which, in conjunction with a sliding indicator on the micrometer screw, recorded the full and part turns of the micrometer. Two and a half of these divisions on the dial corresponded to a second of arc as seen through the telescope, and whilst the movement of the celestial bodies rarely made it possible to read their places with such exactitude, the instrument could be made to measure fixed land angles to a single division [54]. Towneley claimed that the micrometer enabled him to read a foot to 40,000 equal parts, by counts of the screw.

Towneley's micrometer was a direct development from Gascoigne's original instrument and was later to influence Flamsteed [55], but other astronomers were also concerned with the measuring of telescopic angles. Ten years previously, in 1657, Huygens had inserted a diaphragm into the focal point of a 23-ft refractor in an attempt to minimize chromatic aberration, and discovered that it subtended an aperture of $17\frac{1}{4}'$ when a star passage was timed across it [56]. This represented a primitive fixed aperture micrometer, and in *Systema Saturni* (1659) he described how he introduced shaped pieces of metal into the field until they exactly covered the object under observation. On completing the operation, he measured the pieces, and comparing them with the known extent of the field, computed their angular diameters. Hooke and Wren also made measurements of Jupiter's moons in the 1650s [57].

During the 1660s, several Continental astronomers were experimenting with micrometer devices to measure small angles, including Malvasia, Petit, and Auzout, although these men worked independently and in ignorance of Gascoigne [58]. Indeed, it seems to have been the announcement of the French micrometers in 1667 that urged Towneley to publish his own micrometer work in *Philosophical Transactions*.

The convergence of optical and mechanical ideas that brought about the telescopic sight and micrometer in the 1660s was to be of great importance to the future development of astronomy. Though the filar micrometer as an instrument in its own right was considerably refined over the next two centuries, its two essential ingredients — the reticule and screw count mechanism — would be developed independently to serve many diverse branches of science and technology.

THE CLOCK

After Huygens successfully adapted the pendulum to clockwork in the 1650s, astronomers were quick to realize the importance of the clock as a measuring device, by converting temporal into angular units. Though the present book is not concerned with horological mechanisms, the role of the clock in astronomical measurement will be reviewed in Chapter 5.

ROBERT HOOKE (1635–1703) AND HIS CONTRIBUTIONS TO ANGULAR MEASUREMENT

Hooke was closely connected with the early history of the Royal Observatory, founded at Greenwich in 1675, and in addition to having played a part in the design of the fabric, interested himself in the instrumentation [59]. The decade preceding the founding of the Observatory had been one of the great experimentation in the field of astronomical instrumentation for Hooke, and many of his ideas on this subject were embodied in his 1674 Cutlerian Lecture referred to above. His *Animadversions* may be considered one of the most imaginative and far-reaching tracts in the history of practical mechanics. The book was much more than a mere polemic against Hevelius, but an analysis of the principles of astronomical instrumentation as Hooke understood them. He believed that the technical innovations of the past decade at last showed the way by which astronomy could break out of the doldrums into which it had drifted as a result of Hevelius's 'antiquated' methods.

Two dominant themes ran through the work: the vindication of telescopic sights, and Hooke's presentation of a new method of graduating instruments that was totally independent of conventional engraved divisions, and derived from the micrometer. In the method one may trace the culmination of many ideas with which Hooke had busied himself over the previous year: gears, horology, micrometers, and optics. Hooke's ideas, as presented in *Animadversions*, are evident in the design of the early Greenwich instruments, and also influenced the development of the dividing engine in the eighteenth century (Plate 16).

Many times during the course of the *Animadversions*, Hooke's imagination outran the physical limitations of contemporary materials and craftsmanship, but he realized better than anyone else at this time how the telescopic sight and micrometer would allow angles to be measured not only with greater accuracy, but with instruments of smaller and more manageable dimensions than those in current use. He claimed that a quadrant of 3-ft radius, divided by his method, would exceed in accuracy a conventional instrument of 150 ft [60].

Conventional diagonal scales were not only laborious and difficult to draw, but their errors were difficult to detect once the instrument was finished. Hooke sought a more satisfactory mode of graduation, and towards this end, proposed to entirely abandon the use of engraved scales, by furnishing the limb of his quadrant with 1600 teeth, which were to be engaged by a tangential worm-wheel that was attached to the end of the alidade. Turning this screw 17.88 turns advanced the alidade one whole degree, and 0.296 of a turn corresponded to 1′. A circular dial plate attached to the worm-wheel rod would then designate the seconds and fractions [61].

The connection with the micrometer is immediately obvious. By turning the edge of his quadrant into part of a gear wheel, he provided a track along which could be run a precision micrometer screw that carried with it the telescopic sight. Like Gascoigne, he appreciated that the key to this method of dividing rested on the translation of angular quantities into linear units as represented on the straight rod of the micrometer. One may indeed consider the endless-screw micrometer rod as a mechanized form of the tangental cross-piece of the astronomical radius. Astronomers of the seventeenth century were adepts in the art of thinking in terms of mutually related circles and triangles.

In operation, the quadrant would have been fitted with two telescopic alidades that ran on a common pivot at the centre of the arc. This pivot also carried the common eyepiece for both telescopes and contained a pair of mirrors in order to focus the light from both telescopes into the eye of one observer, thus enabling him to take the angle between two objects without the need for an assistant [62].

Hooke paid considerable attention to the practical problems of constructing such an instrument, and in particular, to cutting the gear-teeth. To regularize the motion of the worm-wheel, Hooke knew that the gear-wheel would have to be at a slight angle to the plane of the quadrant, rather than at a right angle. As a preliminary to cutting the teeth he therefore suggested the taking of ten thin brass plates, their combined thickness being the same as the quadrant. The plates would be screwed tightly together to make one piece of brass, and shaped into an arc of the desired size [63]. The requisite number of teeth would then be cut into this arc, but at right angles, square across the combined thickness of the plates. When this operation was complete, the plates would be unscrewed and each one turned slightly on the centre of the arc so that the rows of teeth no longer formed straight, but diagonal, lines, and were then screwed up afresh in their new positions. They could then be finished into a set of diagonal teeth that were much more regular than those filed directly into the edge of a solid arc of cast brass.

Hooke gave no indication as to the best way of making the tangent screw that engaged them, and after describing the more important process of regularizing the main gear-teeth, he probably commended this aspect of the work to the ingenuity of the mechanic. As the diameter of this screw would have been around $\frac{3}{4}$ in, it is likely to have been made by the template method that was current before the invention of the precision screw-cutting lathe. The method derived from antiquity, where it had first been described by the Alexandrian mathematician Pappus, and required the operator to make a triangular template out of thin brass, so that when it was wrapped around the screw-blank, its hypotenuse formed a helix along which one could cut a file, thus incising the helical groove into the blank, as the template was unwound [64]. Alternatively, a piece of paper could be prepared that wrapped exactly around the screw-blank. Upon the paper a set of diagonal lines were drawn, in a ratio that corresponded to the pitch of the intended screw. The paper was then glued onto the blank, making the diagonal lines connect into a continuous helix traversing its length. The mechanic could then file this line, through the paper, and into the metal. Such operations naturally placed great demands on the craftsman to cut and face the screw accurately, so that its pitch was regular, but, with patience, good results could be obtained [65]. Various other screw-generating methods were also known.

Royal Society members who wished to possess a quadrant made according to Hooke's novel specifications, were advised to

imploy Mr Tompion, a watch maker of Water Lane near Fleet Street; this person I recommend as having imployed him to make that [quadrant] which I have whereby *he* hath seen and experienced the difficulties that do occur therein. [66]

Molyneux later purchased a Hooke quadrant, made by Whitehead for £20, which became the subject of several letters that he exchanged with the Astronomer Royal [67].

Hooke listed nine scientific problems that he hoped his screw-quadrant would be able to solve [68]. These included determining the length of the meridional degree, the compilation of accurate tables to find the quantities for atmospheric refraction, and the determination of absolute co-ordinates for important geographical positions. He also recommended the screw-quadrant to be used to see if the fixed stars exhibited small 'proper-motions' one unto another 'which I have good grounds to believe they do'. The existence of these proper motions was eventually confirmed by Halley in 1718 [69].

It is unlikely that Hooke ever undertook any protracted courses of observations with his screw-quadrant 'by reason of his multitude of business', or else he would have been more aware of its shortcomings [70]. Even assuming Hooke's novel way of cutting diagonal teeth into the edge of the limb to have worked satisfactorily, the teeth would have suffered such terrible wear when the steel micrometer screw was racked back and forth as to make them erroneous after a short space of time. Mechanical friction was but imperfectly understood in the seventeenth century, and Hooke failed to appreciate that his endless-screw micrometer would attack the soft brass teeth like a saw.

The principal obstacle to the instrument's success lay in the fact that the screw had to be turned even when moving the telescopic alidade across the scale between observations. As the quadrant carried no engraved divisions, it was impossible to disengage the screw at any time. There would have been no fixed point of reference at which to re-engage it when one wished to re-commence observation, as all angles were measured in screw-turns from the bottom of the arc. Naturally, this constant back-and-forth movement across the quadrant eroded the teeth, and must have made the instrument slow and tedious to use, for a change in altitude of 45° would have required 800 turns to be applied to the micrometer. The successful application of the micrometer to the limb of divided instruments was not achieved until John Bird combined it with conventional divisions in 1745, so that the screw only needed to turn during the critical moment of observation, and was not required to transport the alidade between observations [71]. In this way friction was minimized, and the mechanical efficiency of the instrument vastly improved.

No craftsman in Restoration London could make mirrors to the degree of flatness required to ensure the success of the double catoptric telescopes with which Hooke proposed to equip his screw-edged quadrant. Hooke had also encountered this problem in his attempts to shorten the long telescopes by sending their light through a series of mirrors, in a manner similar to the modern binocular [72]. If mirrors with inaccurately ground reflecting surfaces were placed within the complicated optical system of the screw-quadrant, they would distort apparent star positions, and ruin the crucial lines of optical and mechanical collimation upon which the instrument depended.

In practice, Hooke's quadrant required too many perfect systems — optical and mechanical — to work together, too consistently, through too many operations. A fault of workmanship or adjustment in any one of them was sufficient to render the operation of adjacent systems unreliable. With the exception of testing the screw openings against surveyed terrestrial angles, the quadrant was almost devoid of cross-checks, and allowed errors to accumulate unnoticed. When one considers the inherent play in the supplementary gearing used to turn the micrometer screw, the inevitable racking of this screw on the limb and the complicated optical system involved, one soon appreciates that Hooke's invention far exceeded the practical 'ceiling' of Restoration workshop practice.

It was not until well into the eighteenth century that mechanical technology advanced sufficiently to measure down to those tolerances which Hooke boasted for his quadrant, and by that time, instrument makers had found ways of avoiding the drawbacks outlined above. But what Hooke's tract did contain was an abundance of ideas on how mechanical appliances could be used to enable scientists to make more reliable observations of nature, plus an assortment of incidental devices that later came to be of importance in astronomical instrumentation. Foremost amongst these was Hooke's improved method for making spirit levels, together with his clock driven equatorial mount for the quadrant. To rectify the quadrant accurately, Hooke proposed the use of a spirit level, in which the bubble was enclosed beneath a glass plate, the inside of which was ground concave to represent the segment of a circle of 1000-ft radius [73]. At this radius, Hooke calculated that a 9-in. spirit level would correspond to 2' and single seconds would be clearly discernible quantities. One soon perceives that the logic underlying the level, like that of the quadrant itself, was related to the astronomical radius, where the 9-in spirit level at 1000 ft stood as the equivalent to a tangent on the radius of a circle. Just as it had been impossible for a artisan of 1674 to grind a perfectly flat mirror, so it was equally impossible for him to produce a 9-in spirit level to so large a radius, but when the manufacture of precision levels became possible in the eighteenth century, a level was to provide an invaluable guide when checking the alignment of instruments.

To measure fractional parts of a calculated tangent, Horrox had used moving sights and dividers, Gascoigne a screw in the telescope eyepiece, Hooke a screw on the limb of a quadrant, and, finally, in his spirit level, a bubble in a tube. Each stage of this development depended on the relationship between the tangents, triangles, and radii of the circle.

When in use, Hooke's quadrant was to be mounted upon the polar axis of an ingenious equatorial stand, complete with a counterpoise. Though Hooke had no claim to the invention of the equatorial mount [74], he proposed the original addition of a clock-drive that turned the entire instrument by 'a small automaton which may continue it for many hours exactly in the azimuth of the star desired' [75]. Although the initial hint may have come from Hevelius [76], Hooke obviously recognized the great utility of such a mechanism, which in practice would have relieved the observer from the uncertainty of tracking an object across the sky while trying to measure it — a difficulty which Towneley had already described in his micrometer paper of 1667.

How much of this instrument was actually built is not known, for Hooke was a busy and prolific man who rarely had time to follow an invention through to completion. Tompion seems to have made a geared quadrant with a worm-wheel micrometer, but that he went so far as to equip it with double catoptric sights and a mechanically driven equatorial stand is unlikely, considering the work involved and the general shortage of money for such projects. These finishing details probably lived only in the superb set of plates with which Hooke illustrated his quadrant, although his method of screw graduation was to be used for two of the original sets of instruments at the Greenwich Observatory.

John Flamsteed was the first astronomer to work regularly with a Hooke instrument, when he was supplied in 1676 with a screw-edge sextant, mounted on a geared, hand-cranked equatorial. He found the instrument exceedingly troublesome to use, and after a year was compelled to modify it; attention must now be paid to the use of that sextant, along with the other instruments of the early Royal Observatory.

JOHN FLAMSTEED (1646–1719) AND THE EARLY ROYAL OBSERVATORY

Together with the Royal Society, the founding of the Royal Observatory at Greenwich may be considered one of the most illustrious achievements of the reign of Charles II. The founding and early history of this institution mirrors admirably the mixture of enthusiasm, innovation and organizational ineptitude which so characterized the age. According to the founding Warrant, the Observatory was to complete the 'perfecting of navigation and astronomy' [77], with special reference to finding the longitude by 'Lunars', after Flamsteed had demonstrated to the King the fallacy of St. Pierre's method [78].

Upon assuming directorship of the Royal Observatory in 1675, Flamsteed inherited an empty building. The only instruments he possessed were those raised on his own initiative, or given to him gratis by Sir Jonas Moore. They included a pair of clocks with 13-ft pendulums, a 'Towneleian' micrometer, given to him in 1670, along with an indifferent quadrant and several miscellaneous pieces, which he brought from Derby [79]. His principal instrument was a large sextant provided at the expense of Sir Johas Moore, and a quadrant which he had on loan from the Royal Society, until 'the ill-nature of Mr. Hook forced it out of my hands' [80].

Flamsteed's early years at Greenwich provide an interesting insight into what were considered important astronomical preliminaries, and how an ambitious research programme was mounted with a collection of instruments that were little more than untried novelties of a few years' standing.

The principal clocks mounted in the Octagon Room had 13-ft pendulums beating 'double seconds', and were controlled by ingenious pin-wheel escapements attributed to Richard Towneley [81]. They were built by Tompion to run for a year on one winding, although Flamsteed found them far from trouble-free in operation. It has been suggested that their purpose was to establish 'the equation of the natural days', and confirm the even rotation of the Earth on its axis as a preliminary to his work on the longitude [82]. This was performed by his timing the daily culminations of Sirius with a fixed telescope, to see if any variation was to be detected in the length of the siderial day. The whole logic of longitude-finding pre-supposed the Earth's rotation to be even, and that for every four minutes of time, one degree of sky crossed the meridian. Without secure knowledge of this fact it would have been futile to pursue further the astronomical determination of the longitude. By 1680, Flamsteed had settled this matter to his satisfaction, and henceforth made relatively little use of the 'Gt. Clocks' except to time eclipses and similar phenomena [85].

From 1676 to 1690, Flamsteed's principal instrument was a 7-ft iron sextant made by Thomas Tompion that embodied both telescopic sights and Hooke's method of screw graduation [84]. It was fashioned as a 60° arc with two telescopic sights, but these were plain Keplerian telescopes with reticules each requiring a separate observer, and dispensed with the elaborate catoptric system of Hooke's original instrument (Plate 19). One sight was fixed to the 'zero degrees' end of the arc, the other, being attached to the alidade, was free to move through 60°. To measure any angular separation between two stars, an assistant first sighted one star of the pair through the fixed telescope. Flamsteed then moved the alidade across the scale until he sighted the second. The resulting angular separation was then obtained by counting the turns applied to the worm wheel that were necessary to 'open' the telescopes to the required distance to make the sighting. Prior to commencing regular observations, however, it was first necessary to find out experimentally the angles subtended by a given number of screw turns. Flamsteed determined this by staking out on the ground a line of 8762 in., at the end of which he set a 'strong flat rail' at right angles to it, to act as a tangent. Beforehand, he had computed the exact length that the tangent rail would have to be, so that when viewed from the opposite end of the 8762-in. line, it would subtend an angle of 5°. The ends of the tangent rail were observed with the telescopic sights on the sextant, until, having repeated the observation several times, he was able to compile a table of 'revolves' for the screw [85].

The equatorial sextant was not restricted to meridian work, and could be directed to any part of the sky to track stars in the equatorial plane. Its purpose was to survey, by triangulation, the place of every star in relationship to its adjacent stars, by measuring their separations from the vernal equinox. When the stellar places had been accurately determined, it was possible to chart the lunar and planetary motions against them. Flamsteed's technique was essentially the same as Tycho's, though it was hoped that the optical and mechanical superiority of Flamsteed's instrument would render the problems of the longitude and stellar parallax less intractable.

Within a few months of commencing, Flamsteed discovered that his sextant was afflicted with serious errors. The constant racking of the worm wheel had caused the teeth to wear to such an extent that the instrument displayed errors up to 1′ when tested against specimen angles laid out in Greenwich Park. In 1677, Flamsteed dismantled the instrument, and with his own hands engraved on its brass limb a set of conventional divisions, each being subdivided down to 10″ [86]. The sextant was now equipped with two independent means of reading the same angle, and he soon realized the value of being able to cross-check any given observation, by either screw turns or scale degrees. Furthermore, as the screw was reliable to one-third of a turn over small angles he found it a useful way of reading the interval seconds between any two diagonal lines on the engraved scale [87]. This technique of being able to cross-check readings was to be of great importance, and is to be found in a refined form on all subsequent Greenwich instruments.

In his correspondence with Molyneux, Flamsteed says much about Hooke's screw method of graduation — much of it unfavourable — although it is not always easy to separate his genuine criticism from his undisguised dislike of Hooke as a man. He had little faith in Hooke's screw, and it was only through the inventor's connivance with Sir Jonas Moore and the Royal Society that the sextant was fitted with the device at all [88]. Not even Tompion, the finest metal-worker of the age, could make the gearing to the required order of perfection at this early date, whilst the lack of homogeneity in the composition of the available metals made them susceptible to uneven wear. If Flamsteed seems severe in regarding the 'ingeniose Mr. Hooke' as an impractical dreamer whose imagination soared beyond the skills and materials of his age, it must be remembered that Flamsteed was the only contemporary scientific man to test rigorously a Hooke invention in the daily occupation of research. Even from the very outset of his career at Greenwich, Flamsteed was

> much troubled with Mr Hooke who, not being troubled with the use of any instrument, will needs force his ill-contrived devices on us. Hee talks much of such things as none but those yt. [that] understand them not can esteem possible or probable: yt. an instrument of no more yn. [than] 18 inches radius should measure an angle to less than 6 seconds; that he has an instrument, or quadrant, of 36 foot radius yt. weighs not a pound and which hee can put in his pocket; and several things of the same sort but larger far. [89]

After proving unsuccessful in his attempts to make the screw-turns on his new quadrant read consistently, Molyneux appealed for advice to Flamsteed. The Astronomer Royal replied 'no screw whatever, is so equally made as to have all wayes the same number of revolves in an inch' and that he preferred to repose his trust in his 'diagonals which are unalterable' [90]. Having used the screw-sextant for nearly ten years at the time of writing, Flamsteed may be considered as the voice of experience in such matters.

The Astronomer Royal did not even grant Hooke the credit for inventing the screw, but peevishly stated that he had 'borrowed it from the Emperor Ferdinand as you will find if you read ye *Liber Prolegomena* of Tycho's *Historia Coelestis* page 112', where a form of screw-quadrant is decribed [91]. Mention was made of this and two similar instruments in Chapter 2. Although the instruments described by Tycho did use a toothed limb, the teeth were engaged by an ordinary leafed pinion gearwheel, which served better to steady the alidade than to read the angles. Indeed, many seventeenth-century practitioners experimented with the use of screw-turns in making measurements, and even John Aubrey's friend Francis Potter possessed a spring-bow compass on which the screw-turns were made to correspond to calculated compass openings [92].

The crucial principle embodied in Hooke's instrument depended on the use of a worm-screw, that clearly derived from the micrometer, which he used to engage precision gear-teeth. Worm-screws, unlike ordinary toothed pinions, were capable of engaging several of the limb-threads at one time, thus reducing greatly the possibility of play in its motion, and contributing to the superior accuracy of the mechanism.

Regardless of the low opinion in which Flamsteed held Hooke's instruments, it is likely that they provided more genuine inspiration for his sextant than the Astronomer Royal was willing to give credit for. The Greenwich sextant represented a substantial improvement, both optically and mechanically, upon those of Tycho and Hevelius. It was, furthermore, the first instrument of its kind to be mounted on a geared equatorial. This enabled it to track stars around the pole with a single motion in right ascension, although it had to be cranked by hand instead of by Hooke's proposed clock. Flamsteed found the construction of triangulation surveys with the sextant a painful and complicated business. It required four men to operate it properly — two to observe, one to crank the equatorial and another to keep the clock and make notes — so that in addition to the 'silly surly labourer' permitted him by the Government, he had to employ his pupils as assistants. The sextant was housed in a building with a sliding roof, so that when observations were being made, the entire instrument was open to the sky, and the resulting damp played havoc with the neuralgia, headaches, and other afflictions of which the Astronomer Royal kept diligent record [93]. From the founding of the Observatory, it was considered necessary that Flamsteed should have a large mural quadrant to enable him to take zenith distances. But after paying for the sextant out of his own pocket, Sir Jonas Moore was naturally reluctant to commission a quadrant as well [94], especially as the workmen demanded an 'unreasonable rate' [95]. 'In the mean time', Flamsteed continues, 'Mr. Hook boasts how large and precise an instrument he would make at a small charge, whereupon Sir Jonas Moore allows him the contrivance of it.' Like other instruments which Hooke succeeded in inflicting upon the Royal Observatory, it was novel, cleverly devised, and 'wholly useless'. Hooke was given a free hand to try out yet another of his ideas concerning instrument graduation, which resulted in the total waste of Sir Jonas' money (Plate 18).

Little documentary evidence survives of the 10-ft Hooke quadrant, beyond a fine engraving by Francis Place of c. 1676, a few fragments by Flamsteed, and some words in Hooke's diary [96]. From these remains it is, nonetheless, possible to recognize in the quadrant several innovations that derive from Hooke's ideas on instrumentation. Foremost amongst them was his awareness of how the repetitive operations in conventional dividing could lead to errors, as each degree had to be subdivided by diagonals, and this delicate task repeated 90 times (Plate 18).

In the *Animadversions*, Hooke had suggested a way of avoiding this problem. Taking the full linear extent of one of the limb degrees, he engraved it onto a piece of glass, and accurately subdivided the space by diagonals, so as to give him one whole degree divided down to minutes. The glass was then set in the alidade of the quadrant, so that it passed exactly over the limb, with its full degree divisions [97]. As this 'degree' moved across the other 90, it was possible to make it subdivide the spaces between them, thereby greatly reducing the time taken to engrave the instrument, and, hence, the likelihood of committing error.

On the Greenwich quadrant, the limb was divided into 18 points placed at 5° intervals. Intermediate angular quantities were read by a double index, the exact function of which is not entirely clear from the fragmentary description available [98]. On Place's engraving there appear to be two radial arms projecting from the quadrant's centre pivot. One carries an arc of 5° labelled 'D', the other a telescope sight and a screw mechanism bearing the letters 'A' and 'E'. Flamsteed remarked that one of these arcs — probably 'D' — was capable of being locked down to the main limb 'whilst the other arm ['A'–'E'] was moved upon it'. In the light of Hooke's ideas on scale dividing discussed above, it may be suggested that the arc 'D' was intended to reduce the 5° spaces to single degrees or less, while the alidade 'A–E' delineated the angles and read the fractions.

To make an observation, it is likely that having ascertained the approximate altitude of the star, the 5° scale 'D', was clamped down between the two most appropriate points on the limb, thus dividing the space into degrees and fractions. The star was then sighted through the telescope sight, and the alidade 'A–E' made to travel across the scale 'D' until it finally came to rest at its appropriate degree, thus yielding the desired angle. Nothing is known of how the scale 'D' was subdivided. Individual minutes and seconds may have been read by diagonals, or by a screw mechanism. The motion of the telescope 'A–E' was governed in some way by a screw — the crank of which is represented at 'E' — but whether this served to delineate actual angles or merely to steady the alidade is not known.

In spite of the ingenuity shown by Hooke in the design of this instrument, it failed to work satisfactorily. The principal drawback derived from the great weight of the two indices and the relative weakness of the overall framework that had to support them. Flamsteed complained that the 'weight of a double index suffered not the arc of 5° to remain fixed whilst the other moved upon it' [99], with the inevitable result that it was impossible to keep the 5° arc precisely adjusted between the limb-points when observing. Any piece of apparatus that needed a rope and pulley to move and hold it in position, as this did, must have been difficult to use when attempting to read seconds. Moreover, it must have been impossible to achieve the necessary degree of accuracy in centring a movable index in relationship to its pivot, as a result of the constant wear and tear occasioned by moving the scale. Its reliability must inevitably have proved inferior to that of a permanently engraved scale, as the errors induced by pivot eccentricity and friction completely outweighed the possible advantages of a simpler dividing procedure.

Hooke's quadrant was not only unreliable and difficult to use, it was also dangerous. The great weight of the two alidades located on a common pivot caused them to act like a large pair of scissors, if anything slipped. Flamsteed tore his hands on the instrument, and he complained to Sir Jonas that it 'had like to have deprived Cuthbert [his assistant] of his fingers' [100]. By 1678, the Astronomer Royal had ceased in his attempts to obtain results with the quadrant that had 'so often deceived me and lost its rectification'.

In the absence of an effective quadrant, Flamsteed devised a technique whereby he could set up his sextant in the plane of the meridian to take zenith distances. He used the instrument to observe the upper and lower transits of Polaris, which allowed him in 1677 to obtain the first moderately accurate latitude for the observatory, finding the simple latitude to be 51°29′22″, which after correcting for refraction was reduced to 5l°28′30″ [101]. It soon became apparent, however, that the sextant was scarcely more reliable than the quadrant when used in the meridian. The plane of the limb shifted slightly from the perpendicular every time he moved the alidade, and sometimes the observed value for the same star varied as much as $\frac{1}{2}′$ on two consecutive observations. These early meridian observations were so deceptive that he refused to include them in his catalogue for fear they might 'become a load on the science, and at last turn to his shame and reproach'.

The absence of an adequate meridian arc must have been a severe drawback upon Flamsteed's activities, and in 1681, he decided to order a mural arc out of his own slender finances. Its radius was the same as the sextant, and contained the advantage of bearing a scale of 140°, which enabled him to encompass Polaris in addition to the southern stars. But Flamsteed's expectations were once more dashed, when the 'ill workman, who respected nothing but the getting of wages', to whom he had entrusted the instrument, produced an arc that was too weak and shaky to be of real value [102]. Two years later, Flamsteed attempted to make another arc, probably by salvaging the remains of the 1681 instrument, but it likewise proved so flimsy that 'I durst not confide in the measures taken with it' [103].

The early 1680s must have been especially harassing times for Flamsteed. Following the death of his patron, Sir Jonas Moore, in August 1679, not only was he deprived of the only influential ally who could have extracted funds from the government to buy instruments and pay the arrears in his salary, but his enemies in the Royal Society closed in. A month after Moore's death, a delegation came to Greenwich and

> Mr Hooke produced an order to remove the instruments of the Royal Society to Gresham College. They took away: the small quadrant of 5 inches radius with the screwed limb, another quadrant with two telescopes on it, a dividing plate, an instrument of 3 rulers, Mr Hookes 3 foot quadrant ... [104]

None of these instruments was likely to have been vital to Flamsteed's work, but their removal at this time seems singularly vindictive.

Flamsteed's first decade at Greenwich was also a time of acute financial hardship. So wretched was his salary, that when Baron von Uffenbach visited the Observatory in 1710, the Astronomer Royal told him that he would have achieved little had he not been the 'son of a rich merchant' [105]. His situation was eased, however, after he was presented with the Rectorship of Burstow in 1685, and in 1688 he inherited money following his father's death [106].

Not until 1689 did the Observatory possess an adequate meridian instrument, which Flamsteed provided from his own pocket [Plate 20]. Following the death of his assistant, Stafford, in 1688, Flamsteed engaged the 'very able mechanic and ... expert mathematician' Abraham Sharp to take his place, and construct a new mural arc. It took 14 months to build and cost £120 [107]. Like the unsuccessful instrument of 1681 upon which it was based, the new arc was of 7-ft radius and covered 140° of sky, so that it would be possible to obtain the Observatory's latitude by direct observations of the Pole Star, instead of having to triangulate its position from the circumpolar stars with the sextant. But this instrument was strongly built of iron, the limb being supported upon five rigidly braced radial arms of iron, and the whole securely fixed to the wall with nails and wedges. After enduring nearly 15 years of frustration caused by inadequate instruments at Greenwich, Flamsteed acquired in Sharp's arc the finest and most exact astronomical instrument constructed to date, and it won the praise of all who saw it [108]. With the introduction of this instrument, one may consider the Royal Observatory as having concluded its 'Tychonic' period, when the principal method of measuring celestial positions had been by sextant triangulations. It inaugurated a new epoch in instrumentation that was to lay the groundwork for the techniques of Bradley and Maskelyne.

The principal feature of the new mural arc lay in the high quality of its degree graduations. This was, furthermore, the first major instrument for which we possess an outline of how the graduations were executed. Before the dividing could begin, it was first necessary to establish the zero point on the limb. This was achieved by first setting the undivided arc upon the meridian wall and collimating the telescopic alidade, so that the index was exactly parallel to the optical axis of the telescope. The alidade was first swung from the centre of the arc, facing east, and a plumb-line made to swing so that its wire passed across the alidade index. In this way, several transits of the star Caput Draconis were observed, and on each occasion, a mark placed at the point where the plumb line crossed the index. Several nights later, the alidade and plumb line were turned through 180° to face west, re-hung, and the procedure repeated. From the resulting observations, it was only necessary to bisect the two sets of marks, drawn when the alidade was hung facing east and west, to obtain the true zenith collimation. Once this had been successfully completed, the alidade was replaced on the centre of the mural arc and so adjusted that the new-found point hung behind the instruments' plumb-line. When this was so, a small scratch was made on the polished limb of the mural arc, as a zenith starting point for the divisions [109]. Though no record remains describing the technique by means of which the 140° were laid out from this point, Abraham Sharp later stated that the instrument was engraved *in situ* on the wall, and not on a horizontal table, as was to become the procedure in the eighteenth century. It is also known that the 60° point was struck from the same beam compass opening as was used to draw the radius of the 7-ft arc and that Flamsteed assisted personally by holding the 7-ft compass to prevent it flexing [110]. The remainder of the divisions were probably laid off by bisecting the 60° space to give 30° and 15° spaces, followed by trisecting and quinquesecting, to obtain the single degrees. As with the sextant, each degree was broken down by diagonals until it could be read to 10″ spaces [111].

This was achieved by first dividing the degrees directly to 5′ spaces on the arc. A diagonal line was then drawn across the space. It was reduced to single minutes by the fiducial edge of the alidade, which carried five transversal lines drawn across it. Each of these lines was so placed that they divided the diagonal line into five parts. Whenever an observation was made, one of these lines would either intersect a diagonal, or else come very close to it. By counting which of the five marks touched the diagonal, the scale was easily read to individual minutes. For those cases where no line made exact contact with a diagonal, it was possible to read the interval fraction by means of six intermediary marks drawn between the minute divisions, each of which represented 10″ (Plate 23).

The five principal minute-marks on the fiducial edge were not drawn at equal distances to each other. Because the space covered by the diagonal on the limb equalled the segment of a circle, it was understood that such a curved area could not be perfectly bisected with a straight line. A curved diagonal was required, the exact amplitude of which could be computed. On a 7-ft radius, however, the necessary degree of curvature to bisect correctly a 5′ diagonal was very slight, and difficult to draw. To avoid this problem, Flamsteed drew his diagonals straight and made compensation by introducing a slight spread in the disposition of the minute lines on the fiducial edge. The spread in the divisions was computed to correspond to the following ratio, for each of the 5′ delineated [112] (see Table 3.2).

Table 3.2

Minutes radiating outwards	Ratio in units
1	251
2	503
3	757
4	1013
5	1270

In the construction of the scale on the mural quadrant [113], one discerns what could have been a refinement of Hooke's method for simplifying the drawing of diagonals, discussed above. The Hooke method, of drawing only one or a few degrees in full, and making them move to any part of the quadrant did not work, but it contained an attempted simplification of construction that would have been admirable had the general state of mechanics been sufficiently advanced.

It can be argued that Flamsteed — an eminently practical astronomer who knew better than anyone what the instruments of his day were capable of doing — seized upon this principle in Hooke, whereby he could avoid the difficult task of drawing a number of circular arcs to read the minutes, by drawing only 5′ marks on the fiducial edge of the alidade, which could themselves be used to read all the transversals. Flamsteed's instruments are the only ones known in which the minute lines were reduced and simplified in this way. The instruments of Hevelius, which in terms of accuracy may be considered the immediate ancestors of Flamsteed's, have no such refinement; the Flamsteed mural arc was itself the last major observatory instrument to use the 'diagonal' method of subdividing degrees. There is no written evidence to suggest this line of development from Hevelius through Hooke to Flamsteed, for they were not much inclined to paying mutual compliments, though when one examines their descriptions and engravings, a distinct thread emerges.

Abraham Sharp's practice of observing the places of zenith stars with the alidade as a preliminary to commencing the divisions is interesting, for it also enabled the alidade to be used as a future check on the error of the instrument, as Bradley was later to do with the zenith sector.

Flamsteed was thus able to discover any deviation in the zenith adjustment of the arc by first observing Caput Draconis in the zenith, and then examining how far the original zero point on the limb had strayed. Between July and September 1689, he rigorously checked the collimation of the completed arc by extending this enquiry to the observation of a variety of stars in other constellations. He also kept constant watch on the adjustment of the arc over the following years, and became convinced that the meridian wall which supported the instrument was sinking. By 1715, the displacement had become so great that it was necessary to apply a correction of 14'20" to all observations made with the arc [114].

By 1688, Flamsteed had come to appreciate the advantage of having two independent means of observing any angle, so that one acted as a check upon the other [115]. No doubt this is the reason why he ordered the new arc to be fitted with a Hooke screw similar to that on the sextant, although its function was secondary to that of the diagonals (Plate 21). An additional refinement that had been absent from the sextant was a mechanism to disengage the alidade screw when desired. If the observer wished to quickly alter the elevation of the alidade, the screw could be disengaged from the limb teeth, instead of having to be racked down the arc as was the case with the sextant [116]. As both sextant and arc were of the same radius, with 17 teeth to the inch on their screws, it was obviously useful to be able to compare cross-readings between them, and agreement was found to be satisfactory [117].

Not until Bradley's time, however, did the technique develop of checking an instrument not merely against another of similar type, and hence likely to be afflicted with similar errors, but against one that worked on a different principle, such as the transit or zenith sector. A well-constructed mural arc set in the plane of the meridian allowed Flamsteed to make a greater variety of observations, with a higher degree of certainty and much less inconvenience, than had been possible with the sextant. Declinations could be read with ease and the latitude obtained by direct observation of the Pole. But this did not constitute its sole utility, for 'the observed differences of the times of the transits of any two observable points would give the differences of their right ascensions' [118]. By timing the passages of two objects across the meridian with a good clock, it was now possible to find their respective hour-angles and, if necessary, check them against the sextant's angular values [119]. Both Tycho and the Landgrave of Hesse-Kassel had attempted this method, but with limited success, for it was not until the invention of the pendulum clock that it became feasible [12]. Using the mural arc in conjunction with a clock, it was possible to establish right ascensions and declinations together in one operation, thus greatly simplifying the observing procedure, and allowing the sextant to fall into disuse.

Once the new arc was fully operational, Flamsteed noticed that it possessed additional, unexpected advantages. Observations could now be made in a covered building, through an 18-in. meridian slit in the roof, and no longer in the open air, as had been necessary with the sextant. Apart from sparing him from the 'cold . . . which caused him frequent tortures from the stone and gravel', he discovered that the roof slit reduced the overall glare of the sky, enabling him to see through it with the naked eye stars of the seventh magnitude [121].

The new arc made it possible for Flamsteed to establish accurate solar co-ordinates, from which details of the tropical year and calendar could be derived. These were, in turn, fundamental to accurate timekeeping and the eventual discovery of the longitude. By observing the daily shift in the Sun's declination through the course of the year with the arc, it was possible to determine the precise moment when the sun reached the equinox. The exact period between two such equinoxes gave the duration of the tropical year, from which he could compute the rate of precession.

Without a reliable arc, Flamsteed had been unable to observe his own solar declinations, and had been compelled to rely upon those of Tycho and Hevelius [122]. It was discussed in Chapter 2 how Tycho's sextant triangulations of the sun from Venus had allowed him to arrive at a much more accurate value for the true equinox — and tropical year — than had been possible for earlier observers who had observed the Moon [123]. But even Tycho's value contained an inevitable margin of error as a result of the motion of Venus itself. Using the mural arc, Flamsteed endeavoured to fix the equinox by a technique that dispensed entirely with the use of intermediary bodies, such as the Moon or Venus.

In his equal altitudes method, he commenced by making a series of solar observations at the time of the vernal equinox, by measuring the precise declination above the celestial equator. Around six months later, as the sun approached the autumnal equinox, the observations were repeated. From these observations, Flamsteed could select a pair of days upon which the sun had stood at equal altitudes, or declinations, close to each of the colures. Once these positions had been found it was simple geometry to bisect the encompassing arc, and thus derive the precise time of the summer and winter solstices. The further bisection of these two arcs, containing respectively the winter/spring and summer/autumn paths of the Sun, yielded the precise places of the equinoxes themselves, from which the Astronomer Royal could proceed to determine the tropical year, first point of Aries, and the quantity for precession [124].

For the purpose of celestial cartography, the vernal equinox, or first point of Aries, was the point of reference from which all other positions were measured. Precise knowledge of its place was basic to the construction of a star catalogue.

The mural arc met in every way the exacting demands that Flamsteed made upon it. After settling its errors and adjustments until they were well within those limits 'readily granted to arise from the difficulty of dividing and exactly placing instruments ... over the meridian plane' [125], he set out to revise and remake all his sextant observations with the arc. These observations were eventually to comprise the bulk of the second and third volumes of the *Historia Coelestis Britannica*, and produce the first truly comprehensive star catalogue since the time of Tycho. He settled to a new level of accuracy the basic astronomical co-ordinates, although the 12″ error of his instrument was still too large to provide any worthwhile solution to the longitude [126].

The lunar observations made at Greenwich proved to be of value to Newton's work on the theory of the Moon, and this was especially so after the completion of the mural arc.

'What care I took to observe the Moon ever since the arc was finished', wrote Flamsteed, 'and with what success, will appear from the large synopsis of her places deducted from my observations, and imparted to Mr. Newton.' These observations won the somewhat grudging praise of Newton, who confessed that: 'If I do not make a handsome acknowledgement, they will reccon me an ungrateful clown' [127].

In 1694–1695 alone, the Astronomer Royal supplied Newton with about 150 lunar observations, 'which was more than he could reasonably expect from one of my circumstances of business and ill-health' [128]. It was also Flamsteed's hope that his observations with the mural arc would enable him to detect the

> nutation of the earth's axis propounded by Mr. Newton, but if this were in fact granted, it would be so slight as to be barely perceptible except by instruments of a radius much greater than seven feet. [129]

Flamsteed's work at Greenwich provided the first rigorous trial of the new optical and mechanical innovations that had been brought to astronomical instruments in the 1660s. When the last recorded observation with the mural arc was made, shortly before Flamsteed's death, on December 31st, 1719, the foundation had been laid for the 'astronomy of exactitude' that was to become the hallmark of eighteenth-century scientific achievement.

THE ORIGINAL SOURCES OF THE 'PROLEGOMENA' TO FLAMSTEED'S *HISTORIA COELESTIS BRITANNICA*

Three concerns dominate the 164-page *Prolegomena*, or Preface to Flamsteed's *Historia Coelestis Britannica*: the importance of instruments in the historical development of astronomy, an account of the instruments and techniques used to observe the Great Catalogue at the Royal Observatory, and the vindication of his own life and work against his critics in the Royal Society. Flamsteed's first two objectives were satisfactorily fulfilled, for his study of practical astronomy extending from Old Testament times down to the seventeenth century provided an excellent background to the detailed discussion of his own instruments and techniques developed at Greenwich. Unfortunately, his third intention, which was to consist very largely of an itemized account of the official mishandling of the publication of his Catalogue and an attack on the persons responsible for it, was almost totally suppressed from the posthumously published *Prolegomena*.

This suppression was occasioned by Flamsteed's own death, which took place soon after he had finished the manuscript of the *Prolegomena*, and necessitated the appointment of editors to supervise the publication of the work [13]. As the original *Prolegomena* had been composed in English, moreover, the preparation of a Latin translation further permitted the softening of offensive words and phrases [131].

The editorship of the *Historia Coelestis Britannica* was undertaken by two of Flamsteed's assistants, James Hodgson and Joseph Crosthwait, and because they were relatively obscure men who would have to seek further employment, it was natural that they should have been reluctant to associate their names with the libellous accusations made in the latter half of the original *Prolegomena*. Indeed, the significance of this editorial suppression becomes even more apparent when one considers that the principal target for Flamsteed's attack was Sir Isaac Newton, whose name in the manuscript draft is frequently abbreviated to the letters S.I.N.

Two separate manuscript fragments survive of the original English *Prolegomena*. The first of these, in the Astronomer Royal's own hand, was composed over the years 1716–1717, and is now preserved in the Royal Greenwich Observatory Library [132]. It opens on page 38 of the manuscript volume, with Flamsteed's account of the mural arc, so that pages 38 to 74 correspond to pages 108 to 160 of the printed *Prolegomena*. Yet from half way down page 74 to the last sheet of the manuscript at page 93, and for three pages at the beginning of the volume (to which the account reverts), there is a section of some 22 sheets that was suppressed entirely from the published *Prolegomena*.

The second *Prolegomena* manuscript consists of 11 pages of a 39-page fair copy of the English text prepared by Crosthwait in 1722–1723, comprising pages 1, 2, 3, 4, 9, 10, 11, 12, 37, 38, and 39 of the complete manuscript, copied onto foolscap sheets in a minute hand. It is now included in a volume of letters sent to Abraham Sharp in Yorkshire between 1702 and 1730, located in the Royal Society Library [133].

When these two manuscripts are compared alongside the Latin text, the editorial alterations become immediately apparent. Flamsteed's account of the supposed discovery of a stellar parallax is cut out [134], along with some of his comments on ancient calendar systems and other details. There are numerous changes to individual words and phrases, such as the omission from *MS Flamsteed 32c* of the names of certain inefficient engravers, while in the printed *Prolegmena*, his assistants – designated by Flamsteed as his 'domesticks' – become 'contubernales', or colleagues. But most significant is the complete suppression of the above-mentioned 22 sheets from *MS Flamsteed 32c*, in which Newton's debt to the Astronomer Royal is stressed.

Since the founding of the Royal Observatory, Newton had received hundreds of observations which supplied much basic data for *Principia* and his work on the lunar theory, whilst he had also changed his opinions upon the shape of cometary orbits, following a correspondence with Flamsteed [135]. In particular, Flamsteed emphasized the importance of the new Greenwich instruments to Newton's conclusions, 'especially about the years 1694 and 1695, which on his repeated requests, I imparted to him about 150 places of the moon, deduced from observations made with the Mural Arc' [136]. On this occasion, moreover, he had stressed to Newton that the values were only provisional, for he had still to revise his stellar catalogue, which had been made some years earlier with the less accurate sextant. But Flamsteed received only grudging acknowledgement for all this work, whereas Newton was accredited with having 'perfected the Lunar Theory'. Flamsteed also used the mural arc in an attempt to detect the small terrestrial nutation propounded in *Principia*, although the instrument was not sufficiently accurate to detect this phenomenon [137].

Though some of these complaints seem to savour of jealousy towards Newton, it is unlikely that Flamsteed would have been moved to publish them had he not been deceived and humiliated by Newton's conduct between the years 1704 and 1714, concerning the publication of his observations.

In 1704, Newton offered to intercede with the government on Flamsteed's behalf,

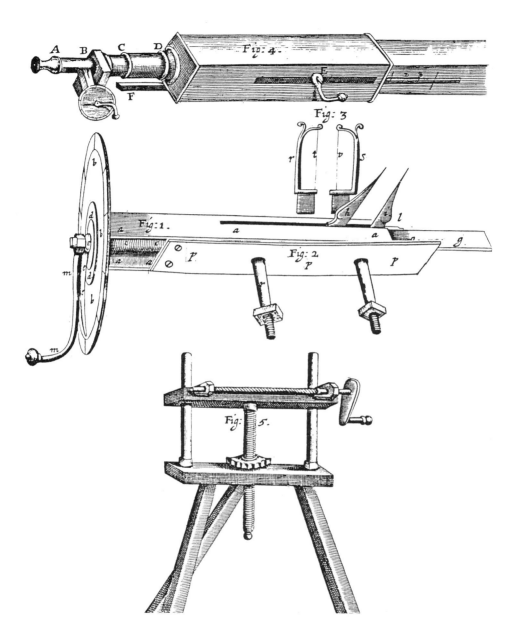

Plate 13 — The micrometer. The specific details included in the plate, and designated figures in the original, depict: Fig. 1 Detail of the micrometer itself, showing the long screw and pointers, visible in the field of the telescope. Fig. 4 The placing of the micrometer into the telescope tube. Fig. 5 Adjustable telescope mount. By means of the two screws, it was possible for the observer to track in right ascension and declination, with a telescope placed across the upper horizontal bar. See Plate 15, below, for a similar stand shown in use. Richard Towneley's Description of his micrometer, *Philosophical Transactions* **2,** (1667) 542.

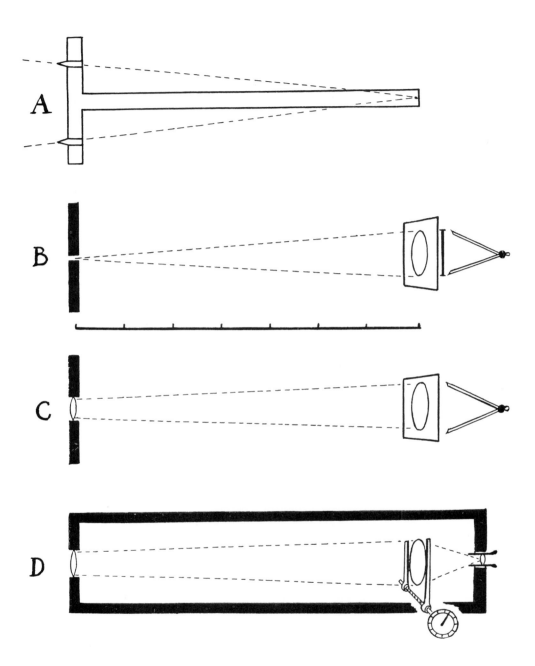

Plate 14 — Suggested geometrical ancestry of the filar micrometer. (A) the astronomical radius. (B) Camera obscura with pinhole. The solar image is measured, with dividers. (C) Camera obscura with single lens. (D) Filar micrometer proper. The image now falls within the telescope tube, and is measured by observing from behind through the eyepiece. Instead of dividers, the image is measured with vertical uprights governed by screws. Allan Chapman.

CAMERAM STELLATAM.

Plate 15 — Interior of the observing chamber in Flamsteed House, at the Royal Observatory, Greenwich, *c.* 1677. The observer on the right works with a long telescope mounted on a stand almost identical to the one depicted in the above Plate 13, Fig. 5. Micrometers were used with long telescopes of this type. The man on the left observes with a quadrant, while the one seated at the table probably 'keeps' the clock, or records time and observation details dictated to him by the astronomers. Engraving by Francis Place, in the Pepysian Library, Magdalene College, Cambridge. For provenance see Derek Howse, *Francis Place and the Early History of the Greenwich Observatory* (New York, 1975) 'Plate IX'. Science Museum, Neg. No. 4534.

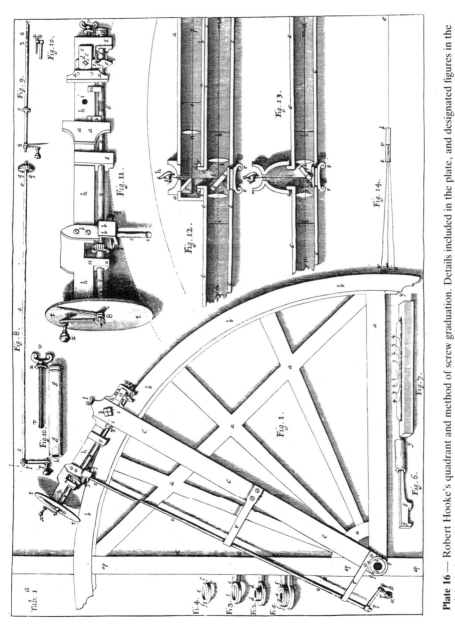

Plate 16 — Robert Hooke's quadrant and method of screw graduation. Details included in the plate, and designated figures in the original, depict: Fig. 1 The complete quadrant. The outer limb is denticulated and engaged by the endless screw, set in the mount marked 'h' 'h' 'h'. By turning this screw, the whole alidade and telescopic sight is advanced through a prescribed angle, as read off on the dial plate. Fig. 11 Detail view of the tangent screw mount. Fig. 13 Hooke's special catoptric sights, intended for use with the instrument. R. Hooke, *Animadversions* (London, 1674) Tabula 1a.

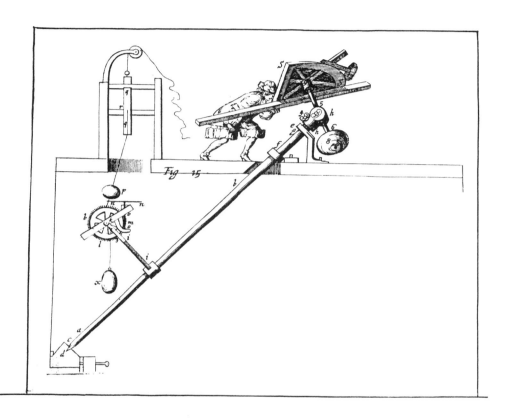

Plate 17 — Clock-driven equatorial, devised by Robert Hooke, on which to mount his screw quadrant. The observer works at the double catoptric sights, placed over the centre of the instrument. The screw-count mechanism and circular dial plate are clearly visible on the extreme edge of the quadrant limb. Though it is not known whether this instrument was built in its entirety, it represents the first use of a graduated instrument set in the equatorial plane the tracking motion of which was governed by a clock. Flamsteed's sextant of 1676 incorporated many of its features, but without the clock drive. R. Hooke, *Animadversions* (London, 1674).

Quadrans Muralis Meridie pedum Rad.

Plate 18 — Mural quadrant of 10-ft radius, designed for Flamsteed by Hooke in 1676. The elaborate graduation mechanism is clearly visible at 'E'. Engraving by Francis Place. See Derek Howse, *Francis Place and the Early History of the Greenwich Observatory* (New York, 1975) 'Plate Xb'. N.M.M. Neg. No. A7121

Plate 19 — Seven-foot sextant, built for Flamsteed by Thomas Tompion, 1676. The basic design of this instrument derived from the sextant of Tycho Brahe (Plate 3, *ibid.*) and probably the one of Hevelius (Plate 10, *ibid.*). The instrument is here refined with the addition of telescopic sights, screw graduations and an equatorial mount with geared setting circles, probably inspired by Hooke. Engraving by Francis Place. This, like the other Place engravings, was orginally intended to adorn Flamsteed's future star catalogue. When the *Historia Coelestis Britannica* was eventually published, in 1725, this was the only Place engraving to be actually included. See also Derek Howse, *Francis Place and the Early History of the Greenwich Observatory* (New York, 1975) 'Plate XI'.

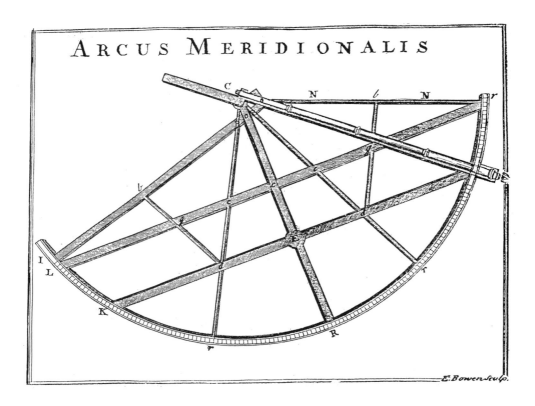

Plate 20 — Mural arc, built for Flamsteed by Abraham Sharp, in 1688. This arc, of 140° compass, was secured to a meridian wall in the Royal Observatory, and formed Flamsteed's principal instrument after 1688. The engraving is incomplete, and does not include the gear, or screw-count mechanisms on the end of the telescopic alidade. J. Flamsteed, *Historia Coelestis Britannica* I, (London, 1725).

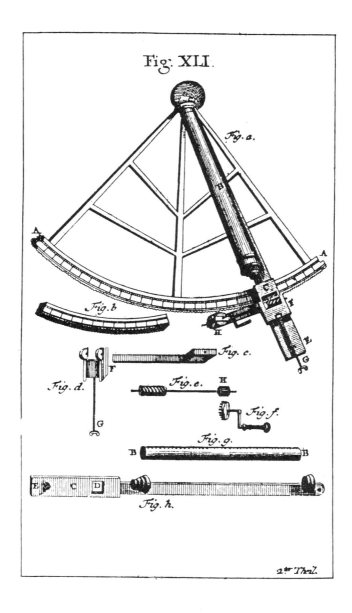

Plate 21 — Exploded view of screw mechanism of Sharp's mural arc. The graduated limb was denticulated, the precision teeth being engaged by a tangent, or endless screw, at 'H–F'. By counting the screw turns, a cross-check could be applied to the scale graduations. Sketched by Z. C. von Uffenbach in 1710, and included in his *Merkwurdige reisen durch...* (Ulm, 1753) 'Plate XLI'.

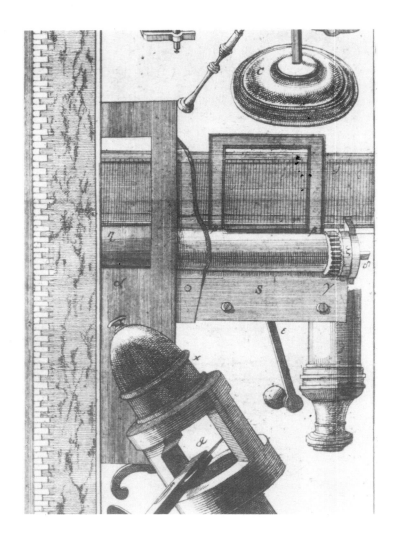

Plate 22 — Detail of the scale and screw mechanism of Flamsteed's sextant. Note the diagonal scale, telescopic sight and screw cranking handle. Both the sextant and mural arc were equipped with similar mechanisms. The illustration forms part of the border decoration of Francis Place's engraving of Flamsteed's 'Well' telescope, *c.* 1677. See Derek Howse, *Francis Place and the Early History of the Greenwich Observatory* (New York, 1975) 'Plate XIIb'. N.M.M. Neg. No. B653.

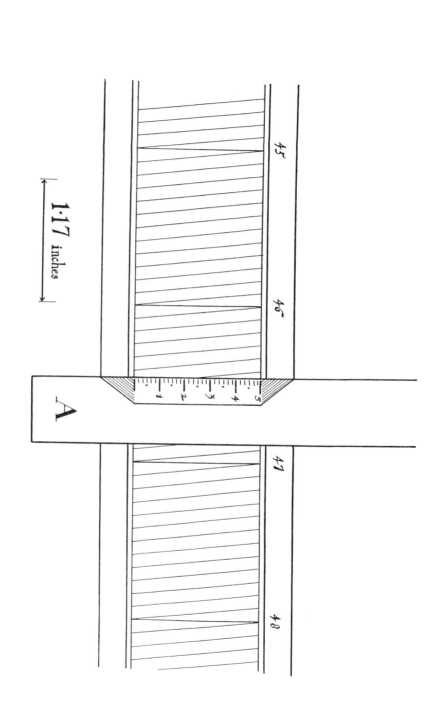

Plate 23 — Reconstruction of the diagonal scale of the Sharp/Flamsteed mural arc of 1688, from its description. The limb is divided into 5′ spaces, and the alidade 'A' to single minutes and 10″ spaces. The angle represented is 46° 16′ 40″. Allan Chapman.

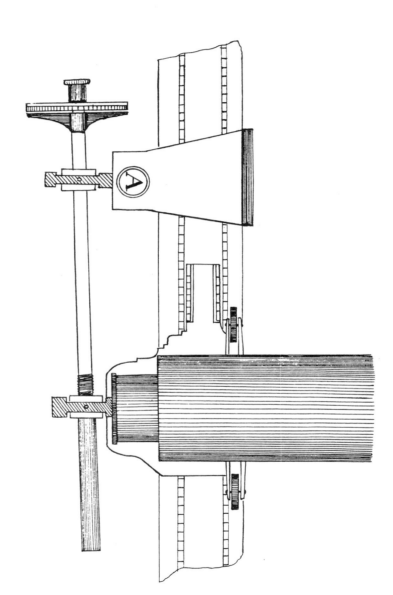

Plate 24 — Micrometer and vernier for mural quadrants as perfected by John Bird, drawn two-thirds full size. The locking plate 'A' can be secured to any part of the limb, and the telescope and verniers moved by rotating the micrometer head. After an observation, the double verniers, on the alidade, were read off against each other, and the single seconds deduced from the screw turns on the micrometer. Allan Chapman.

to obtain funds to print the *Historia Coelestis Britannica* [138]. Yet as soon as publication got under way, and Newton had the Astronomer Royal's observation books in his possession, the presses virtually stopped, and Flamsteed was left helpless [139]. The treachery became complete in 1712, while Newton, who had been entrusted with the observation books under covenant not to divulge their contents without permission, permitted the publication of a pirated edition under the editorship of Edmond Halley. To add insult to injury, Halley's *Historia Coelestis in Libri Duo* contained a Preface accusing Flamsteed of sloth and neglect of public duty [140], whilst failing to mention that all the Greenwich instruments were the Astronomer Royal's private property and that his salary was both inadequate and often months in arrears. Not until the change of government following the death of Queen Anne in 1714 was Newton obliged to surrender the observation books to Flamsteed, so that he could commence his own publication — at his own expense — of the Great Catalogue [141].

As Flamsteed was now meeting his own publication costs and had no debts of gratitude to acknowledge, he was determined to counter the accusations made in Halley's *Historia*, explain the long delays in placing his observations before the public, and vent his anger against Newton, 'who would have all things in his power to spoil or sink them' [142].

As he chronicled his dealings with Newton, during the latter's transition from scientist to courtier, he spared no courtesies. 'I always found him insidious, ambitious . . . exceedingly covetous of praise and impatient of contradiction' [143], stated Flamsteed. For Newton was a man who loved flatterers and refused to do anything for those who would not fawn or 'cry up' to him.

When these personal assessments and recorded details of conduct are taken together, it is clear the Newton was guilty of several moral, not to mention legal transgressions. But as by the time of publication Flamsteed was already dead, and Newton was President of the Royal Society, it is understandable that Hodgson and Crosthwait proved discretion to be the better part of valour, by drawing the venom from their master's bite.

It is interesting to consider what the consequences might have been had the *Prolegomena* been published in the form intended by Flamsteed. Almost certainly, Newton's debt to the Royal Observatory, and the importance of accurate observation to the foundation of theories, would have been emphasized, along with the connection between the Newtonian lunar theory and a specific set of developments in scientific instrument making.

As things remained, there was no apparent association between instrument standards and Newtonian theory until Maskelyne and Cavendish undertook to demonstrate the action of gravity between non-planetary bodies, in the late eighteenth century [144].

Lastly, it is unlikely that Newton's image would have come down through history in quite the way that it did. Hardly anything prejudicial to Newton's 'heroic' stature was published in England during his lifetime, and it is surprising how his followers succeeded in casting a mantle of purity over and above his undisputed mantle of genius. A forthright appraisal of his character and conduct written by a contemporary and professional equal might have gone a long way towards providing posterity with a more human view of Newton, and a greater sympathy for the efforts of his fellow scientists [145].

OLE RÖMER (1644–1710) AND HIS CONTRIBUTIONS TO INSTRUMENTATION

Most of the papers and instruments of Ole Römer were lost in the destruction of his observatory by the fire which razed Copenhagen in 1728, and his uniquely original contributions to practical astronomy have come down to us through the writings of his assistant, Peter Horrebow [146]. Römer recognized the potential of the new instrumental innovations that had appeared in mid-century, and how measurements could be made much more exact by the utilization of optical devices.

Ideally, the graduation of a quadrant requires the embodiment of two properties: (a) the construction of a perfect quarter-circle, and (b) the division of the same into 90°, each of which is identical in extent to the other. While it is possible in practice both to divide a circle into four parts *and* to draw equally spaced divisions along a curved arc, it is extremely difficult to bring them both together so that a perfect quadrant contains 90 perfect divisions. Using the beam compass technique already mentioned to lay off a radius and build up a full 90°, seventeenth-century instrument makers stood a better chance of scribing a perfect quarter-circle than of breaking it down into perfectly equal divisions.

Römer knew that as very few astronomical observations required the reading of a full 90°, the most frequently used part of the instrument, namely, the integral degrees, often contained the greatest number of defects, as the divisions were invariably 'adjusted' to fit the 60° and 30° spaces. He recognized that what was of primary importance for a good set of graduations was the perfect equality of the degree and not the overall extent of the arc to which they belonged. To this end he scribed a circumference line from the centre of the intended instrument, along its limb [147]. Computing the approximate linear extent of a degree for the radius of the instrument, Römer proceeded to lay off the divisions by a method that was independent of the beam-compass. Taking two sharpened steel rods, he bound them strongly together, so that the distance between their points corresponded to about $\frac{1}{6}$° which for a 3-ft instrument comprised approximately $\frac{1}{12}$ in [148]. He then proceeded to 'step' the points around the circumference line, to make a row of equally spaced dots that were sufficiently small to be covered by a human hair [149]. Römer fully understood that this method of dividing would not fill the quadrant with 90 *equal* degrees, but rather, divide a line of indeterminate length into an equal number of parts [150]. Once such a scale of equal parts had been constructed and the instrument set up in the observatory, a conversion table to turn them into conventional degree equivalents could be computed, and checked against an instrument with ordinary degrees. Alternatively, if instead of a quadrant the points were drawn on to the circumference of a full circle, as Römer preferred, one first selected a dot to correspond to the celestial equator, from which one could easily find the pole, and hence determine the number of *equally spaced* dots drawn between them [151].

In spite of the obvious ingenuity of Römer's equal divisions, his method contained two fatal flaws. The first, and most important, stemmed from the way in which the divisions were to be executed. In laying off his line of dots, Römer was 'stepping the compasses' with his two tightly bound steel rods. This practice came to be held as an anathema by eighteenth-century dividers, for as Smeaton pointed out in 1786, a 'stepped' compass could easily be diverted from its course by slight irregularities in the metal of the limb, and once this had occurred, every successive dot would be incorrectly placed [152]. The operator had no control over these errors, or ways in which he could detect them. It would, indeed, have been an impossible task to accurately 'step' the compass through all the 540 intervals necessary to divide 90° into 10′ spaces.

Secondly, even assuming that Römer had succeeded in producing 540 perfect divisions, he was still dependent upon ordinary, and much less accurate, instruments to set it up and determine their extent. To this end, he recommended setting up the instrument in the plane of the equator, to observe the meridional culminations of the stars of different declinations, in conjunction with an assistant who made a simultaneous observation with an ordinary quadrant.

The differences in declination between the two stars made it possible to equate the conventional degrees with a given number of 'equal parts' on Römer's instrument [153]. But no matter how skilfully constructed the new instrument happened to be, if the extent of its divisions were derived from another — and, by the logic of Römer's argument, an inferior — instrument, it could never fulfil his expectations, as the sins of the father descended upon the son! Indeed, the only way in which he could have obtained independent degree equivalents for the equal division would have been to extend them through at least 180° on a full circle. Then, hanging a fine plumb line across the circle so that it crossed both the exact centre of the circle and opposite edges of the limb, it would have been possible to have counted the 'equal divisions' enclosed in a natural arc of 180°, and thus construct a conversion table accordingly.

In the subdivision of his instruments, Römer showed both originality of invention and a keen awareness of the drawbacks of the conventional methods then in use. Diagonals demanded too much painstaking care from the maker, and he realized that only one inaccurately scribed line was needed to throw many others out of sequence. The use of screws was also rejected for a similar reason [154]. Like Hooke, he endeavoured to find a method that would avoid placing too much stress on either the concentration, steadiness of hand, or sharpness of vision of the craftsman. His solution provided the first instance in which a compound microscope was used to read divided scales.

Römer placed a low-power microscope on to the alidade of his instruments, so that the centre of its field passed over the row of dots on the limb. Taking the angle between two dots as seen through the microscope, he then set a series of equally spaced silk threads at the focus in the field of view, so that when the two outermost threads passed over the two dots on the limb, the space between was broken into equal parts. The number of threads placed in the microscope varied in number, depending upon the fineness of subdivision required. To make an observation, after sighting a star through the telescopic sight, one looked through the microscope to see which numbered dot on the limb appeared in the field of view. Then, counting the subdivisions that stretched between the dot and the centre of the microscope's field, one read the total angle. As there was no physical contact between the limb divisions and the subdivisions in the field of the microscope, the usual abrasion, change, and displacement that always existed when delicate divisions were scribed onto contiguous pieces of metal were avoided [155].

The chief limiting factor upon the eventual effectiveness of Römer's method was the skill of the craftsman, who had to set ten or more fine silk threads across the field of his microscope. Several of Römer's instruments illustrated in Horrebow's *Basis Astronomiae* are equipped with microscopes to read their subdivisions, and in particular, the scale attached to his transit instrument, where an exploded engraving depicts a microscope. But how many of Römer's instruments that carried microscopes also carried his 'equal degrees' on their main scale is conjectural. It is likely that microscopes were also used to read conventional degrees.

Römer's use of the microscope is precocious. Not until after 1787 did the instrument come into general use for reading scale divisions, and by this time the full circle was beginning to replace the quadrant as the astronomer's principal instrument, bringing in its wake a new technology of instrumentation [156]. The only optical assistance used in reading scales before this time had been the simple magnifying glass.

In addition to his work on scale graduation, Römer made important contributions to the general design of instruments, and it is to him that credit is granted for the invention of the transit instrument. Delambre suggested that the discovery was made accidentally [157], but this is not substantiated by the letter sent by Römer to Leibniz, which describes the transit as a deliberate creation made in 1675 [158].

Although Römer's transit was fitted with a short scale of degrees to measure altitudes, its real purpose was simply to observe the passage of objects across the meridian, find their right ascensions, and regulate the clocks. It consisted of an ordinary telescope, mounted on a rigid east–west axis, so that it always designated the meridian. With the development of reliable clocks in the eighteenth century, it succeeded the sextant as a simpler and more certain way of taking right ascensions. It will be recalled that Flamsteed used his mural arc in a similar way.

Quadrants, and instruments that employed detached *fractions* of a circle, came to be held in suspicion by Römer, who considered that the greatest consistency of results could only be obtained from a scale that was part of a full circle, being less likely to distort and move out of shape. On these grounds, Römer claimed that he would place more confidence in a circle of 4-ft radius than he would a quadrant of 10 ft [159]. He constructed a fine meridian circle of 5½-ft radius, which he collimated with the aid of meridian marks, along with an altitude/altazimuth instrument [160]. They were the only circular instruments of their kind to be used in astronomical research before the 1780s.

Like Flamsteed and Hooke in England, Römer had a keen awareness of the technical limitations — or 'ceiling of accuracy' — within which the astronomers of his day were compelled to operate. He attempted to isolate the qualities that were required for accurate measurement, and embody them in instruments which combined simplicity of operation with a capacity for cross-checking. What he recognized as fundamental towards this end was the simplification, or rationalization, of the techniques of scale division, which in his day were the source from which so many errors sprang.

It is indeed interesting to note how Römer, who was independently striving to solve the same technological problems as Hooke and Flamsteed, should have produced a solution which so closely resembled theirs. All three practitioners used a 'master' subdividing scale that could be applied to any degree on the instrument, with the purpose of simplifying division. Whereas Römer had placed his scale at the focus of a microscope, Hooke engraved his onto a piece of glass, as a mobile transversal, and Flamsteed on to the brass fiducial edge of his alidade. Although the technical resources available to Römer in the late seventeenth century had been insufficient to give his instrumental precepts proper articulation in practical terms, their value came to be recognized in the eighteenth century, when the construction of instruments bearing equal degrees came closer to reality.

4

Dividing as a high art

Perhaps no part of the science of mechanics has been cultivated with more assiduity, or more deservedly so, than the art of dividing circles for the purposes of astronomy and navigation.

John Smeaton, 1786 [1]

To eighteenth-century minds, positional astronomy represented the epitome of precision and exactitude in measurement. The astronomical achievements which justified this belief will be reviewed in a subsequent chapter, but it is first necessary to examine the technical basis which made them possible. This basis depended on the refinement of inventions and techniques already discussed in previous chapters. At its most fundamental level, however, it depended upon the greatly improved quality of graduated scales that became available during the eighteenth century. Positional astronomy advanced at a rate that was proportional to the increasing precision with which instrument makers could engrave exact angular scales, for in the eighteenth century, precision dividing was the 'High Art' upon which astronomical science depended. During the course of the century, the developments through which this art progressed were to be of profound importance both for astronomy and precision engineering. By 1760, the best dividers in London possessed such an understanding of their tools and materials that they were able to achieve standards of accuracy that would have been deemed impossible 60 years before.

If any one individual can be seen as having set this sequence of events in motion, it was George Graham, whose school of dividing — as exemplified in the works of his successors — became characterized by the use of certain tools, workshop techniques, and experimentally derived canons of procedure.

GEORGE GRAHAM (1675–1752)

Graham stands as a figure of primary importance in the development of eighteenth-century precision measurement. Not only was he responsible for far-reaching innovations in graduation, but he remains the first craftsman of whose working techniques we possess a detailed description, albeit at secondhand. This description, in Smith's *Opticks*, refers to the 8-ft quadrant built by Graham for the Royal

Observatory in 1725, which was in itself the first of a sequence of instruments in which the features of the Graham school assume importance [2]. One can only conjecture as to the models or prototypes that may have led Graham to so original an instrument, for craftsmen preferred to document their ideas in works rather than words. But his own training and education had placed him at the hub of the London precision trade, where he would have had ample opportunities to learn and experiment with innovations in his profession. Graham had been in the employ of, and then was successor to, Thomas Tompion, the constructor of Flamsteed's original instrument [3]. Both men were primarily clockmakers, but as Tompion's interests frequently led him outside the field of timekeepers, so it was only natural that an intelligent successor should follow suit.

Like Abraham Sharp, Graham used the beam compasses to execute the primary dots on the 90° limb. But unlike Sharp, Graham worked with a quadrant flat on a table, rather than vertical on the wall. In a letter by Joseph Crosthwait, Flamsteed's executor, it is related that Graham performed the delicate task of graduating the quadrant in the Great Room of the Royal Observatory itself [4]. Prior to commencing division, Graham set up the quadrant on a flat bed and planed the limb with a 'scraper' until it was perfectly smooth and ready to receive the divisions. The framework holding the scraper was pivotted, and braced into the ceiling of the work room, to guarantee the perfect flatness of the metal [5]. This complete, a strong beam compass, set to a radius of 8 ft., had its point set in the geometrical centre of the quadrant, whilst its steel cutter was gently drawn across the limb, to incise the circumference line (Plates 29 and 30).

The compass point was next located at one of the ends of the circumference line, in a dot that would represent 0° on the finished scale. From this point, the radius compass could strike off 60°, on the principle that a radius, as a chord, will divide into a full circle six times exactly. The 60° space was accurately bisected with a shorter compass. To do this, two bisecting arcs were drawn from each end of the 60° arc, in such a way that the scratches they made on the metal just failed to touch. If, indeed, the two bisecting arcs *had* touched, it would have been difficult to determine exactly the point of contact, but as they fell just short, Graham found it easy to fix the precise point between them by the aid of a strong magnifier. In all probability, he determined the initial point by estimation, but checked its accuracy with a spring-bow compass. Once the 30° point had been found, the compass was set into the 60° mark, and a full 90° arc constructed. Each 30° space was likewise bisected to contain 15°.

In the art of dividing, Graham strove to evolve a technique that was simple in operation. The more operations through which it was necessary to go, the lower the chance of achieving flawless workmanship. In pursuit of this end, Graham attempted to draw a whole scale using bisections alone, in deference to the geometrical axiom that it is impossible to trisect or quinquesect an angle perfectly with the compasses [6]. But a scale of pure bisections was found to be impossible in practice, and Graham was forced to trisect his 15° spaces to form 5° and then to quinquesect, to obtain single degrees.

To avoid damaging the limb by the trials that were necessary when trisecting, Graham drew a faint, 15° arc at another centre, away from the circumference line, and proceeded to divide it. Once the 5° and 1° spaces had been divided, they were transferred back to the circumference line by means of beam compasses [7]. Each degree was then broken into 12 spaces, to represent 5′ arcs. At each stage of the operation, the newly inscribed points were checked for accuracy against their adjacent points by reversing the compasses to ensure the correctness of their places. Graham's technique aimed at making every angle answerable to every other angle of similar amplitude, and thus enforce a rigid system of cross-checks.

Though he had been unsuccessful in his attempts to produce a 90° scale using bisection alone, Graham searched for a number around 90 that could be divided to single units in that manner. He found it in the number 96. On such a scale of 96 equal parts, the radius would strike off 64, which was itself bisectable, in the ratio 32, 16, 8, 4, 2, 1. In consequence of this discovery, the Greenwich quadrant was equipped with two sets of scales of 90 and 96 parts, drawn on the same limb, about 1 in. apart. The 96-part scale was easily converted to conventional degrees by a table. Two such scales formed an admirable cross-check on each other and followed the same principle after which Flamsteed had equipped the mural arc, with a diagonal and screw, to make independent determinations of the same angle. But the new method of using two scales, drawn to accord with different geometrical ratios, was greatly superior to the Flamsteed screw, being free from wear and more accurate in execution. Though the 96-part scale was said to be the more reliable of the two, the two arcs never disagreed by more than 5″ or 6″, which was a substantial improvement on Flamsteed's arc [8].

Although Graham introduced the use of two cross-checking scales into eighteenth-century practice, he was not the original inventor of the method. Tycho's steel quadrant in a square, it will be recalled, carried a linear sine scale to corroborate its conventional divisions and thus afford a cross-check. Graham's enduring invention was his use of the 96-part bisectable scale to cross-check the 90°, and this came to be embodied into many of the instruments of his successors.

With the exception of his 96-part scale, the thing which had so far distinguished Graham's use of the compasses from the efforts of his predecessors had been his remarkable manual dexterity rather than any technique as such. His special innovation in compass technique was his method of transferring the 90 'primary dots', obtained as above, into the actual incised marks that would be read by the astronomer. This required that the dots be transferred from the 'primitive circle', on which they had been originally laid off, to the reading edge, where the astronomer would read his angles.

Up to Graham's time, it had been customary to draw the divisions with a dividing knife and ruler. This knife was a form of scriber that 'exactly resembles the butcher's cleaver; and perhaps we might add, is commonly directed with about equal science' [9]. In operation, it was held like a pen, and drawn towards the operator along the ruler, the displaced metal rising at each side as a burr. To locate the cutting point of the knife *exactly* inside the primary dot, and draw an accurate straight line from it, must have been well-nigh impossible to maintain through the 1080 operations necessary to break a quadrant into 5′ spaces.

All too aware of these disadvantages, Graham dispensed with the dividing knife, substituting in its place a beam compass of short radius, one end of which carried the fine scribing tip [10]. Running close to the arc of the reading edge for the divisions, Graham scribed a faint 'occult' circle of about 8-ft radius. The scribing-compass was located with its point in the occult circle, and its scribing tip seated exactly inside the primary dot on the circumference arc. The length of the compass was such that when its scribing point touched the degree circle it formed a tangent, and at the application of slight pressure would boldly incise the degree mark into the metal. That the resulting degree mark was slightly curved was of no consequence, for what really mattered was that it commenced from the exact centre of its original dot, thus making the point more conspicuous and easy to read against the fiducial edge. Later eighteenth-century dividers tended to devote their energies towards devising more reliable methods of laying down the primary dots, but their efforts would have been futile had the Graham scribing compass not been available as a superior way of transferring and incising these points into the limb, to form the eventual scale.

Not until its application to the Greenwich quadrant by Graham had the vernier scale been used to read the degrees on a major observatory instrument. From Tycho to Flamsteed, instruments had been equipped, almost universally, with diagonal scales. Only Hevelius, the significant exception, had used verniers as supplementary scales on some of his instruments.

Diagonals were easy to read, and, at least in theory, should have been easy to construct. In practice, however, the execution of a reliable diagonal scale demanded many hours of concentration, as *each* diagonal line had to bisect a pair of points — one at each end — and this had to be done with the dividing knife and ruler. To lay off the diagonals on Flamsteed's arc, it had been necessary for Sharp to bisect accurately some 3360 dots. Failure to bisect any of them exactly would render a whole sequence of readings untrustworthy. As none of these dots was larger than a pin-prick, one realizes that the likelihood of accurately joining each pair by a semi-free-hand technique was infinitesimal.

The main scale of Graham's quadrant required only 1080 divisions to be drawn on the limb; each dot was only bisected once, and then with the controllable beam compass. It was traversed by a short vernier, attached to the sighting telescope, and could be read to 30″ directly, or down to 15″ or 7½″ by estimation [11]. The vernier itself was divided into 12 equal parts, a ratio that was made to correspond with 1° on the main scale (Plate 28). Although later in the eighteenth century John Smeaton was to despair of the possibility of making a perfect vernier scale, the opportunities for committing major errors in the engraving of such a scale were substantially less than with a diagonal scale. Indeed, if the vernier did contain an error, its quantity could easily be discovered by trials, and a correction applied at each reading. Even in engraving his vernier, Graham remained constant in his rejection of the dividing knife, cutting all its divisions by the controlled strokes of the scribing compass. By rejecting diagonals, Graham simplified the whole procedure of graduation and reduced the likelihood of error accumulation, while making any errors that did occur easy to detect. Both the 90- and 96-part scales were read by their respective verniers, which were engaged on opposite edges of the same piece of brass (Plate 28).

Great attention was paid to ensuring the exact line of collimation between the telescope's axis and the vernier, as the telescope was offset from the quadrant's centre to give freedom to the pivot. To collimate the instrument, both the axis pivot and the vernier has to be set exactly at the same distance from the optical axis. Graham accomplished this by placing the telescope in a shallow wooden box, so that it was supported at one end by the centre pivot, and at the other by the zero point of the vernier. When so adjusted, a sighting was made through the telescope of a distant object. Next, the telescope was reversed through 180°, and if its cross-wires returned to the same place, the collimation was considered satisfactory [12].

As originally supplied in 1725, Graham's quadrant was not fitted with a micrometer, but only verniers. The instrument was equipped, however, with an adjustable screw by which the elevation of the telescope could be delicately controlled to secure a star in the cross-wires [13]. Graham was certainly familiar with the construction of micrometers, and in the same year, 1725, fitted one to the zenith sector that he was then constructing for Molyneux [14]. No doubt he considered the two cross-checking scales to be sufficiently accurate to meet all demands, and it was not until 1745 that Bradley commissioned John Bird to convert the screw-set on the Greenwich instrument to a micrometer proper, thus enabling him to read single seconds [15].

A significant part of the success of Graham's instrument derived from the improved way in which he mounted the graduated parts of his quadrant. Flamsteed's arc had comprised a limb supported on the ends of five bars that radiated outwards like the spokes of a wheel, together with several light intermediary braces. Large parts of the engraved limb were quite unsupported, and could easily shift their place and alignment.

To prevent this recurring, Graham carefully apportioned the weight of his limb across a heavy framework of wrought iron bars, riveted together to form a lattice. The limb was thereby supported on an iron portcullis, and the sighting telescopes centred and delicately counterpoised to prevent uneven wear [16]. On its meridian wall, the quadrant was mounted on a set of iron brackets, gripping the frame and evenly distributing its weight. To guarantee easy rectification to the zenith and meridian, the screw-set adjusters within the mounting brackets [17] allowed the plane of the quadrant to be altered in a way that had not been available to Flamsteed, whose arc was simply nailed to the wall.

Jonathan Sisson is said to have constructed the framework of the Greenwich quadrant, which supported Graham's scales [18]. What part Sisson played in the overall design of the instrument is hard to establish, although the initiative probably goes to Graham.

In spite of the care taken by Graham to graduate and mount the instrument, it was not entirely free from flexure, and *did* change shape. When examined by Bradley in 1745-6, it was found to be 16″ less than a quadrant [19]. The mischief stemmed from the bi-metallic fabric, the brass limb being supported on an iron frame. Numerous instruments had hitherto been made in this way, but not until the 1720s were scales sufficiently accurate as to render the quantity of flexure noticeable.

It is to some extent ironic that, even whilst working on the Greenwich quadrant, Graham was himself engaged in researches to determine the effect of temperature changes upon the materials from which pendulum rods were constructed [20]. A leading characteristic of the subsequent 'Graham school' of dividers was their awareness of the sensitivity of precision instruments to temperature change, and its effect on graduated scales.

The design and execution of the 1725 Greenwich quadrant shows great originality, and established new standards in the art of instrument graduation. Subsequent adherents to Graham's school were unaminous in their rejection of the dividing knife and diagonals; they adopted the scribing compass, and realized that the best graduations were always performed with the greatest simplicity of technique and economy of effort. Graham commenced a school of instrument graduation that secured the priority of English craftsmanship until well into the nineteenth century, numbering in its rank Jonathan and Jeremiah Sisson, Ramsden, and the brothers Troughton, although it is agreed that the finest exponent of these techniques was John Bird.

JOHN BIRD (1709–1776)

> Bird ... enjoyed the undisputed reputation of being the most accurate divider of the age in which he lived [21].

Bird's initial interest in scale dividing came from his desire to make clock dials of greater accuracy than those produced by the local craftsmen in his native Durham [22]. He later worked under Graham and Sisson, and was already a craftsman of substantial reputation by the 1740s. Bird was Graham's natural successor in the art, learning from his master's innovations, and adding many of his own. Foremost, Bird was a geometer, and this is reflected in the way he approached his work, seeking a purity of technique that aspired to angular perfection by the simplest of operations.

Bird's enduring reputation rested on his construction of a number of larger observatory instruments, the divisions of which set wholly new standards of accuracy. Their success stemmed from Bird's novel technique of graduation, which he used to divide a new quadrant for the Greenwich Observatory in 1750. The instrument replaced the original Graham quadrant on the southern meridian [23], though Bird modelled it carefully on the original: indeed, the dimensions, principles, and overall resemblances between the two instruments show clearly that Bird's instrument was inspired by the work of Graham. Both were of 8-ft radius, and carried scales of 90 and 96 parts, read by cross-checking verniers. Like Graham, Bird dispensed with the dividing knife, using the scribing compass and occult circle. A rigid lattice of braced angle bars gave even support to the limb. In this way, the novel features of Graham's 1725 prototype came not only to be incorporated into its successor at Greenwich, but also in those instruments built by Bird for the observatories of Oxford, Shirburn, Göttingen, St Petersburg, Glasgow, and elsewhere.

Bird's outstanding innovation lay in his technique of dividing a 90° scale into equal parts, using bisection alone [24]. This was performed with great ingenuity, but at the expense of compromising a pure geometrical technique by the introduction of an accessory that in the hands of any but the finest craftsman would have constituted a source of hazard: a scale of equal parts. Bird faced the alternative of using either a pure beam compass technique, but being obliged to trisect the 15° angles, or an external aid to the beam compasses that would enable him to work exclusively by bisection. He considered the latter to offer the greatest scope for original work, and employed it with great success.

The secret of his success came from his development of Graham's 96-part scale. What Bird sought was an angle less than 90° that was perfectly divisible by two. By computation, the angle 85° 20′ was found to suit this requirement, and if this point could be accurately laid off on the limb, the rest of the degrees would fall into place without trisecting. Indeed, it was on the exact establishment of this point that the success of Bird's method was to stand or fall.

For a given radius, Bird computed the lengths in inches of a sequence of chords that would strike off six angles on the limb. The first of these was the radius itself, just under 8 ft, at 95.938 in., with five further chords corresponding to 30°, 15°, 10° 20'; 4° 40', and 42° 40'. To measure these chords in inches, Bird constructed a 'scale of equal parts' of great accuracy, which carried a vernier scale calibrated to five decimal places. Read direct, the vernier could be relied on to 1/1000 in, and through a 1-in. magnifier, Bird could consistently estimate its divisions to a third of this quantity. To guarantee the accuracy of the scale of parts, its own divisions were determined by bisection alone, for the 8-ft scale contained 96 in., and could be bisected to linear units using an identical technique to that used by Graham to divide his quadrant scale [25]. The chords were measured off the scale of parts with the beam compasses, which were applied in turn to the limb of the quadrant to delineate the angles.

After drawing the circumference line, Bird struck off the point 60° with the same compass, but this is as far as he proceeded by 'open' division. Instead of bisecting the 60° space, he measured his 30° point from the scale of parts and added it to the 60° arc, to build up a full quadrant. Then, with a compass opened to 15° from the scale, the 75° point was laid off, to which was added 10° 20', to complete the bisectable angle of 85° 20'. Before this crucial point could be reliably employed in further division, each of its angles had to be cross-checked and the compass openings used to strike them off. This was achieved by reversing the compasses, to see if the points of the bisecting compass read the same when set from opposite ends of the angle. In this way, every compass opening was integrated into those of its neighbours, until the 85° 20' point was finally read off from 90° by means of the 4° 40' compass. Confirmation by the 4° 40' compass was especially significant, as it had been used during none of these earlier operations to build up the 85° 20' points, and thus formed an external cross-check. The compasses opened to 42° 40' and 21° 20' provided further independent cross-checks on the crucial point. Once satisfied that the point 85° 20' had been laid off with all possible accuracy, Bird then filled in the remaining 1024 points that were necessary to divide the angle into equal five-minute spaces. A similar process of bisection was used to finish off the 56 remaining divisions between 85° 20' and 90°. This bisection procedure imposed a third and final check on all those points used to build up the angle 85° 20', for it not only filled in the scale degrees, but also tested the places of the 30°, 60°, 75° and 90° measured angles, which, however, 'fell without any sensible inequality'.

Bird's use of measured compass openings to denote angles contained all the simplicity of a great invention, but such a technique could only work in the hands of a highly gifted operator. By introducing the scale of parts alongside the conventional compass methods, Bird had placed the theoretical maxim of purity of technique one step further back, and only the most skilled of operators could hope to use the mixed method successfully. Indeed, relatively few craftsmen were capable of making the scale of parts to the requisite accuracy, and this was but the starting point of Bird's method. As division advanced, the whole process had to be hedged within an elaborate system of cross-checks to guarantee linear tolerances of less than 1/1000 in.

Bird had gained a detailed knowledge of the Graham quadrant when modifying and adjusting it for Bradley, and was aware of the errors that had arisen from the different coefficients of expansion of the brass and iron parts. These experiences made him extremely watchful of temperature-induced errors in his own work, and he became the first craftsman to take systematic precautions against them. During dividing itself, Bird recognized two ways in which temperature-based errors were most likely to occur. The first came from possible temperature disparities beween the scale, compass, and quadrant; the second from a variation of temperature taking place in the metal of the limb or compass whilst undergoing division, so that degrees marked out at the beginning would be of different size from those marked out at the end.

Against the first contingency, Bird took strict safeguards. The compasses were delicately adjusted the previous evening, and left lying on the quadrant all night, to render their temperatures homogeneous. After re-checking in the morning, the work was begun at dawn, whilst the air was cool. No fire was allowed in the workshop, and only one assistant permitted, so that the room should not be affected by body heat. Once division had commenced, Bird saw that his best defence against temperature change was to execute the work as quickly as possible. Haste was essential. The most important part of dividing — laying off the 85° 20′ point — could be successfully accomplished in two or three hours [27]. The remaining divisions could be filled in more slowly when the thermometer permitted. The dividing of the south quadrant for the Radcliffe Observatory at Oxford was performed between June and September 1772, and Troughton later said that Bird's method required about 52 days to divide a circle [28] or about 13 for a quadrant.

The above-mentioned innovations were concerned with laying off the points from which the divisions were to be cut. Like Graham, Bird set these dots into a 'primitive circle' close to the intended reading edge, and struck them with the beam compass to form small arcs, about 1/20 in. long, rendering their places 'very conspicuous' with a punch-prick 1/1000 in. in diameter [29]. By working initially in a primitive circle, Bird avoided encumbering the reading edge with superfluous dots. The dots were eventually transferred in the last stages with a scribing compass, though here he improved upon Graham's method by introducing several refinements, so that if any change took place in the length of the scribing compass it would not impair the divisions it produced [30]. In rejecting the dividing knife he formulated the canon: 'That a right line cannot be cut upon brass so accurately as to pass through two given points; but that a circle may be described, from any centre, to pass accurately through any given point' [31]. Furthermore, Bird was no doubt aware that the brass of his day was not homogeneous, but contained 'hard particles' that could easily deflect the path of a hand-held tool, such as the knife, to produce a bad division. These difficulties were all overcome by using the scribing compass.

To guarantee maximum sensitivity whilst graduating, Bird devised a special cutter, which he fitted to his compass. Unlike the normal compass, it did not have a flat chisel blade, but rather a faceted cutting edge with a pointed cutting surface inclined to it at 60°. This enabled Bird to locate the pointed edge of the cutter at the very bottom of any punch hole with extreme precision. With the scribing compass securely located, any number of light strokes could be applied, to build up an incised degree mark without distortion.

Bird's entire technique of graduation placed stress on the faculty of touch, as opposed to vision, when achieving high accuracy. In this respect, he was at one with most of the quadrant dividers, but at odds with those men who later in the century were to specialize in the division of full circles, where the faculty of vision was to achieve primacy. He developed a remarkably acute sense of touch when using beam compasses, and worked in accordance with his pithy maxim that 'contact is more subtle than vision' [32]. It was Bird's claim that a skilled operator could usually *feel* marks on a polished surface that it was impossible to discern visually.

The compass scribing technique outlined above was also extended to the construction of the quadrant's 96-part scale, with the difference that its units were obtained by continuous bisection, without recourse to the scale of parts.

Great care was taken by Bird to ensure that the verniers were cut and adjusted with the highest degree of accuracy. The dimensions and ratios of both vernier and main scale divisions on Bird's quadrant were the same as on Graham's, and on the 90° scale the length of the vernier was made to correspond to 11 divisions on the limb, or 55'. This quantity on the vernier was then broken down to ten equal parts. The specimen arcs were first laid off faintly on the limb, between the 90- and 96-part scales, and transferred to the chamfered edge of the vernier plate with the scribing compass. To prevent temperature distortions occurring at this stage, it was Bird's custom to hold both compass and vernier-plate in his hands together, to render their temperatures homogeneous. For the actual business of scribing, the vernier plate was secured to the limb with hand vices at a point where the 90- and 96-point scales coincided, at 60°, so that the zero points on the verniers would read the same quantities on their respective scales. Both the verniers were engraved onto the opposite edges of the same rectangular piece of metal, like Graham's verniers. After engraving, their plates were rigidly secured to the lower end of the telescope, and collimated to the optical axis [33].

In addition to the verniers, which read down to $7\frac{1}{2}''$ by estimation, Bird's quadrant was fitted with a micrometer. Bird's first micrometer had been fitted to the Graham quadrant in 1745, and consisted of a steel rod, accurately cut with $39\frac{1}{4}$ threads to the inch [34]. One end of this rod was anchored, by a bushed pivot, to a plate that was capable of being secured to any part of the quadrant's limb by means of a thumb screw. The other end engaged a female screw on the telescopic alidade. By turning this rod through one revolution, the alidade was elevated through 53'', thus enabling the quadrant to read single seconds. The micrometer fitted to the new quadrant was identical to this original in appearance and operation [35] (Plate 24).

By counting how many turns were required to bring a given star to the cross-wires of the telescope, it was possible to read declinations to single seconds of arc. Micrometers of this pattern were to become standard features on all Bird's instruments, and exhibited a significant advancement on the screw-edge micrometer used by Flamsteed. Unlike Flamsteed's instrument, it was not necessary to turn the micrometer merely to move the sighting telescope across the scale to make the adjustments. During this operation, the Bird micrometer was disengaged, and only turned at the critical moment of observation, reducing wear and friction to a minimum. It should also be noted that Bird avoided the use of achromatic glasses in his quadrants, until he was persuaded to fit them to the two instruments he made for the Radcliffe Observatory in 1772–1774. He considered that the additional weight of achromatic doublets would cause uneven wear on the quadrant's centre pin [36].

This may seem over-fastidious on Bird's part, even considering that a doublet could be three or four times heavier than a single lens. Bird does not record whether or not he verified his suspicions experimentally, and his non-use of achromats could have been due to over-caution. Achromats were not essential, after all, where one invariably observed through the centre of a well-stopped-down glass, with little need for peripheral vision. In 1770, the success of Bird's quadrants depended upon the exploitation of a design that was over 20 years old. Bird's quadrants were mechanical, not optical, instruments, and aimed to eliminate every possible source of tension or imbalance in the fabric, for which they employed the simplest optical systems.

Both Graham and Bird developed elaborate bracings for the telescopic alidades of their quadrants, although eccentricities did occur in the Graham quadrant, as Bradley discovered in 1742. No doubt Bird considered that additional weight could only cause mischief to what, by 1770, had proved to be a brilliantly successful and efficient design.

In addition to the 96-part scale on the quadrant, Bird laid off an arc of 96 equidistant dots between the two engraved scales, as a strict cross-check upon them. The dots were read by a silver wire 1/600 in. thick, mounted on a little frame at the end of the vernier. When this wire fell between two dots in making an observation, the micrometer screw was rotated until it exactly bisected the nearest dot to the left, as seen through a strong magnifier. The full and part turns that had been applied to the micrometer were then converted into minutes and seconds by simple calculation [37]. This was not part of the usual observing procedure, and was designed as a check on the verniers. In 1753, Bird engraved a similar row of dots onto the limb of the old Graham quadrant, so that its scales could be compared with his own whenever necessary. At the point 64°, Graham's scale was found to be 10.6″ less than Bird's, which corresponded well with the known error of 16″ for the full 90°, as determined by a different method [38].

The essence of Bird's techniques of graduation comprised simplicity and vigilance. Practical geometry was his touchstone, and he strove to place it as close to the ideal geometry of axioms as brass and beam compasses would permit. No error was too small to escape his scrutiny, for he bequeathed to later instrument-makers an awareness of minute flexures, temperature discrepancies, and other hazards to perfection that at times almost appears obsessive. No man before 1750 had acquired a better knowledge of contemporary workshop materials, or a more perceptive understanding of the limiting factors on practical mathematics. Constant correction and checking were of fundamental importance, and this principle was to be of basic importance to astronomers and craftsmen alike, and made possible the great achievements for which eighteenth-century astronomers justly earned their fame [39].

Bird published a description of his method in 1767 as a condition of a Board of Longitude reward for his services to precision mechanics, and this constitutes the first document of its kind to be written *under* the hand of an eminent craftsman. It was followed some years later by an amplified version, written by William Ludlam, the Cambridge astronomer, appointed by the Board to adjudicate the value of Bird's method. These two papers comprise the first systematic treatise on graduation ever to be written.

Astronomers were unanimous in their praise of Bird's instruments. Even in the hands of different observers, on different parts of the Earth's surface, Bird's instruments performed with singular uniformity. Observing with two Bird quadrants, of different radii, from England and Germany respectively, Bradley and

Mayer obtained values for the obliquity of the ecliptic that differed by only 2″, corresponding to an annual diminution of 0″.5 [40].

JEREMIAH SISSON (flourished 1736–1788)

'Jeremiah Sisson, the son of Jonathan Sisson, was of Graham's school for dividing, and did nearly as much to the method as Graham himself [41]. In mid-century, he was Bird's contemporary, and the closest thing Bird had to a rival in the art of geometrical dividing. Unfortunately, Sisson (whose father, Jonathan, had made the ironwork for Graham's quadrant) left no description of his methods under his own hand, although in 1766, Jeremiah's own son communicated an account of his father's methods to William Ludlam in Cambridge, who related the same in his treatise on John Bird [42]. This short account quoted by Ludlam, along with occasional comments from his contemporaries, comprises most of what survives concerning Jeremiah Sisson's approach to graduation.

Sisson's technique was basically the same as Graham's, with the addition of a scale of parts. He endeavoured to work by bisection, and scrupulously avoided trisecting. After bisecting the radius in the traditional manner, he built up his full 90°, after which he resorted to a scale of equal parts. Two beam compasses were adjusted to carry the computed chords of 21° 20′ and 8° 40′ respectively, so when laid off together they cross-checked the 30° openings. Each of these openings, moreover, could be reduced to 5′ spaces by continuous bisections [43]. Scribing compasses were used to incise the circumference degrees proper, though Sisson employed a more primitive cutting tool than did Bird, for whereas Bird's was prism-shaped, and capable of impressing a dot into the metal, Sisson's was flat and knife-edged [44]. This had the disadvantage that its flat cutting surface could never exactly fill the dot from which it was to cut a division, but had to stride across it, thus rendering it prone to error.

At first sight, Sisson's method appears to have the advantage of fewer operations and greater 'purity' of technique than Bird's, requiring only two cross-checking compasses. In reality, however, this was not the case, for Sisson represents not so much a simplification of Bird's technique, but rather an abbreviation. Bird's five compasses compelled more rigorous checking than did Sisson's two, provided the operator possessed the skill to adjust and use them properly.

To divide the quadrant, Sisson had to use the same compass opening at least three times, once within each 30° space. This came close to the practice of 'stepping' the compasses, or of using a given opening several times to build up an angle. Stepping was a method regarded as anathema by eighteenth-century dividers [45], as it allowed tiny errors to build up between each 'step' as a result of irregularities in the metal. To build up his 85° 20′ point, Bird had used each compass once only, and thus avoided stepping them.

Sisson differed from the rest of the Graham school in the respect that he disdained to equip his quadrants with a 96-part scale, arguing that such a scale was only of assistance to a bad workman. Perhaps Bird's retort was tinged with sarcasm when he replied that only a *bad* workman had cause to fear the stringent checks of a 96-part scale, and that it was an added advantage to an accurate craftsman [46]. Such comments, passing between practitioners on given points of technique, are rare to find, and the anecdote was published by William Pearson in the early nineteenth century, who presumably obtained it at second or third hand from the instrument makers with whom he was acquainted.

Sisson was conscious of the need to eliminate error from his work, and it was no doubt in pursuance of this end that he began to equip his circular instruments, such as theodolites, with indices placed at 120° intervals around the circle so that each observation could be submitted to three cross-checks [47]. This prospect, of making errors reflect in other parts of the scale so that they could be more easily detected, was a unique property of the circle, as opposed to the quadrant. When full circular instruments began to replace the quadrant in observatory practice a quarter-century later, it may have been Sisson's triple indices that encouraged the craftsmen, Ramsden and Troughton, to equip their astronomical circles with two, three, or six micrometer microscopes for reading celestial angles.

One of the principal instruments divided by Sisson was the 5-ft quadrant for the Earl of Macclesfield's Observatory at Shirburn. This instrument *was* fitted with a 96-part scale and was examined by Bird in 1745, when he found, from a sequence of bisections drawn by himself, that Sisson's divisions showed an error of 10″. Six years later, when Bird re-examined his own divisions upon this quadrant, the ensuing error was found to be only 1′ [48].

The mutual connections that subsisted between Graham, the Sissons, father and son, Bird, and Ludlam would be interesting to unravel if they were better documented. It is known that both Jonathan Sisson and Bird originally worked for Graham [49], and that Bird and the younger Sisson, Jeremiah, were rival craftsmen in the post-1750 period, but how far they exchanged ideas is difficult to assess.

William Ludlam knew both Bird and Sisson, and their names appear in his account books, along with those of some 17 other craftsman from whom Ludlam bought instruments and tools [50]. Though Ludlam's notebooks say very little about the connections existing between craftsmen, they say a great deal about what they stocked, and what they charged. In addition to his graduated instruments, Sisson also sold 'scales' (balances?), pencils, and a variety of miscellaneous requisites. Bird sold similar items; for instance, he retailed black lead pencils at 4d each, and red ones at 3d [51]. These minor bread-and-butter items of trade were almost certainly made elsewhere, but sold over the counter as part of the stock in trade of mathematical practice [52]. In a letter of 1747, recorded by Ludlam [53], Bird mentions that it 'is usual to charge 5s per day for a good workman', although John Hacking, Ludlam's jobbing artisan, was regularly docketed at 2s 6d per day.

In his day, Jeremiah Sisson was highly regarded in his craft, as his father had been before him. He was a member of the Clockmakers' Company, made instruments for George III's collection, and in 1788, the year of his death, was appointed 'Instrument Maker to his Royal Highness' [54].

JOHN TROUGHTON (*c.* 1739–1807)

Troughton's aim was to secure the advantages of Bird's bisected arc, whilst dispensing with the scale of parts. His efforts towards this end were documented by his brother, Edward, as part of his own treatise on graduation, published in 1809 [55]. Initially, it had been John's 'mere want of a scale of equal parts on which he could rely' [56] that had urged him to obtain the coveted 85° 20' point without one, although he soon recognized the special virtues of his novel technique. But the freedom from a possible secondary source of error that resulted from the absence of the scale was only obtained at the expense of breaking the geometer's canon against trisecting. Troughton vindicated this lapse by using his trisections sparingly, and then only to break down small angles. Moreover, even if the eventual point, 85° 20', was erroneously located, the 1024 intermediary divisions between it and the zero point would at least be equal one to another, as having been obtained using bisection. It appears from his brother's account that John Troughton realized that what was of primary importance was not that the arc should be a perfect 90°, but rather that each of its divisions be homogeneous in extent [57]. Troughton began in the conventional way, with radius bisections, to build up the 90°, but instead of concluding bisection at 15°, he proceeded to 7° 30', and in turn to 3° 45'. Using these irregular numbers, it was possible to build up the angles 82° 30' and 86° 15', which between them embraced the desired point.

A carefully drawn trisection between these angles denoted the point 85°, and a further trisection from this point to 86° 15' yielded the angle 85° 25'. A final quinquesection between this last point and 85° brought Troughton to the point of 85° 20', from which he could proceed using bisection [58].

Because the angles trisected were so small, Troughton was probably capable of laying down this point with great accuracy, but the principal drawback of this method was its relative lack of cross-checks. Reversing the compasses was the only way of testing the verity of each point, and this was only possible over a small sweep of angles. It was only feasible to check large angles *after* all the divisions had been engraved, and by then it was too late. Edward Troughton wrote that his brother was 'justly considered the rival of Ramsden' in the art of dividing, although he confessed that his fame was less widespread, and more specialized to the hand-graduation of quadrants and sextants [59].

Perhaps one reason for John's relative obscurity lay in his failure to publish, along with the eclipse of his fame by his illustrious brother. More fundamental is the fact that his method was devised specifically to graduate quadrants, and by the 1770s, when he was working, the quadrant was beginning to yield priority to the full astronomical circle — the instrument to which both Jesse Ramsden and his own brother Edward were to apply their genius.

JOHN SMEATON (1724–1792)

Both by training and in his approach to instrumentation, Smeaton was an engineer rather than a geometer. Unlike the other men discussed in this chapter, he was not a working instrument maker, but rather a scientific gentleman with a gift for mechanics. Furthermore, it is unlikely that his proposed method of quadrant dividing, presented as part of his treatise on instrumentation given to the Royal Society in 1786, was ever tried in practice.

Smeaton was well aware of the potential hazards of Bird's geometrically impure technique, involving as it did the use of the radius and scale of equal parts, but realized that it was impossible to avoid both trisecting *and* the scale of parts. He sought, therefore, a means of fixing the cardinal points from which the divisions were to be drawn, without even the necessity of laying off the radius to form 60°. This was to be the closest approximation to a 'pure' technique of all the dividers.

Without the use of the radial compass to strike 60°, Smeaton realized the uncertainty of laying off a perfect 90°, but did not consider this of primary importance. He agreed with Römer that what *was* of crucial importance in astronomy was that the divisions should be equal, one to another, rather than that the quadrant as a whole comprise a perfect 90°, but in which the individual degrees varied slightly as a result of 'impure' graduation techniques [60].

Smeaton suggested that the beam compasses should be adjusted to strike off the computed chord 16° from the scale. The chord would then be laid down five times, to make 80°. As 16° is an angle capable of bisection to single degrees and 15′ spaces, it was possible to measure off an 8° and 2° opening, and thus build up a full 90° [61].

A variation of this method could fix the point 85° 20′ by using four compasses, set to the computed chord 21° 20′. None of these alternatives produced any improvement on Bird. They aimed to simplify, but succeeded only in cutting corners. By rendering his technique independent of the 60° compass, Smeaton did not lose a source of error, but rather a valuable cross-check, whilst putting a double dependence on his scale of parts. The technique, moreover, was by no means pure, for it still mixed the use of a scale with the open compass work of bisection.

Smeaton's method contained one grievous shortcoming: in laying off the bisectable points, he was compelled to step the compasses four or five times. Perhaps more than any other mechanician. Smeaton was cognizant of the dangers of stepping the compasses more than once, for irregularities in the metal made it impossible for two, let alone five, steps to be perfectly equal. Once more, the wisdom of Bird, using half a dozen complementary compasses, becomes apparent.

It was the problem of stepping that eventually led Smeaton to suggest the laying off of 85° 20′ by means of a single compass opening. But the disadvantages are obvious: a compass of such prodigious length — about 11 ft on an 8-ft quadrant — could never be sufficiently braced against flexure to be used with confidence, and there was a total absence of cross-checks.

Smeaton's contribution to this aspect of graduation was essentially academic, although he did make valuable contributions elsewhere. The problems inherent in precision graduation had been of lifelong concern to him, and he remains the only surviving source on Henry Hindley, the Yorkshire pioneer of the dividing engine.

In his experiments to ascertain the effect of heat on metals, conducted with a sensitive pyrometer of his own invention, he showed great originality [62]. It is not unlikely that Bird's awareness of a quadrant's reaction to temperature changes could have been influenced by Smeaton's researches, which were published in 1754. Smeaton had not been the first man to use a pyrometer, and he records that George Graham possessed an apparatus by which he could detect temperature variations producing a 1/4000 in. expansion in metal bars, with the aid of a micrometer [63].

The pyrometer reinforced in Smeaton's mind two of what he considered the fundamental principles of precision graduation; first, his recognition that touch was the most sensitive of all human faculties; second, the supreme reliability of the micrometer above all other ways of making measurements. Smeaton claimed, on the grounds of his pyrometer experiments, that a well-practised hand in conjunction with a fine micrometer could detect 1/24 000 in. as a sensible quantity, whereas the eye could only discern 1/4000 in. [64]. These conclusions gave him a natural affinity to the Graham school, where the pre-requisite of accurate workmanship was a delicate sense of touch to accurately manipulate the beam compass points into holes that were otherwise indiscernible. It also supplied further experimental proof for Bird's maxim that 'contact is more subtle than vision'.

Smeaton was convinced of the impossibility of making wholly reliable vernier scales, and recommended their replacement by micrometers, to read off the interval seconds between any two degree marks during observation [65]. He argued that it was unlikely that both vernier and main scale were always at the same temperature, and Bradley's zenith sector had been capable of regularly measuring down to 1″, using only a micrometer.

The 'high art' of geometrical quadrant dividing underwent no appreciable improvements after the 1760s, and, while it is difficult to assess the number of skilled practitioners flourishing in London at this time, it is unlikely that they produced any significant innovations that were in advance of those discussed above.

REFINED PRACTICE

Definite canons of practice evolved around the graduating of quadrants and part-circular instruments, for it was upon them that the concept of exact instrumentation was to stand or fall. Some were purely empirical in origin, whilst others were framed with respect to specific theoretical or mathematical considerations.

It might be argued that the canons of purity and simplicity of technique to which all the craftsmen aspired — the construction of a 90° scale without resort to trisections or external scales of parts — were not only empirical, they were also aesthetic. To eighteenth-century minds, geometry was a pure demonstrative science that stood on classical axioms, and to deviate from the only true Euclidean way of dividing an angle, by bisecting it, one was somehow contaminating not only its practical but also its intellectual exactitude. All the dividers examined above were *geometers*, and these twinges of conscience must have been strong.

A scale of parts could never be more than a second-best way of working, but its introduction made instrument makers doubly aware of the need to cross-check every angle, with the result that by mid-century, empirical standards of division and error awareness had greatly increased. The growth of this idea of a web of cross-checks proved to be invaluable not merely in the workshop, but also in the observatory, as astronomers themselves came to realize that the web of checks used in constructing an instrument must also be carried over to its use in the observatory if the instrument's potential was to be fully realized. The observing techniques adopted by Bradley in the 1750s far transcended in delicacy those of Flamsteed.

During the course of the eighteenth century, quadrant dividers came to place greater importance on the equality of divisions, rather than on the quadrant comprising a perfect quarter-circle, for when in use in the observatory it was easier to apply a correction to homogeneous divisions than to an irregularly divided quarter-circle. Yet it was no longer possible to construct these equal divisions by stepping because of the ease with which a stepped compass could be deflected.

Though never an explicit canon of procedures, like purity of technique or the prohibition of trisecting, the primacy of the tactile faculty in their work was recognized by most quadrant dividers. So long as the beam compass remained the principal tool of graduation this was inevitable, the practice receiving empirical support in the maxims of Bird, and scientific substantiation from Smeaton's researches [66]. This procedure, however, was to pass wholly into abeyance with the demise of the quadrant.

With the introduction of the astronomical circle after about 1780, not only did the whole technology of instrument graduation change, but also the attitudes and approaches of the craftsmen involved. The division of the quadrant was a geometrical exercise, but the division of the full circle became a piece of mechanical engineering, and gave rise to a new and distinct school of practice. Graham, Bird, Sisson, and John Troughton worked within a tradition that may be termed classical, whereas Ramsden and Edward Troughton are best identified with that tradition which was to produce the Industrial Revolution.

It is now appropriate to examine the success of the eighteenth-century quadrant dividers, how their instruments were used by contemporary astronomers, along with their reliability in seconds of arc.

5

The techniques of eighteenth-century positional astronomy

The progress of astromony has always been found to have so great a dependence upon accurate observation, that till such were made, it advanced but slowly.
James Bradley [1]

The Tychonic school had aspired to accuracy by making each observation with as many instruments as possible, so that a good average value could be derived from them. When instruments still had open sights and there were relatively few independent cross-checks that could be applied to them, multiple observation was the only answer. This explains the large assortment of sextants, armillaries, and quadrants described by Tycho and Hevelius.

Eighteenth-century observatories were, by contrast, Spartan in their instrumentation. Astronomical observation had become greatly simplified by 1740 in the number of instruments required to perform a given task. A star catalogue, which had demanded all the resources of Uraniborg in 1590, could be performed with a maximum of four instruments, and a 60-fold increase in accuracy, at Bradley's Greenwich. This great improvement in the efficiency of instruments stemmed directly from the efforts of the London craftsmen, allied with the recognition on the part of the astronomers themselves of how stringent cross-checks could be applied that would improve the working quality of their instruments without needing to duplicate them in quantity. Attention has already been paid to the improvements in instrument-making technology in the eighteenth century, but these alone would have been of limited utility had not astronomers evolved a new system of observing, which allowed fundamental breakthroughs in the workshop to reach fruition in the observatory. Observing procedure depended upon a realization of the mutual interdependence of four quite different instruments: the mural quadrant, transit telescope, zenith sector, and regulator clock. All observations were now confined to the meridian, and were performed by the transit and mural quadrant. The development of accurate pendulum clocks enabled right ascensions to be measured (as Flamsteed had done) by timing the successive meridional passages of two objects, thus rendering the sextant and armillary obsolete.

The transit and zenith telescopes were relatively new instruments in the eighteenth century, and were used to designate two regions of the sky to assist in the true setting of the quadrant. But the true secret of success stemmed from the fact that these four instruments worked on four distinct mechanical principles: the quadrant its scale, the clock on its pendulum, the transit upon balanced pivots, and the zenith sector upon gravity. To obtain harmony of operation between four different systems of making a measurement was much more rigorous than Tycho's method of reading off one quadrant against another. Used together, these four instruments extended the system of interdependent cross-checks perfected by the scale dividers, and applied them to the practical business of astronomical observation.

THE TRANSIT TELESCOPE

The transit telescope was an instrument made possible by the technical advances of the seventeenth century. Before it could be used in astronomical measurement, it was first necesary to have a reliable regulator clock, and this would have been impossible before the invention of the pendulum and anchor escapements in 1658 and *c*. 1670 respectively. The transit instrument was simple in form, but demanded great exactitude in adjustment, being first employed by Römer at Copenhagen.

A transit consisted of an ordinary telescope, firmly secured to an axis at right angles to the optical tube. The ends of the axis were mounted across a window frame or similar aperture in the observatory wall, so that the telescope commanded a view to the south [2]. In use, the instrument could traverse the 180° from northern to southern horizons through the pole, but could not be moved from side to side. Its purpose was to delineate a meridian, and maintain it, as a standard of adjustment for the other instruments in the observatory (Plate 25).

James Pound, the uncle of Bradley, was one of the earliest astronomers to use a transit in England, which he set up at his observatory at Wanstead [3]. Graham also constructed a transit for Halley at Greenwich in 1721, which was the first of the Royal Observatory's new instruments, made to replace those removed by John Flamsteed's executors [4]. Its use was first to determine a meridian that could serve the collimation of the less movable quadrants, and second, to act as an instrument in its own right to determine right ascensions.

Meridian finding could be performed in several ways, depending upon the situation of the instrument. A line could be surveyed with shadow staves and plumb lines to establish a meridian mark against which to adjust an instrument [5]. A more accurate method was to follow the noontide sun with a quadrant to observe the moment of its highest culmination, or alternatively, if one had a good clock, one could calculate from the daily equation of time the precise second when the sun would occupy the meridian. All that remained was to observe the sun at that instant, and 'bring down' the telescope vertically to a horizon mark [6].

The Greenwich transit enjoyed a superior mounting to that of Römer, in the respect that it commanded the meridian through 180°, the roof of the transit house being fitted with shutters that could be made to open, thus giving an unimpeded view across the entire sky [7]. Once it was possible to observe a circumpolar star with a transit, one could fix a meridian by simply observing the star's 'upper' (southern) and 'lower' (northern) culminations.

If the star took longer to pass through, say, the western arc of its journey around the pole, it indicated that the axis was set too far to the east. Its angular quantity could be determined arithmetically, a correction applied, and the observation repeated. When the star took exactly 11 hours 58′ 28″, or half the siderial day, to pass through both eastern and western arcs, the instrument was considered to be true to the meridian.

When Bradley came to Greenwich in 1742, he discovered that Halley had allowed the transit to go badly out of alignment. After the method outlined above, he observed Capella, and discovered a westward displacement of 12″ from the meridian in the axis of the instrument [8]. Capella was a favourite object for such work, being the brightest of the circumpolar stars and placed at a moderately large angle from the pole. Its large polar displacement gave it a faster apparent movement and allowed its culminations to be timed with greater precision than the more sluggish Polaris.

When a transit was mounted to command 180° of sky, as at Greenwich, it not only permitted the instrument to find its own meridian, without the need for a quadrant, but also enabled it to designate its own horizon check. This was done quite simply by 'bringing down' the transit from its polar position, so that it could be made to view the horizon. A convenient object thereupon gave a permanent point of reference for the adjustment of the instrument in routine observation. It was normal practice to observe two meridian marks on the northern and southern horizons respectively. Halley's transit had been set up to align to the north on a chimney stack in Greenwich, and in the south, to a line chiselled into the wall surrounding Greenwich Park [9]. During his examination of the transit in 1742, Bradley found that although the instrument stood true to the northern meridian mark (when tested on Capella) its southern counterpart had become displaced by a couple of inches.

The reliability of meridian marks was always a difficulty with transits. On setting up the new Bird transit in 1750, Bradley devised more conspicuous marks. An iron plate drilled with small holes was secured to the chimney of a house on Shooter's Hill. Light shone through the holes, and when viewed with the transit, could be bisected exactly with the instrument's cross-wires. A similar mark was set up to the north, but instead of viewing the sky through holes, Bradley adjusted it to the silvery light reflected from the surface of the Thames [10]. Their alignment was regularly checked by the stars, thus resulting in a meridian line of great accuracy.

When Hornsby set up the Bird transit at Oxford's Radcliffe Observatory in the 1770s, he incised a mark on the wall of Worcester College, which stood exactly 680 yds due south of the transit room. By a series of experiments, Hornsby determined that the width of the line subtended an angle of 5.7″ from the observatory [11]. Terrestrial meridian marks remained in use for transit instruments until the invention of the collimating telescope in the 1840s [12].

One of the foremost advantages of the transit lay in its capacity both to apply and to receive cross-checks upon its accuracy. It was relatively light in weight and was reversible upon its pivots. Reversing (or inverting) was the critical test of the transit's alignment, in which the entire instrument was lifted out of its bearing pivots and turned around, so that the left-hand axis pivot now occupied the right-hand socket. After being permitted time to settle in the new position, the instrument was again brought down to the meridian. If its reversed wires still read the same places as formerly, then its collimation error could be considered as zero. If the reversed instrument did not fall upon the established meridian marks, then adjustments were applied by turning the pivot screws to bring the axis into line (Plate 26).

Each end of the transit's axis had to be rigidly supported. On the Greenwich and Oxford instruments, each end of the axis was mounted into an adjustable socket, set in a great stone pier that went deep into the earth. It was essential that these pivot sockets be absolutely horizontal if the transit was to bisect the zenith and pole.

Though this could be tested astronomically, by observing the transit of zenith stars, it became standard practice to apply the independent cross-check of a precision spirit level to the sockets. Several references occur to the use of levels on Halley's and Bradley's instruments [13], and the principal transit in Bradley's time was checked by means of a spirit level, in which a displacement of 1/50th in. in the place of the bubble corresponded to a deviation in the support sockets of 1' from the horizontal [14]. When the axis was found to deviate, it was brought to the horizontal by screw-set adjusters [15].

It was often difficult to keep a transit in adjustment when the Earth supporting the piers was soft or unstable. Hornsby in particular found this to be the case, between 1774 and 1778, at the Radcliffe Observatory. Applying the level to his transit piers about eight times a year, he found the western pier to be annually sinking out of adjustment by a couple of seconds. But the sinking ceased after the completion of the Observatory tower, 'since the centre-part of the building has been finished and the ground has received its full weight, the western end of the axis has ceased to sink' [16]. Probably the best level to be made in the eighteenth century was that used by Sir George Shuckburgh to test the Ramsden equatorial instrument, which he described in 1793. Its glass was ground to a curvature that corresponded to a radius of 1100 yds, so that the foot-long tube containing the liquid represented about 1'. A shift of $\frac{1}{6}$ in. in the bubble represented 1'' from the horizontal plane [17]. Hooke had been one of the earliest practitioners to suggest the grinding of spirit level glasses to large-radius curves to obtain precision alignments, as discussed in Chapter 3.

On Römer's original transit, the telescope had been placed away from the centre of the supporting axis. On Halley's 1721 instrument the telescope was also offset to one end of its $3\frac{1}{2}$ -ft axis, which made it impossible to reverse to the same meridian mark. To help rectify this problem, Bradley later devised a board with two marks set at $26\frac{1}{2}$ in apart (the difference between the 'normal' and 'reversed' collimation marks), and set it up a mile away from the Observatory when the alignment had to be checked [18]. The transit built by Bird in 1750 once more located the telescope in the middle of the axis, as well as fashioning the axis from two hollow cones, which were less liable to sag than a straight iron bar [19].

Another source of error when using transits came when observing the Sun, for the heat falling upon the axis invariably caused expansion problems. Bradley, indeed, even found that the body heat of the observer could distort the alignment if the axis were touched [20]. He attempted to 'defend' the axis from direct sunshine by a wooden casing, as well as by using narrow shutters in the transit house in an attempt to minimize the direct light falling upon the instrument. An identical procedure was followed by Hornsby at Oxford [21].

If the angular separation between two stars was required, the transit was used to observe the moment of culmination of the first star, and the time on the clock recorded. When the second star came to the meridian, its exact time of culmination would also be taken, and the interval hours, minutes, and seconds between observations would yield the hour angle between the stars. If the duration was timed between the passage of the first point of Aries (the start of the sidereal day) and any other star in the sky, the right ascension would thus be obtained [22]. Angles expressed in time could easily be converted to degrees by simple arithmetic. Such a practice was very much superior to sextant observation, and was a refinement of the quadrant and clock technique of Flamsteed. Its reliability, however, was much greater, because the reversible transit provided a much more easily verified standard than Flamsteed's mural arc, where the plane or pivots could be out of true without it being obvious at the time of observation [23].

In the transit's field of view were at least two wires — in the vertical and horizontal planes. Halley's original transit carried only two, but Bradley ordered Sisson to fit two extra vertical wires, each one 15′ from the centre wire, when he overhauled the instrument in 1742 [24]. The Bird transit had five wires, and before commencing regular observation, Bradley determined their exact separations from each other by timing star passages. [25]. Eyepiece field-wires were usually made of silver, and Maskelyne recorded that those in the Bird quadrant were only 1/750th in. thick [26]. Multiple wires carried with them the advantage of multiple observations of each transit, for one observed two transits before and two after the meridian. When it was cloudy, or the unsteadiness of the atmosphere caused stars to 'flutter', it was especially useful to be able to have three or five chances at making a good sighting, depending on the number of wires in the field.

To obtain the central transit of the Sun, it was customary to observe the two limbs and divide the resultant figure by two, as it is almost impossible to estimate accurately the Sun's centre. Therefore, if both limbs were observed as they ingressed and egressed each wire, it was possible to obtain no less than ten sightings for a single culmination of a five-wire instrument.

To make an actual observation it was customary for the astronomer to work with an assistant who 'kept the clock' and noted down the stars' times as they passed each wire. Observations were timed with a regulator clock, the pendulum of which was adjusted to beat sidereal seconds. As the transit room was in almost total darkness during observation, the astronomer listened carefully to the deliberately heavy beats ,of the clock, as a way of timing the star's movement from one wire to another across the field of the telescope. A skilled observer could frequently break a second down into quarters, and Bradley was capable of estimating them to a sixth part, to be designated by special symbols in the log-book [27], when he called them out to his scribe. By timing their meridional passages with the transit in this way it was possible to obtain the hour angle and right ascension of every object in the sky. When the same stars were re-observed with the quadrant, to obtain their declinations, an identical observing procedure was followed.

Hornsby, who never had an assistant, was forced to keep his own clock, and to scribe and observe all at one time. Moreover, it was his custom to make routine observations in both right ascension and declination on the same star-passage. He did this by observing a star on the first and second wires of the quadrant to obtain its declination. He then quickly transferred to the adjacent transit instrument to see it actually come to the meridian, after which he would switch back to the quadrant, to see it leave the field across the fourth and fifth wires. Such a technique must have demanded considerable physical agility, a flawless sense of timing, and an exact memory [28]. In this manner did the observers of the middle of the century compile their catalogues and reform the basis of positional astronomy.

The transit instrument was simple, manageable, and capable of great accuracy. It achieved its results, however, not by any superiority of scale division, but by guaranteeing a reference point in the sky, around which astronomers could develop other techniques of observation. As an instrument in its own right, it was invaluable, and as a check upon the quadrants — the instruments with which critical angular measurements were made — it was to become indispensable.

THE ZENITH SECTOR

The invention of the zenith sector came as a response to seventeenth-century attempts to measure a stellar parallax. Its working principle was simple: it consisted of a telescope of long focal length, supported on pivots or gimbals at its object glass, and left free to hang down, so that it pointed to the zenith. The length of the tube was considered as a radius, from which could be computed the precise size of the degrees through which the eyepiece would pass when the tube was moved. When adjusted, its pivots prevented it from moving more than a few degrees from the zenith, and even then only along the plane of the meridian. It was a somewhat specialized form of transit instrument, designed to measure the meridional culminations of zenith stars. In operation, the design of the instrument embodied two advantages that were considered essential to accurate parallax work: as the instrument 'hung dead' like a pendulum, it found its own zenith automatically, by gravity. Furthermore, the light of zenith stars could pass straight through the atmosphere free from distortion or refraction, which was a great advantage for critical observation, at a time when the laws of atmospheric refraction were only imperfectly understood (Plate 32).

It was hoped that as the Earth moved around the Sun, in the course of a year, it would be possible to measure a parallax at six-monthly intervals, if one observed in the zenith with a long-radius tube that would be sensitive to even the smallest deviation. To measure the precise quantity that the star actually moved, a scale or micrometer was secured to the lower end of the tube, to designate how far it had been necessary to move the instrument from the zenith to track the star. This figure, it was hoped, would correspond to the star's parallax.

Robert Hooke was the earliest practitioner to recognize the advantages of the zenith sector, as outlined above, in the measurement of parallaxes. In 1669, he constructed a 36-ft sector and installed it in his rooms in Gresham College, securely fixing it to a chimney stack to poke through a hole in the roof. He set out to observe γ Draconis, which passes almost directly overhead in London, and eventually obtained a 'parallax' figure of 27″ for the star, but this was regarded with suspicion by his contemporaries [29]. Almost certainly, this excessive value had been caused by the then unknown and unrecognized aberration of light, which continued as a source of uncertainty until Bradley discovered its true principles in 1728.

It is interesting to note that another of Hooke's reasons for preferring a zenith sector in the parallax measurements was that it allowed him to dispense with a fully divided arc. As the angle of parallax was so small, he appreciated that only a very large arc would be capable of showing the necessary divisions, and it is in this context that he provides the first recognition by an astronomer that the larger the quadrant or sextant, the more prone it was to distortion as a result of temperature changes. 'The heat of summer, when the summer observations are to be made, will make the quadrant swell, and the cold of winter will make it shrink, more than to vary a minute' [30]. Hooke's 36-ft sector was fixed in the vertical, with no pivots.

Also in the year 1669, Picard began his attempts to measure the length of a meridional degree, for which he used a portable zenith sector to take the places of the zenith stars at each end of his surveyed line [31]. But neither of these seventeenth-century sectors was capable of great accuracy, primarily because they did not carry micrometers to measure their angles, but rather short scales, broken down with transversals, attached to the eyepiece ends of the instrument, and read off with a plumb-line wire [32].

The 24-ft sector constructed by Graham for William Molyneux in 1725 was to become the prototype eighteenth-century sector, being fitted with delicate adjustments and a weight that kept the tube in permanent contact with a precision micrometer screw used to read the zenith distances. It had a field of view that covered 28', and was rectified to the zenith by a long plumb-line, the bob of which was damped in a dish of water to prevent excessive oscillation. Bradley made a number of observations with this instrument, and become convinced that it was capable of extremely high accuracy [33].

When Bradley commissioned Graham to build a sector for him, in 1727, it was closely modelled on that of Molyneux. It was first installed at Wanstead, where it guaranteed Bradley's scientific immortality by being the instrument with which he established the laws of aberration and nutation. After becoming Astronomer Royal he installed it at Greenwich, where it acted as a collimator for the quadrants down to the early 1800s [34].

Before its installation at Wanstead, Bradley carefully determined the sector's optical and mechanical characteristics. He realized that accurate measurements were only possible if his observing techniques equalled in rigour the workshop techniques of the instrument maker. After repeated trials on land objects, the object glass of the new sector was found to have a focal length of 12 ft 6.3 in. This meant that when the 12-ft tube was moved in an arc around its pivots, $1''$ at the eye-piece end would correspond to 1/1375 in. The motion of the telescope was governed by a fine micrometer, of which one revolution corresponded to 0.0246 in. At the end of the micrometer rod was a circular head, so that to turn the micrometer 1/80th of a turn moved the telescope 1/3252 in. When this linear quantity is applied to the moving of a $12\frac{1}{2}$-ft-radius telescope, it was found to advance the same through an angle of $\frac{1}{2}''$ [35].

As one may consider Graham the founder of a school of instrument graduation, so Bradley was to teach astronomers a new approach to the use of their instruments. Whatever the instrument — quadrant, sector, or transit — Bradley tested it almost to destruction before he would rely upon it. He was fortunate in being able to work with the finest instruments that were available in his day, but understood that if the skill of the maker was not complemented by that of the user, nothing worthwhile would be achieved. Bradley was the first to devise an observing technique in which the quadrant, sector, transit, and clock provided four interdependent cross-checks to catch errors, and his influence was reflected at home by Hornsby and Maskelyne, and abroad by Mayer and Bessel. It was with his zenith sector observations in the 1720s that the origins of his technique were first established, which were to grow to full maturity at Greenwich after 1750. Bradley himself was confident that the sector was reliable in practice up to $\frac{1}{2}''$ [36]. Molyneux's zenith sector was limited in the number of stars that it could encompass in the respect that it was only capable of being moved a few minutes out of the zenith [37]. To avoid this problem, and extend his observations as far as Capella, Bradley made his own sector movable through $6\frac{1}{4}°$ on each side of the zenith [38]. The exact zenith angle through which the telescope moved was designated on a $12\frac{1}{2}°$ scale attached to the telescope and read against a plumb-wire. The small seasonal variations in the position of the star as the Earth moved around the Sun were read with the micrometer [39].

Like the transit, the sector was easily cross-checked. The exact horizontality of its pivots was capable of being adjusted by a spirit level, and the whole tube could be reversed by lifting it out of its pivots and turning it through 180°. It was also possible to dismount the tube altogether to test its optical collimation against land objects. Like the quadrant, its micrometer could be checked against its own scale as well as being itself 'reversed', for on most sectors, the micrometer could be engaged by thumb-screws to push against either the north or south faces of the tube. If it read off the same quantities in either direction, it could be considered reliable.

THE REGULATOR CLOCK

While the development of timekeeping devices falls outside the scope of the present study, the regulator will be considered briefly because its own development was an integral part of those changes in observational technique brought about by the sector and transit, neither of which could have functioned without an accurate timekeeper. Although the mechanical clock had been known since the fourteenth century, it did not assume scientific consequence until the successful application of the pendulum by Huygens in 1658 [40].

The regulator progressed through three stages before it became the perfected instrument known to Bradley. Once the properties of the pendulum were understood, it was first necessary to discover how its swing was governed. Then an escapement was required so that the pendulum could govern the gear train, and finally, it had to be protected from variations in length that occurred through seasonal temperature changes.

Huygens himself contributed a great deal towards the solution of the first problem, which centred largely around the application of cycloidal cheeks to the pendulum suspension spring as a way of making it beat in equal quantities. Huygens had determined that a pendulum of 39.2 in (English) would beat seconds, although Lord Brouncker and Lawrence Rooke found that in London, 39.25 in was the true length, thus giving rise to the 'Royal Pendulum' [41]. By 1670, the first problem had been largely overcome, but there remained great sources of error in the working of these clocks — especially when fitted with 39-in pendulums — because of the inadequacies of the verge escapement. A crown wheel and verge required a swing of up to 100° to lift the pallets high enough to release the escape wheel, and whilst this was no impediment to a foliot bar, it was impracticable for a seconds pendulum [42]. Pendulums had to be heavy to be stable, and an immense source of power was necessary to throw one through 100°, once every second. Heavy weight trains were required, and the ensuing wear and tear was considerable.

A solution was found to this problem by the invention of the anchor escapement, around 1670, to which both Hooke and the clockmaker Joseph Clement claimed priority [43]. The anchor escapement allowed a reduction in the angle of swing to about 8°, which resulted in a great improvement in the clock's mechanical efficiency [44].

At the Royal Observatory, Flamsteed set up three clocks. One of these, his 'degree clock', completed in 1691, was fitted with an anchor escapement, and stood in the Sextant House [45]. In the Octagon Room, he mounted two Tompion regulators with 13-ft (2-s) pendulums, controlled by a pin-wheel escapement which has been attributed to Richard Towneley [46]. Their function was to confirm to Flamsteed that the Earth's axial revolutions were isochronous, as a prerequisite to finding a solution to the longitude. His use of a long pendulum was no doubt inspired by Hooke's discovery that a 14-ft pendulum, on the right escapement, was more stable, needed only $\frac{1}{2}$ in of swing, and made more economical use of the clock's power to give a longer running time [47].

The anchor was not completely satisfactory for astronomical purposes, as a result of its being a recoil escapement. When the pallets on the anchor engaged the escape wheel, their curved faces caused the wheel not only to stop, but to recoil backwards through a fraction of a turn. This always introduced an error into the exact timing of seconds. George Graham developed the mechanism in the early eighteenth century, when he modified the shape of both the teeth and pallets of the anchor to eliminate the recoil and make a dead-beat action [48].

By 1720, the reliability of timekeepers had improved more than 100-fold since 1650 [49]. Astronomical clocks were simple in design, unencumbered with striking trains or ornamentation, but made to the highest possible degree of mechanical reliability. Seconds pendulums, moving through small arcs of swing, were standard features on these clocks, with those pronounced 'ticks' which made them easy to 'keep' when working in the dark.

The only substantial problem that remained came from variations in their rates induced by temperature changes. Most clocks carried either thin iron or wooden pendulum rods. Unvarnished white fir rods were considered to be less affected by temperature fluctuations. But around 1715, John Harrison produced his 'grid-iron' pendulum rod, which utilized the expansion coefficients of brass and steel to maintain an even length [50].

Graham's attention was drawn to the expansion of metals in 1715, but he could devise no practical way of compensating for these almost imperceptible quantities until his attention was drawn to the expansive properties of mercury. Beginning in 1721, he experimented with a pendulum bob containing mercury, in which the upward expansion of the mercury in hot weather compensated exactly for the downward expansion of the pendulum rod. He stated that a good quality clock with a common pendulum ran into error about 12 or 14 s per day in a temperate room, and in exposed conditions 'it altered 30 seconds a day between y^e. hottest and coldest weather in the year 1722' [51]. But when he fitted a mercury bob to a similar movement, he discovered that in variable conditions its error fell to around one-sixth

Plate 25 — Römer's transit instrument, 1675, P. Horrebow, *Basis Astronomia*, (Copenhagen, 1735). Science Museum, Neg. No. 4496.

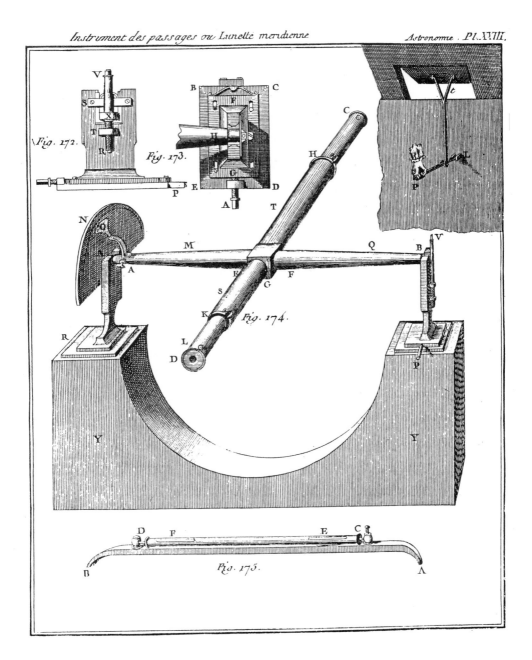

Plate 26 — Transit instrument and fittings. Note the level, 'Fig. 173', and gimbal type adjustments, 'Figs 172–173', J. le François LaLande, *Astronomie* (Paris, 1792), 'Plate XXIII'. LaLande discusses the transit in Vol. II, p. 624.

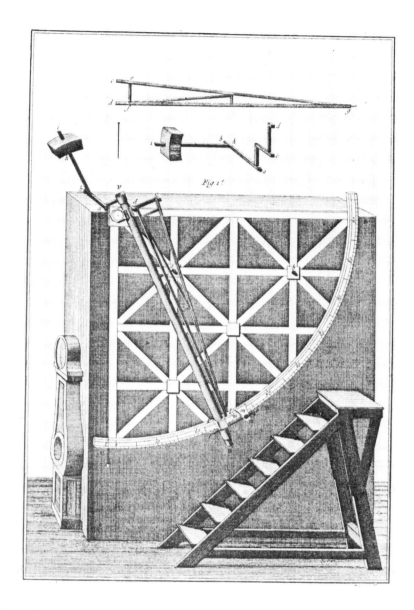

Plate 27 — Mural quadrant of 8-ft radius by George Graham for the Royal Observatory, 1725. This became a prototype mural instrument for the remainder of the eighteenth century, being developed by Graham from the Sharp/Flamsteed arc, and later perfected by Bird and the Sissons. D. Diderot, *Encyclopédie*, XIII (Neufchastel, 1765). The engraving accompanies the article 'Quart du Cercle Astronomique', pp. 667–671.

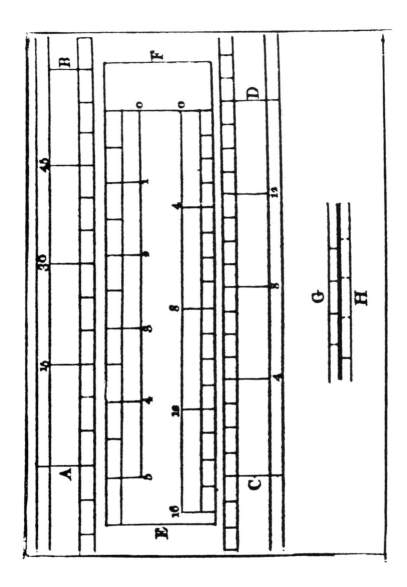

Plate 28 — Vernier scales on Graham's quadrant. The central pair of scales 'E–F' are attached to the telescopic alidade, and move across the 90° arc with it, between the 90- and 96-part scales engraved onto the quadrant limb. 'A–B' is the scale of 90°, and 'C–D', 96. The angle is derived from the congruence of pairs of lines, as shown at 'G–H', and in the present illustration reads 53′ 30″. N. Bion, *Construction and principal uses of mathematical instruments*, edited by E. Stone (London, 1758). See Supplement, 'Plate II, Fig. 10'.

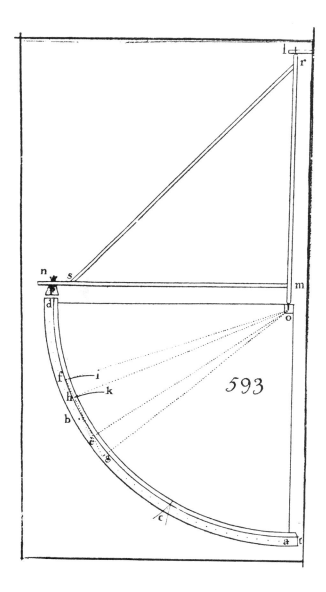

Plate 29 — Graduation of Graham's quadrant, 1725. This is the working drawing, from Smith's *Compleat System of Opticks,* showing the unfinished quadrant on the graduating bench, with the pivoted radius 'n–m' moving upon it. 'P' is a tool used to polish the limb to perfect flatness, and is braced vertically into the roof, at 'm–r'. The limb marks 'f–i', 'h–k' and 'c' are preliminary graduation points. R. Smith, *Compleat System of Opticks* (Cambridge, 1738), 'Fig. 593'.

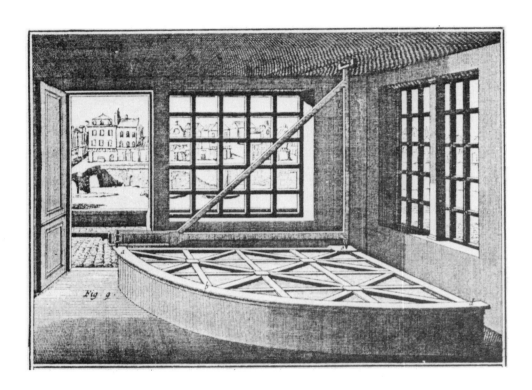

Plate 30 — The same scene as Plate 29 artistically re-drawn for Diderot's *Encyclopédie*. The technical plates in the *Encyclopédie* were frequently artist's copies of working drawings published elsewhere. D. Diderot, *Encyclopédie* XIII (Neufchastel, 1765).

Plate 31 — John Bird, 1709–1776. The foremost hand-graduator of the eighteenth century. Before him lies the unfolded plate from his *Construction of Mural Quadrants*, on top of which is placed a beam compass. Mezzotint, by V. Green, 1776.

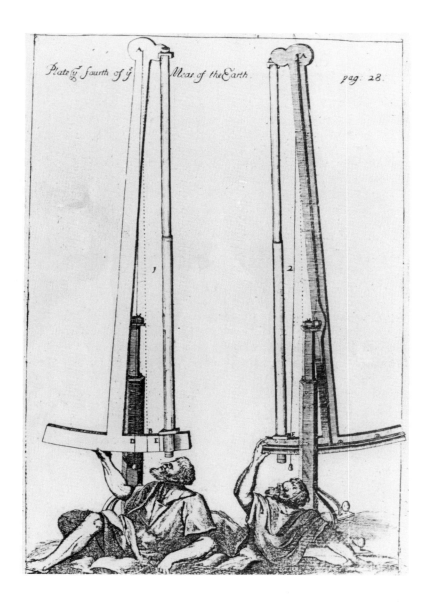

Plate 32 — The zenith sector in use. By moving the vertically suspended telescope along the plane of the meridian, it was possible to measure variations in the zenith culminations of the fixed stars. R. Waller (editor and translator), *The Measure of the Earth* (London, 1687) p 28.

of that for a common pendulum, and in a temperate room, to less than one-eighth. His experiments were conducted over a period of three years and four months, being presented to the Royal Society in April 1726.

Halley's original clocks at Greenwich do not appear to have had any temperature-compensating devices, for in July 1742, Bradley spoke of having to raise the bob of the clock in the quadrant house to 'a proper length for the season of the year' [52]. But one of Bradley's first priorities upon becoming Astronomer Royal was to get his clocks in good order, for in September 1742 the transit clock 'was taken down in order to have a new pendulum, contrived of bars of brass and steel, to remove in good measure the effect of heat and cold from retarding or accelerating its motion'. Two years later the quadrant clock was similarly modified so that it 'now has the same sort of pendulumn as [the] transit' [53].

By the mid-century, regulator clocks were capable of keeping time to within a couple of seconds per day, and when used in conjunction with sector, quadrant, and transit could determine co-ordinates with great accuracy. What was of primary importance was not so much that the clock had *no* error, but that it was constant and capable of being monitored over a period of time. An error of several seconds per day was quite acceptable, provided its quantity never varied. The clock supplied by John Arnold to the Dunsink Observatory in 1788 was capable of short runs when its daily error was less than 0.8 s [54]. John Arnold, along with John Shelton, were two of the leading makers of the middle to late eighteenth century, and supplied clocks to Greenwich, Oxford, Glasgow, and several foreign observatories [55].

Accurate timekeeping demanded that clocks be wound regularly to maintain even tension on the wheel trains. Most regulators had 30-day winding barrels, and it was Maskelyne's custom to wind the Shelton clock on the first day of each month [56]. The reason for installing 'month work' or even longer running periods between windings was to avoid disturbing the clocks once they were in motion. The pair of clocks by Tompion for Flamsteed ran for a year on one winding [57]. One of the primary hazards of winding derived from the fact that the clock invariably lost several seconds as the weights were re-hoisted. Bradley recalled, in 1726, that upon each winding of Molyneux's regulator at Kew it lost about 5 s [58]. The problem was finally solved by the invention of the maintaining power mechanism, in which an auxilliary weight was made to engage the wheel train and keep it in motion during winding [59].

Maskelyne also used a pair of 'assistant' or 'journeyman' clocks, that were made to keep time with the regulators. They had especially loud ticks, so as to be heard in windy weather, and were fitted with bells that sounded once per minute [60]. This made them easy to check against the main regulator, by simply opening the windows of the Octagon Room so that their rings could be heard across the courtyard and thus checked alongside the standard clock.

On several occasions in this book, attempts have been made to obtain assessments of the accuracy of early scientific instruments, unclouded by the estimates of their original users. Though this may be safely attempted when an instrument of non-critical accuracy has survived — such as an astrolabe — or when angular observations can be reduced, there is virtually no way of knowing the original accuracy of a clock.

Several early regulators have survived, but modern tests can only give a rough indication of their original accuracy, as decades of wear, combined with modern lubricants, affect their present-day running. It would, furthermore, be impossible to obtain useful information by reducing the results of horological observations.

Astronomical clocks were used to time right ascension angles, but as each timing was only of short duration — as successive stars culminated to the meridian — nothing significant is likely to be gained by reducing the right ascensions to their original positions. At best, this would only give the clock's rate for two or three hours out of 24, and without knowledge of local conditions, such as lubrication, temperature and position of the weights, a reduction would be little more than a mathematical speculation.

Little can be done beyond accepting the astronomer's own estimate for a clock's accuracy, and for this reason, the graph compiled by Dr F. A. B. Ward has been accepted as a reliable guide [61]. It would seem that the clocks used by Flamsteed to establish the length of the sidereal day, on 17th June 1690 and 16th June 1694, as 23 h 55m 50 s and 23 h 56 m 15 s respectively [62] (being close to the modern mean value of 23 h 56 m 4 s), agree well with Ward's estimated error of 8 or 10 s per day for a clock of 1700, as does Graham's 1¾ s per day for a clock of 1730, although it is likely that Ward incorporated these same figures into his graph.

ASTRONOMICAL INSTRUMENTS IN USE: OBSERVING PRACTICE IN THE EIGHTEENTH CENTURY

It is now appropriate to examine the working methods of the eighteenth-century observers, to understand how the instruments discussed above were made to function one with another [63]. One may consider the workshop as the starting-point in the quest for improved scientific accuracy, but it was in the observatory that the goal was to be attained. Bradley stressed

> . . . it is incumbent upon the practical astronomer to set out at first with the examination of . . . his instruments, and to be assured that they are sufficiently exact for the use he intends to make of them, or at least to know within what limits their errors are confined. [64]

After establishing a meridian line and 'southing' the transit, the latter was used to adjust the mural quadrants. Flamsteed's arc had simply been secured to the wall with a great nail and wedges, making it almost immovable once mounted, but the quadrants of Graham and Bird rested upon screw-set adjusters, which made it possible to secure critical alignment to the vertical. When correctly brought to the vertical with plumb lines, the meridional passage of selected stars would be observed with the quadrant, and compared with simultaneous observations of the same stars made with the transit.

The quadrant's deviation from the meridian would thus be obtained, and by turning the adjusting screws, corrected. This was the procedure followed by Bradley when he re-adjusted the Graham quadrant in 1742, after Halley had let it go out of adjustment [65]. To bring a quadrant to the meridian involved a more complex series of operations than to do the same with the transit, because of the quadrant's large flat surface area, each part of which had to be accurately aligned. When rectifying the Graham quadrant, Bradley selected 60 stars covering some 84° of altitude. At each of the selected altitudes, he compared the star passage in the transit with that of the quadrant, and thus obtained exact quantities for the deviation of each part of the quadrant's plane [66]. Maskelyne made a similar study of the Bird quadrant when he became Astronomer Royal, and found that when adjusted to the transit, its limb never deviated from the meridian by more than 6 s in right ascension [67].

Mural quadrants were heavy instruments, not easily moved. With the invention of the transit, the quadrant's reliability was greatly enhanced, by rendering its alignment and meridian setting amenable to immediate and easy cross-checking. Plumb lines were also used to check the plane of the quadrants. In December 1726, Bradley and Graham rectified the new quadrant so that the wire stood above the limb by half 'the thickness of a sixpence' [68]. In June 1734, while Halley was still Astronomer Royal, Bradley carried out further tests upon the Graham quadrant with plumb lines and discovered that the instrument was now badly out of true. When hung from the pivot at the quadrant's centre, the wire of the plumb line should have bisected a tiny dot 8 ft below on the limb. When tested, however, it was found to miss the dot entirely and Bradley estimated that the instrument was reading zenith distances 20″ too small [69]. The following year, he and George Graham submitted the instrument to a more rigorous examination, noting exactly the place of the wire in relationship to the dot it was supposed to cover. Using a small beam compass and scale of equal parts, he determined that the error amounted to 7/1000 in, which corresponded to about 15″ [70].

In 1742, Bradley commenced to re-determine the instrument's error after a seven-year lapse. He affixed the thin wire of the plumb line onto the plate of a good micrometer, and then made it hang exactly across the centre of the quadrant. It was then necessary to turn the micrometer screw through 26/40ths of a revolution before the wire was brought to bisect the beginning point for the divisions. Tests showed him that the micrometer had to be turned through 11 and 12/40th revolutions before the wire was advanced across 10′ on the scale, from which he determined that the angle of error in vertical adjustment amounted to $34\frac{1}{2}$ s for 1742 [71]. Assuming a steady rate of error accumulation since 1726, when it was first set up, and a 15′ error in 1735, Bradley estimated that the quadrant was shifting 2″ per year.

Plumb lines were again used as a preliminary to check the plane of the instrument when it was examined in 1735. Bradley found that the lower part of the limb had 'got further from the wall, near as much as the thickness of half a crown, for I found it necessary to force in the limb so much before the wire of the plummet could play freely' [72]. As the wire had originally hung half 'the thickness of a sixpence' in the opposite direction in 1726, it is obvious that Halley had failed either to notice or remedy an error of at least 3/16 in. in the plane of the quadrant.

Considering his reputation as an astronomer, Halley was remarkably slipshod in the adjustment of his instruments. Even granted the fact that he was a very old man during his Greenwich years, he seemed to have retained his vigour and energy in other aspects of his profession [73]. After the setting up of the quadrant in 1726, he used it for all meridian observations, and so neglected the transit that Bradley was obliged to cut down the trees that had overgrown the meridian marks before he could test it [74]. But one advantage emerged out of Halley's negligence: in the correcting of the Greenwich instruments Bradley was not only scrupulously exacting, but also recorded precisely the operations that it had been necessary for him to go through. His notebooks provide invaluable historical material.

The Bird quadrant was similarly rectified by plumb lines, and Maskelyne records the used of a silver wire 1/200 in. thick to make a critical alignment to the vertical. An explicit account of how to rectify a small Bird quadrant was also given by Ludlam [75].

Bradley rigorously tested the scales of both the Graham and Bird quadrants at Greenwich. By 1746, he had become aware of an eccentricity in the Graham quadrant in which the 45° part of the scale stood slightly further from the centre than did either of the ends. He determined the quantity to amount to some $15\frac{3}{4}''$, which he checked firstly with a spirit level, and later with a micrometer — obtaining the same figure in both cases [76]. Initially, he attributed the error to a displacement from the centre of the pivot, after detecting an error of 1/191 in. in its place, but in 1747 he reduced this figure to 1/400 in. [77]. The likeliest cause of the error, however, lay in the bimetallic construction of the instrument, discussed previously. Bradley was already aware that the quadrant was temperature-sensitive, for in 1742, he had noticed that in hot weather the vernier plate did not quite extend down to the divisions [78]. Slight variations of expansion and contraction between the brass and iron over 20 years would have been sufficient to have created an error of $15\frac{3}{4}''$.

The internal errors of the quadrant were tested up to 1745 by plumb lines, levels, and cross-checks with the transit instrument, but in that year Bradley had a micrometer fitted to the limb of the instrument, very similar in form to the one on his zenith sector. It permitted him to make more accurate observations, and provided a superior method of detecting scale errors. It needed $39\frac{1}{4}$ turns to move the micrometer through exactly 1 in, and on the limb, one turn corresponded to $53''$ [79]. One end of the micrometer was secured by a bushed pivot to a brass plate that could be locked to any part of the limb by a thumb-screw. Its opposite end engaged a female thread at the lower end of the sighting telescope near to the micrometer, so that one turn on the micrometer elevated the telescope through an arc of $53''$. By commencing at the start of the divisions on the limb, it was possible for Bradley to move the telescope and vernier through all 90° and read each one with the micrometer, to provide an independent check. Using this method in 1753, he confirmed that at the division 64°, the Graham quadrant had an error of $10.6''$, which accorded well with a $16''$ error for the full scale [80]. In turn it was straightforward to test the accuracy of the micrometer by noting consistent errors in its readings. Micrometers could also be 'reversed' in their motions and errors thus rendered complementary. Bradley extended a similar series of tests to his new Bird quadrant in the 1750s. After a most rigorous examination, he found that it retained its figure and had a scale of 90 perfectly equal divisions.

Upon moving the $12\frac{1}{2}$-ft zenith sector to Greenwich, Bradley began to use the instrument to collimate the quadrants, thus completing the sequence of cross-checks devised to eliminate error from his work. It was possible with the sector 'to determine with ease and precision the error of the lines of collimation of both mural quadrants', because it tested not only the alignment of the quadrant's frame — as did the plumb line — but also the accordance of the frame with the telescopes, verniers and micrometers [81]. Before commencing, it was necessary to check the zenith sector's own collimation, which was done by 'reversing' it, or turning its pivots through 180°, similar to the transit. If the observed star returned to the same place in the field after reversing, the instrument was considered reliable.

Simultaneous observations were made of the zenith star, with the sector and quadrant, after bringing the latter's telescope down to the zero mark on the limb. The sector was taken as the 'standard' and any deviation in the quadrant's reading noted and corrected. In 1768, Maskelyne found that the Bird quadrant was showing zenith distances 1.1″ too small, and the Graham quadrant 7.4″. The observation of 18 zenith stars in that year indicated that the collimation error was 0.4″ smaller than in 1765. Between 1765 and 1772 the quantity did not change, and then in August of that year, the error increased to 2″ after achromatic glasses had been fitted to the Bird quadrant [82]. The above-mentioned adjustments and checks to bring the quadrant to the meridian and zenith completed, it was now ready for observation of the stars in declination.

The thumb-screw that locked the micrometer plate to the limb was first loosened, thus allowing the whole telescope to turn around the centre pivot. Its motion was steady, being counterpoised on one side of the pivot by a lead weight [83]. Looking through the telescope, the observer would watch the desired star enter the right-hand side of the telescope's field and, after centring it aproximately, he would firmly lock the thumb-screw on the micrometer plate, to hold the telescope fast. Next, he turned the micrometer screw, until the star was exactly bisected by the horizontal wire in the field. The turns which it had been necessary to apply to the micrometer were then used in conjunction with the vernier scales to obtain the declination angle. The vernier read to 30″ direct and $7\frac{1}{2}$″ by estimation, but the micrometer yielded the single seconds. An equivalent reading was made on the 96-part scale, the micrometer giving the intermediary seconds on the vernier [84].

In the late 1740s, Bradley made a discovery which, he said, rendered all his previous quadrant observations useless, when he realized that the local state of the atmosphere affected refraction [85]. Since the late sixteenth century, astronomers had been aware of the necessity of applying a refraction correction to observations of a quantity that diminished with altitude. A prepared refraction table allowed a standard quantity to be subtracted from an observed angle, to obtain what was believed to be the true astronomical figure. When Bradley realized that this mean refraction was dependent upon local pressure and temperature conditions prevailing at the time of making the observation, he appreciated that his pre-1750 observations could never be corrected for absolute refraction, and were of limited value [86]. All post-1750 observations at Greenwich were accompanied by a barometric record and the height of the two thermometers, one inside and one outside the quadrant house. His precepts on refraction were followed by Maskelyne and Hornsby, who regularized the practice of accompanying astronomical with meteorological observations.

To make observations by the instruments discussed above, only a small staff was required. Bradley had one full-time assistant — his nephew — and the drudgery endured by Maskelyne's assistant was bequeathed to posterity by Thomas Evans [89]. As observations had become confined to the meridian and so were more accurate, they also became physically easier to make. Tycho had required a small army of assistants, Flamsteed's arc two, but Hornsby at Oxford eventually devised a technique that permitted him to do everything single-handed. It is indeed ironic that the Radcliffe, which, in 1777, Thomas Bugge considered the best equipped observatory in Europe [88], should have denied its director a single assistant. In addition to his novel one-man observing technique, discussed above, Hornsby was an almost exclusively daylight observer, considering that the daytime sky provided a more even illumination to the eyepiece wires than the candle lanterns used at night [89].

Our judgement of the success of early positional astronomy depends upon the standard of accuracy that may be attributed to the observations themselves. Estimates of the absolute accuracy of early instruments may be made from two sources, the first of which is the astronomers' own values.

Flamsteed had been capable of working to 10″ or 12″ in the use of his instruments, and the Graham arc could be relied upon, after the making of standard corrections, to 7″ or 8″. Bird claimed that his own arcs had total errors amounting to no more than 3″ [90]. This was indeed a formidable claim, but it was well substantiated. As a final flourish to his paper on the division of quadrants, Bird concluded with a eulogy to his own craftsmanship that was drawn from the results of two of the leading astronomers in Europe. James Bradley, using the new 8-ft Greenwich quadrant, and Tobias Mayer at Göttingen using a 6-ft instrument (both of which were made by Bird) gave independent determinations of the obliquity of the ecliptic that agreed to within 2″ [91].

It is also possible to obtain modern determinations of these instruments by reduction and analysis of the observations made with them. Modern reductions of this sort can often reveal information about the peculiarities of an instrument that eluded even the most diligent of their original users. When Knox-Shaw and his colleagues made a reduction of Hornsby's observations in the 1920s, they discovered that the overall scale-error of the Oxford quadrant was almost linear — thus indicating a great regularity in the instrument's divisions [92]. From 1774, when it was installed, to 1779, the error was constant, then between 1779 and 1786, it increased substantially. This was later correlated with the fitting of a new counterpoise on the quadrant, which probably occasioned uneven wear on the centre-pivot. Between 1786 and 1794 the error became stable once more and then rose sharply after 1798. A study was also conducted to discover if the instrument's performance varied with the seasons and temperature, but nothing emerged from the reduction.

From a series of observations made between 1788 and 1790, E. J. Stone was able to deduce a revised value for Hornsby's North Polar distance, along with several instrument errors [93].

Henry Safford's reduction of the Greenwich planetary observations made in 1891 provided additional substantiation for the high quality of Bird's first quadrant, in spite of the fact that the observations reduced by him came from a period when the instrument had begun to show the signs of hard usage. From observations made in the early 1780s he detected an error of +2.3″, which suddenly increased to 12″ in 1787. No cause for this sharp increase could be found in Maskelyne's notebooks [94]. This was, no doubt, the root cause of the large error discoverd to be present in the quadrant by Pond in 1806 [95]. Correlation was also made in the reduction between recorded temperature and the observed angle. This demonstrated a connection between the error in North Polar distance and the height of the internal thermometer, although as with the Oxford quadrant, there was no overall seasonal error. Safford drew a number of interesting conclusions about the performance of the instrument, stating that 'in studying the observations it is clear that the quadrant was a pretty troublesome instrument to use, and that it was frequently employed by quite unskilled persons, perhaps for practice' [96]. His conclusions about Maskelyne, who made the observations, are no less penetrating, stating that the Astronomer Royal 'was a good observer in detail, but very negligent in the handling of his instruments. He seems to have been methodical, without understanding the importance, which Bradley well knew, of keeping a close watch on the adjustments' [97].

What emerges from the two sets of reductions is that the quadrants were remarkably trustworthy instruments. But the most eloquent single testimony to their worth emerges from Rambaut's notes on Hornsby's observations, where he states that, in reduction, his mean error from 33 observations of Arcturus was 0.80″, and the overall error from the other observations examined, 1.62″ [98]. This accords closely with Bessel's original reduction of Bradley's observations published in 1818, when he found the mean error from 300 sightings of five selected stars to be 1.45″ [99].

6

The achievements of eighteenth-century positional astronomy

The great exactness with which instruments are now constructed hath enabled the astronomers of the present age to discover several changes in the positions of the heavenly bodies, which by reason of their smallness had escaped the notice of their predecessors [1].

The seventeenth century had been an age of innovation in its approach to astronomical research, whereas the eighteenth was to become one of consolidation and fulfilment. The Earth's motion in space, the shape of the globe, the lunar theory and the discovery of the longitude all became important issues in the seventeenth century, but it was not until the later century that practical instrumentation became sufficiently advanced to give them decisive substantiation. The effective solution to these problems gave dramatic proof of how technological barriers acted as a 'ceiling' upon the solution of scientific questions, but it was in their observational vindication of Newtonian theory that the astronomers of the eighteenth century claimed their greatest victory. This was only possible after instruments had become capable of measuring down to those critical few seconds of arc that allowed Newton's pronouncement on the shape of the earth, the 'three-bodies problem', and the lunar orbit to be demonstrated in the observatory.

THE ABERRATION OF LIGHT

Although aberration and nutation are two quite separate phenomena, they are often associated for several reasons. They were both discovered with the same instrument, both arose quite unexpectedly out of a separate astronomical inquiry, and between them they established James Bradley as the foremost positional astronomer of the eighteenth century. Bradley's two papers in 1728 and 1748, treating respectively the aberration of light and nutation, were models of practical scientific method, in which he first described his discoveries made with the zenith sector, and how his results were employed to deduce the laws that the phenomena obeyed. His approach was cautious, yet perceptive, and at all times constrained within the physical confines of the evidence. Even a modern scientific reader cannot help being impressed by the scrupulous care and attention to detail that made Bradley's work possible.

In 1725, George Graham completed a 25-ft zenith sector for Samuel Molyneux, who erected the instrument in his observatory at Kew. Its purpose was to repeat Hooke's observations of γ Draconis and establish a reliable figure for the stellar parallax. Bradley was well aware that the reason for Hooke's original failure lay in the fact that his great zenith sector at Gresham College was subject to instrumental errors of considerably bigger magnitude than the actual parallax he was endeavouring to measure. Molyneux's sector, on the other hand, was carefully collimated, and measured zenith distances with a micrometer rather than Hooke's diagonal scale.

Bradley began to make observations with Molyneux's instrument in December 1725, and after several nights he noticed that γ Draconis was continuing to culminate more southerly than he expected for a true parallax motion, and on past the solstice. The star continued to move southerly until March 1726 when, after having moved 20″ away from its December position, it began to advance northwards again. By June it had returned to its original position and then continued to move northerly until September, after which it veered south once more until December, when it occupied the same place whence it had begun 12 months before [2].

After a minute examination of possible errors in the instrument, Bradley was convinced that he had discovered a genuine motion, quite distinct from the parallax. This conviction was further enhanced by the regularity of the motion and the fact that its direction changes bore direct relationship to the equinoxes and solstices. Indeed, it was fortunate that Bradley commenced observation at a time when the star occupied its 'middle position' at midwinter solstice.

Bradley had to frame a hypothesis to account for the phenomenon in physical terms, and in furtherance of this end, ordered a zenith sector of his own from Graham. As the house in which he planned to mount the new sector was incapable of accommodating a 25-ft tube, he ordered one of $12\frac{1}{2}$ ft, as described above. As γ Draconis had been the only bright star within the range of Molyneux's sector, the instrument could only be moved 7–8′ from the zenith. The new sector which he set up at Wanstead could be moved through $12\frac{1}{2}°$ of the meridian, which enabled him to observe Capella.

On finding that the new sector substantiated his original observations, Bradley addressed himself to the star's motion. Eliminating the possibilities of instrumental error, he considered the likelihood of its arising from a nutation of the type predicted in Book I of Newton's *Principia* [3]. But Bradley discounted the chance of detecting a Newtonian nutation on account of its predicted smallness, and explained the phenomenon in terms of the changing direction of light from the star entering the sector's tube, as the Earth moved around the Sun [4]. The effect arises from a combination of the velocity of light and the velocity of the Earth in its orbit, so creating the illusion that the star was traversing back and forth across a mean point over the course of the year.

Although Bradley had been the first to recognize aberration as an astronomical phenomenon, evidence suggests that several earlier astronomers had detected quantities which they sometimes mistook for a parallax, but which were in fact due to aberration. Hooke's 'parallax' of 27″ for γ Draconis was almost certainly disguised aberration [5]. In 1692–1693, Römer discovered a quantity that he knew was not a parallax, but to which he could not ascribe a cause [6].

Flamsteed is the first observer from whose work a reliable quantity for aberration may be deduced. The first of these derived from this discovery of a 40″ displacement in the position of Polaris which he attributed to parallax [7]. But the more reliable value comes from Peters' reduction of Flamsteed's observations, which revealed a figure of 20.676″ (±1.1″) for aberration, which accorded well with Bradley's own figure of 20.00″/20.25″ [8].

Bradley acknowledged to the Royal Society that the key to his own success was 'depending very much of the accurateness of the instrument', for which praise was 'chiefly owing to our curious member, Mr. George Graham' [9].

In the late seventeenth century, instruments were just approaching the level necessary to detect aberration, but not until the 1720s had they progressed sufficiently for its quantity to be accurately measured and its laws established. So was the scientific 'ceiling' elevated.

Though Bradley failed to measure a parallax, he nonetheless provided the first 'proof' of the motion of the Earth in space from observational evidence, and his 1728 observations represent a new standard of astronomical achievement in the eighteenth century. One feels that Bradley had every justification for his claim that had the stellar parallax been as large as 1″, he would have detected it [10].

NUTATION

The researches which finally led to Bradley's discovery of the nutation of the Earth's axis originated from the same series of observations that first enabled him to derive the aberration of light. He noticed in these observations that certain stars close to the equinoctial colure showed a shift in declination which was greater than could be accounted for by the accepted figure of 50″ per year for the equinoctial precession [11]. Stars situated opposite to them on the solstitial colure, however, exhibited a change in declination which was less than expected. The pole appeared to dip down to those stars which culminated with the sun at the vernal equinox and winter solstice and to recede from those that culminated in autumn and summer.

Bradley first detected the phenomenon in 1727, but was unable to produce a satisfactory explanation until he had observed it over a number of years. He came to attribute it to the variable pull of the Moon on the Earth's equator as the inclination of the node shifted through all its positions over the course of its 18-year cycle. The constant changes in the intensity of lunar gravity upon the terrestrial equator resulting from the movement of the nodes induced a slight rocking of the globe. This was most apparent when the place of the pole was observed, for it produced a slight oscillation or nodding (hence 'nutation') of the Earth's axis, as the nodes moved [12].

The Moon was already known to affect the equinoctial precession, and Bradley realized that as the nodes of the lunar orbit shifted constantly in the sky, they would also exert an oscillatory motion upon the precession. When the 18-year cycle of the lunar nodes was complete, the oscillations should be restored to their starting point.

When he commenced observations in 1727, the lunar node was in the constellation of Aries, and by 1736 — half way through the cycle — it had receded to Libra. By this time it is likely that Bradley had recognized the cause of the new phenomenon, but withheld any announcement until he had observed the completion of the cycle, with the return of the node to Aries in 1745 [13]. He also made additional observations of star declinations, by noting the behaviour of stars that stood directly opposite to γ Draconis in the sky. While γ Draconis was found to be advancing northwards, he noticed that the small star 35 Camelopardi Heveli, which stood opposite to it across the pole, had advanced an equal distance to the south, when it culminated at Wanstead, 12 hours after γ Draconis. This demonstrated that the movement was indeed regular, and could be interpreted as an apparent motion occasioned by the oscillations of the terrestrial axis [14].

Having satisfied himself of the cause of the phenomenon, he commenced to substantiate it from a larger number of observations. He set out to compute the mean declination of γ Draconis from some 300 observations, and after applying the necessary correction, obtained such a consistent sequence of numbers for the place of the star that only 11 varied from it by as much as 2″ [15]. These observations, with some equally satisfactory ones made of other stars, enabled Bradley to determine the coefficient of nutation at 9″, which is within a fraction of a second of the modern figure [16].

Although it is true that what Bradley had discovered was not the same nutation as that predicted in *Principia*, Book I (which was solar rather than lunar in its origin), it nonetheless had a bearing upon the 'three-bodies problem', and gravity theory generally.

Much of Bradley's paper on nutation is concerned with his instrument and observing technique. He stressed the need for regularity in the making of such observations, for 'the more exact the instruments are that we make use of, and the more regular is the series of observations' [17]. He considered himself fortunate in being able to leave the zenith sector undisturbed at Wanstead for over 20 years, during which time the instrument's performance was faultless. Graham, the builder of the sector, once more received the highest praise on account of 'the most perfect manner' of his workmanship [18].

To make his discoveries of aberration and nutation, it had been necessary only to measure the relative declination of γ Draconis and its adjacent stars, as they moved in relationship to Bradley's local zenith at Wanstead. The observations did not require the determination of the stars' absolute angles from the pole or equator, and this was fortunate, for Bradley possessed no instrument with which he could then establish them with sufficient accuracy. Even after moving to Greenwich in 1742, he possessed no north-facing quadrant with which to observe the declinations of the circumpolar stars, and hence redetermine the observatory's latitude. The only quadrant at Greenwich was the Graham instrument built for Halley, and it faced south.

Bradley dedicated his paper on nutation to the Earl of Macclesfield, who, in 1748, maintained at Shirburn Castle in Oxfordshire one of the best-equipped meridian observatories in England.

Prior to the installation of the Bird quadrant at Greenwich in 1751 — which gave Bradley two quadrants, one of which could now face north — the Astronomer Royal had been indebted to the co-operation of the Earl of Macclesfield in the determination of the latitude of Greenwich. This has been performed by making observations of selected stars at Shirburn, and measuring their exact declinations, with relationship to a north-facing quadrant at Shirburn. By this procedure it was possible to find the declinations of stars that lay within the angular compass of the south quadrant at Greenwich. After re-observing these stars at Greenwich, and finding how they differed in terrestrial latitude, or absolute zenith distance, from their places as seen at Shirburn, it was relatively easy to compute the latitude of the Royal Observatory [19].

Bradley's observations with the zenith sector permitted the reliable measurement of unprecedentedly small angles in the sky. His discoveries and techniques became examples to his fellow astronomers, while his own often-repeated indebtedness to the skill of George Graham provides an exemplary demonstration not only of the dependence of practical astronomy upon the instrument maker, but also of its power to substantiate the truth of what had hitherto been held upon largely theoretical grounds: namely the Earth's motion in space, and the oscillations of its axis.

THE DETERMINATION OF THE SHAPE OF THE EARTH

The true shape of the Earth, and the length of a meridional degree of arc, had become questions of fundamental importance to the scientists of the early eighteenth century. The issue was further complicated by the fact that for 50 years the members of the French Académie had been making diligent observations in pursuit of a solution — and produced conclusions that were diametrically opposed to each other. One set of observations showed the Earth to be a *prolate* spheroid — pointed at the poles — whilst another set indicated it to be *oblate*, or flattened in those regions. By the 1720s, the issue had assumed considerable importance as it bore directly upon the conclusions of *Principia*, Book III, for Newton's treatment of lunar and terrestrial dynamics postulated an Earth that was oblate in shape. As with other critical issues in eighteenth-century astronomy, the decisions on the eventual outcome related directly to improved standards of instrumentation.

The first experimental evidence that indicated the Earth to be an irregular spheroid was derived from the pendulum observations made by Richer at Cayenne in 1672. He found that a pendulum adjusted to swing seconds in the Paris Observatory ran slow by two minutes per day at Cayenne, and had to be shortened by $1\frac{1}{4}$ lignes (1 French ligne $=0.0888$ English inches) before it would beat true seconds [20]. Richer carefully repeated these experiments many times over a period of ten months, by timing the swings of a free pendulum with an 'excellent clock'. As Cayenne is some 40° closer to the equator than Paris, it seemed to indicate that the terrestrial attraction diminished towards the equator as witnessed by the slowing down of the pendulum, while it would be at its greatest at the pole.

Newton appreciated the significance of Richer's findings, and after dismissing other possible causes for the pendulum's change in length (such as temperature expansion) concluded that 'the Earth is higher under the equator than at the poles, and that by an excess of about 17 miles' [21]. The shape of the Earth was important to Newton's conclusions on the nature of rotating bodies, the motion of the Moon, and the precession of the equinoxes.

Alternatively, the overall cogency of Newtonianism was threatened by those savants whose observations of the length of the degree of arc within various parts of France tended to demonstrate a prolate Earth. These observations, the first of which was made by Picard in 1669, required the accurate measurement of a base line on the Earth's surface, from the ends of which observations would be made of selected stars. In this way it was possible to correlate a linear quantity on the globe with an angular amplitude in the sky [22]. In 1701, Cassini laid down a set of survey triangles in the south of France, and concluded that as each degree appeared to be 1/800th shorter than its predecessor as they approached the equator, the globe was prolate [23]. Cassini's son added further substantiation to the arguments in favour of an Earth with 'pointed' poles when, in 1718, he published his findings derived from a more extensive triangulation survey [24].

None of these contrary observations induced Newton to change his ideas on the shape of the Earth, and he continued to consider it an oblate spheroid in both the 1713 and 1726 editions of *Principia*. The reason was simple. Whilst no one challenged the care with which Picard and the Cassinis had made their observations, they had all been made within the confines of France, and the geographical extent of that country was too small to provide a reliable guide to the shape of the whole Earth. Furthermore, a succession of observers who had repeated the pendulum experiments over a distance that extended from St Helena to Archangel all pointed to the contrary conclusion: that the Earth was more massive at the equator than the poles [25]. It was even possible to tabulate the precise variation in the pendulum length corresponding to the place of making the observation.

In the 1730s it was decided that the Académie should undertake a series of observations that would be decisive. Two expeditions were projected, one to be sent to measure a degree in the Tropics, the other within the Arctic Circle.

It was the expedition dispatched to Lapland that provided the decisive pronouncement, and Maupertius' memoir to the Académie described in detail the techniques and instrumentation that made it possible [26]. Although it is true that the Arctic expedition returned to Europe long before the tropical one, its results provided the immediate answer when its polar degree was compared with those made previously in France itself. When the expedition returned from Peru several years later, its findings provided substantiation to what had already been determined rather than decisive proof.

The Académiciens commenced their Polar survey in 1735 on the frozen surface of the river Tornea to the north of the Gulf of Bothnia, in Lapland. A triangulation was completed that provided a baseline of 55 023½ toises (1 toise $= 6\frac{2}{5}$ ft) in length [27]. From each end of this line the astronomers began to make observations of the stars, α and δ Draconis. To make these observations, they used a zenith sector by Graham of London, which was modelled on the instrument used by Bradley to detect aberration. On many occasions in his monograph, Maupertius speaks with deference of the work of Bradley and the instruments of Graham, both of which he considered as the ultimate in achievement in their respective fields. In addition to the sector, the expedition carried other Graham instruments including a 2-ft quadrant and a pendulum with knife-edge suspension [28].

The nine-foot sector carried a scale of $5\frac{1}{2}°$ at its lower end, and was read by means of plumb line and micrometer. Before using the instrument astronomically, it was tested rigorously on a computed terrestrial angle by five of the expedition's astronomers, each of whom performed an independent test. At a distance of 380 toises from the intended point of observation a line of 36 toises was laid out so that the shorter line formed a right-angle to the longer, thus subtending an angle of exactly $5\frac{1}{2}°$ to the observer. The sector was then secured in the horizontal plane and observations made of two markers placed at each end of the 36-toise line. Between them, the five astronomers concluded that the sector read the angle at $5° 29' 56\frac{1}{4}''$, or $3\frac{3}{4}''$ too small [29]. The error was considered extremely small, and attributable more to the contraction of the instrument through extreme cold than to erroneous dividing.

When the overall error of the sector had been determined, it was possible to make the astronomical observations. The instrument was set up vertically at one end of the baseline, the positions of the stars δ and α Draconis carefully observed, and their places taken on the micrometer. After careful dismantling, the sector was conveyed to the opposite end of the baseline and the observation repeated. An angular displacement of $57' 28\frac{3}{4}''$ was thus obtained, for a baseline of 55 023½ toises [30].

Before a reliable figure for the meridional degree could be computed it was necessary to establish the exact homogeneity of those degrees used to measure δ and α Draconis. A fine pair of wires were thus extended out across the scale, to subtend a computed angle of 1°. Using the micrometer, it was possible to advance the sector's scale beneath these wires, and test the equality of each degree through a viewing microscope [31]. Once again, a high degree of agreement was discovered, the degree space used to measure the star δ being only 0.95″ larger than that to measure α Draconis [32]. An opening was then made with the microscopes so that every 15′ space on the limb could be compared with every other to discover the internal consistency of the dividing and the micrometer. As with all preceding tests, it was performed five times, each one by a different astronomer, and the astonishing consistency of results that emerged confirmed their trust in the craftsmanship of George Graham [33].

In addition to the purely astronomical surveys, the Académiciens completed an extensive series of pendulum observations in the Arctic Circle. After taking great care to keep the temperature constant over the duration of the experiments, it was discovered that the pendulum accelerated 59 s per 24 hours in its swing, between Paris and Lapland [34].

From an astronomical amplitude of $57' 28\frac{3}{4}''$, it was calculated that the length of a degree on the Arctic Circle would correspond to 57 437 toises. This was 377 toises larger than the degree measured between Paris and Amiens by Picard. But Picard had known nothing of aberration, and he had failed to correct adequately for refraction and precession. When these quantities were allowed for, Maupertius argued, his value for the degree was reduced even more, to 56 925 toises, which was 512 toises shorter than the Polar degree. The quantity for the Polar degree given by Maupertius of 57 437 was after corrections had been applied, otherwise its length would have been 57 497 toises [35]. Maupertius was insistent upon an adequate correction for the aberration in measuring the initial amplitude in the sky, and indicated that had Picard and the Cassinis known of it when making their surveys, their results would have been substantially different. He concludes, 'Le degré du Meridien qui coupe le Cercle Polaire surpassant le degré du Meridien en France, la terre est un sphéroide applati vers les Poles' [36].

In his 1748 paper on Nutation, Bradley discussed the French determinations of the shape of the Earth, and how the new observed quantity for the equatorial bulge was greater than allowed by Newton as an adequate cause for precession [37].

But this was of minor importance to the general vindication of Newtonianism that emerged so strongly from the work of the Académiciens. Before it could deliver a final pronouncement on this part of seventeenth-century astronomical theory, the eighteenth-century scientific world required the cumulative experience derived from a new knowledge of aberration, allied with the new standards of precision measurement. Without either of these, a satisfactory conclusion could not have been reached, for the aberrational constant was sufficiently large to throw any series of observations into confusion if not allowed for, and without improved instruments, aberration would have remained undiscovered.

THE MEASUREMENT OF GRAVITATIONAL ATTRACTION BETWEEN TERRESTRIAL BODIES

Deriving initially from the problems involved in determining the shape of the Earth and how it was affected by astronomical bodies, the question inevitably arose of how gravitational attraction operated between bodies upon the Earth's surface. This inquiry was especially valuable, for it opened the possibility of providing a yardstick by which the relative masses of attracting bodies could be computed and expressed in terms of a stable substance, such as water.

The Académicien Bouguer, who went to Peru to measure an equatorial degree in the 1730s, had noticed that when making zenith observations in the proximity of Mount Chimborazo, an error of several seconds occurred in his readings, which he attributed to a displacement on the plumb line of his instrument, caused by the mass of the mountain [38]. In the 1770s the Royal Society showed interest in the matter, with the result that Maskelyne was sent to Scotland to make zenith sector observations at the foot of the mountain Schahallion (variously spelt Schaehallion, Schiehallion, etc.)

Schahallion was selected because its main axis stood east to west across the meridian, it possessed clearly defined boundaries, and it was not joined into a chain of other mountains. This localized its gravitational pull for the purpose of the experiment, and made it more readily calculable [39].

A temporary observatory containing a zenith sector, transit, theodolite, and Shelton regulator clock was set up to the south of Schahallion; these, after being adjusted, were used to survey a meridian line [40]. The sector was then used to observe the zenith passage of selected stars. When satisfied with the south-based observations, a second observatory was set up to the north of the mountain, and the observations repeated. Great care was taken to ensure that the two observing positions were exactly on the same meridian, and Maskelyne established this by careful cross-checking of results 'to confirm every deduction by another found in an independent manner' [41].

An exacting trigonometrical survey was conducted at the base of the mountain to find its precise dimensions and determine the distance between the north and south observing stations, which Maskelyne calculated from a series of triangles to be 4364.4 ft. This length was then used as the difference in latitude between the two stations, from which it would be possible to obtain the altitudes or zenith distances of the observed stars by simple arithmetic. Using Bouguer's tables for the variation in the length of the terrestrial degree. Maskelyne calculated that at the latitude for Schahallion

(56°40′ N) a second of arc would correspond to 101.64 ft. A baseline of 4364.4 ft, which he used as the basis for his observations, corresponded, therefore, to a celestial arc of 42″.94′.

The observations, however, yielded an angle of 54.6″, and he correctly attributed the additional 11″.6 to a deflection in the place of the sector's plumb line, due to the gravitational pull of Schahallion [42].

At all stages in the observations, Maskelyne paid great care to the adjustment of the instruments, for he fully realized that worthwhile results were only possible if the experiment was conducted in accordance with the strictest observational accuracy. Special attention was paid to the collimation of the sector, and he gave its maximum mean error as 0″.4, which was a very small quantity considering the terrain over which the instrument had to be conveyed [43].

After satisfying himself that the 11″.6 'is to be attributed to the two contrary attractions of the hill', Maskelyne considered the significance of the observations. Primarily, they proved that Schahallion exerted an attraction that was no less real upon the plumb line than that of the Sun upon the Earth. This provided the first demonstration of gravitational attraction between bodies of non-astronomical dimensions and illustrated by analogy the truly universal character of gravitation.

The Schahallion experiment also provided a demonstration of the inverse square law, and by this means, opened a way to deduce the density of the whole Earth. By comparing the computed volume of the mountain to that of the globe, Maskelyne estimated that the terrestrial density was between four and five times that of water [44]. This figure was later refined to 4.713 as a result of the researches of Hutton and Playfair between 1778 and 1811 [45]. It remained slightly less, however, than the value of 5.48 times the density of water, as obtained in 1798 by Cavendish from his torsion balance experiments. The modern value is 5.517 [46].

Maskelyne produced no surprises in obtaining a value for the pull of Schahallion, for the theoretical existence of the phenomenon was implicit in Newtonianism, though he was pleased to discover that it further demonstrated 'the analogy of nature'. Once a figure for the terrestrial density was available, moreover, it was possible for Hutton to ascribe water-density values to the hitherto relatively expressed densities of the planets [47].

The universality of gravity formed the cornerstone of *Principia*, but, like the Earth's motion, nutation and shape, it could not be demonstrated empirically until the old instrumental ceiling had been surpassed. The success of this achievement lay in the new capacity of scientists to measure the necessary quantities within a century of their predicted existence, and this indeed was the triumph of practical mechanics.

THE REVISION OF POSITIONAL ASTRONOMY

Discussion has already been devoted to four of the century's most significant discoveries made possible by improved practical mechanics, but it was from a host of less dramatic achievements that the eighteenth century assumed its true complexion.

Flamsteed's Great Catalogue of 1725 had been fundamental in providing a wholesale revision of practical astronomy that was to be invaluable to later generations of observers. Most other astronomers of Flamsteed's generation, though eager to experiment with micrometer and pendulum clock, had not been personally dedicated to a lifetime of systematic observation, and so much of Flamsteed's achievement stemmed from his half-century of devoted routine research. When the Great Catalogue eventually appeared, the 12″ error of the 4500 fundamental stars represented a five-fold improvement upon the accuracy of the 1000 stars of Tycho's Catalogue [48]. His comprehensive revision of basic astronomical constants, and the system of instrumentation that made them possible, formed the bedrock of eighteenth-century practice.

One of the most significant eighteenth-century advances, from the utilitarian point of view, was Tobias Mayer's improved lunar tables, which, after their simplification in the *Nautical Almanac* (1767), offered, at last, a solution to the longitude [49].

Though Halley had observed the Moon through an entire 18-year cycle, his own tables proved inadequate [50], and it was from Mayer's original 1755 tables and the theory that emerged therefrom that it first became possible to find a longitude to within the limits prescribed by the Act of 1714 [51]. In acknowledgement of this service, the Board of Longitude paid a posthumous reward of £3000 to the astronomer's widow [52]. Yet none of Mayer's work would have been possible but for his ability to measure more accurately than Halley, and this advantage derived from his access to a fine 6-ft Bird quadrant installed at the Göttingen Observatory.

Although they did not rely on the use of graduated instruments for their successful observation, the 1761 and 1769 transits of Venus were of great importance to the derivation of the solar parallax in the eighteenth century. An exact knowledge of the solar parallax was an essential requirement for further developments in Newtonian theory, for it was used to compute the distance of the Sun, which in turn was vital to the determination of planetary distances, which at that time were generally expressed in terms of the Astronomical Unit. A change of a few seconds in the accepted parallax value could alter the calculated solar distance by several million miles, with obvious repercussions for accepted solar system dimensions [53].

The instruments used to observe the transits were the telescope, eyepiece micrometer, and regulator clock, although these had to function in accordance with the general standards of accuracy as derived from graduated instruments. The average value of around 8″.6 derived from the total observations of the 1769 transit accords well with the modern value of 8″.794 [54].

Eighteenth-century astronomers were rightly proud of their discoveries and the new precision of their science. Newton, they believed, had explicated the Creator's very thoughts, and these in turn could be demonstrated with the increasingly delicate instruments which the age afforded. Indeed, the instruments formed a link between the manual and intellectual aspects of nature and human understanding. For Bradley, Maskelyne, Maupertius and others, there was no sense of dichotomy between the two realms of enquiry, and no concealment was made of their dependence upon skilled craftsman. Now that precision had been achieved, it seemed that perfection would inevitably follow.

7

The precision graduation of full circles

The superiority of circular instruments is, I believe, too universally admitted to render it probable that quadrants will ever again be substituted in their place [1].

The dislodgement of quadrants and other part-circular instruments from the fore-front of astronomical research that began in the late eighteenth century indicated not so much a new level of scientific aspiration, but rather the establishment of new engineering technology. Astronomers were always aspiring to new levels of precision, and by the late eighteenth century their demands had become constant. Every new discovery promised richer rewards once they could reliably enter the 'next decimal' into their observation books, and with the stellar parallax still unfound, the exact solar parallax open to conjecture, and the lunar theory in an unpolished state, the astronomers of 1770 had plenty with which to keep themselves occupied.

At many points of *impasse* in scientific endeavour, one is aware of the operation of a law of diminishing returns, where effort has to be trebled or quadrupled to secure a single unit improvement. In the realm of instrumentation, this law exerts itself at critical stages, for instruments are the fundamental implements of research, and when the brass and steel of which they are fashioned prove themselves inadequate to new scientific demands, one encounters a physical barrier that only a breakthrough in technology can hope to surmount. It is at such times, when the vital proof of experimental vindication is demanded, that the science of pure intellect is imprisoned within the artisan's pocket.

When the technical demands of science were relatively simple, a researcher could substantiate his ideas with a dramatic *experimentum crucis*: thus Galileo set two lenses in a disused organ pipe and Horrox measured the solar diameter with two needles set in a stick. But in 1770, astronomy had outgrown this blissful state. It had become the most technically demanding of all the sciences, and even basic research demanded heavy capital investment in equipment. Each new decimal was won only at the price of formidable effort in terms of craft dexterity, and it could not be advanced much further if astronomy still continued to operate within the technical confines of the quadrant.

New techniques of graduation and mounting had been sufficient to give Graham an improvement of about 5″ on the mural of Abraham Sharp, and Bird in turn reduced Graham's error of 7–8″ down to 1–2″ by 1750, but these few seconds were won at a price that would have been unthinkable to Hevelius. In terms of mounting, construction, and beam compass graduation technique the quadrant had reached its zenith with Bird, and no hand or eye could make it go further.

The eclipse of the quadrant may be seen as the third such deadlock in astronomical technology, the resolution of which demanded an influx of new skills and techniques. The first had been experienced by Tycho, who found that instruments constructed in accordance with classical principles could be developed no further. His use of diagonal scales and improved sights enabled him to build a 6-ft instrument that was more efficient than a conventional one of 20 ft, while at the same time elevating the ceiling of accuracy from 10′ to single minutes of arc [2].

The second deadlock came in the 1660s, when Hevelius and the other Tychonic astronomers had developed graduating and observing techniques to a level that surpassed the resolution of the naked eye. Further improvements in metalwork would have been futile had not the telescopic sight made its crucial appearance, thus placing within the reach of every astronomer a visual acuity which transcended that of Hevelius himself.

Both of these technical improvements — in conjunction with a host of minor ones — had been applied to the quadrant, but by 1780 the shape itself had become an object of suspicion. Its reaction to temperature change was less uniform than that of the full circle, and it was more difficult to centre exactly, because the alidade could not be cross-checked in the 180° position. As it was divided by striking off the radius, its graduation procedure involved beam compasses, and as hand-held tools they were subject to severe limitations. The superiority of the circle was discussed by Shuckburgh in 1793 [3].

To win the 'next decimal' it was thus necessary for astronomers and craftsmen to look to a new type of instrument, the fabrication of which placed it within the newly desired parameters of accuracy.

Ole Römer's recognition of the merits of the full circle has been discussed in Chapter 3, though with the exception of his assistant Horrebow, his example was not followed elsewhere [4].

Henry Hindley of York invented what must rank as the first proper technique of circular division to be devised to suit the requirements of the engineer rather than the compass geometer. It consisted of a regulated stepping technique, but as it was devised primarily for the graduation of dividing engine plates rather than astronomical circles directly, it will be treated more fully in a later chapter.

THE DUC DU CHAULNES (1714–1769)

The circular division procedure published by the duc du Chaulnes in 1768 was also intended primarily for the plate of a dividing engine, but as it contained several features that were to become integral parts of astronomical circle dividing and laid the foundation for a new instrumental tradition, this aspect must be considered under the present heading.

The method involved the total abandonment of the beam compasses. The faculty of touch, which lay at the heart of compass-division and was enshrined in Bird's maxim, was also cast out, and the faculty of vision put in its place. But its operation was strengthened and made more positive by the use of the microscope. Instead of feeling for a point on the limb, the duc had the operator see it through a microscope, where it could be easily bisected by a cross-wire. Circular division was to stand on principles quite different from those of the quadrant.

The essential element in the success of the duc du Chaulnes' method lay in his exploitation of a unique property of the circle — its reversibility. Once centred upon is axis, a circle could be broken into fractions simply by reversing it through 180° and checking its turns against two fixed points [5]. Two fixed microscopes A and B were set up facing each other across a mounted circle, so that when rotated, its limb passed beneath their object glasses at the point of focus. A fine scratch was drawn upon the limb of the circle and brought beneath the cross-wires of the microscope A. Taking a small slip of brass onto which a similar scratch had been drawn, an assistant positioned it beneath the cross-wires of the second, facing microscope B, and secured it with wax. When this operation had been successfully performed, the circle was reversed through 180° upon its axis, to bring the wax piece under microscope A, and the original scratch under microscope B (Plate 35).

Any errors in the position of either of these two marks, or of the microscopes, would now become immediately apparent, for if they deviated from 180°, it would be impossible to make both marks and circle coincide when reversed. If deviations did occur, slight re-positioning of the wax pieces and microscopes were made until cross-wires and scratches agreed perfectly in all positions. Once divided into two equal parts, the first stage of graduation was complete.

Another microscope was then placed at an angle of 60° to A, from which the places of 60° and 120° were located on the circle, until both halves had been accurately divided into six segments of 60°. When the positions of the wax pieces had been established with certainty, lines were drawn from them to make permanent divisions.

This procedure was repeated with the 30° and 10° spaces until one had a circle divided into 36 equal parts. Because wax pieces were used at all stages of the trial-and-error process of division, it was unnecessary to make preliminary construction marks on the circle, which must have given it a clearer finished appearance.

It will be noted that the duc du Chaulnes used the technique of trisecting, which had fallen into disuse amongst the best quadrant dividers. But trisecting was less hazardous in circular division, where the use of microscopes, reversible circles and the abundance of checks which they afforded allowed much more certainty than beam compasses.

Great ingenuity was displayed in the subdivision of the 10° spaces into single degrees. His method was based on the irregular properties of the number 9, being borrowed from 'Clavius the Jesuit' whose contributions to scale division were discussed in Chapter 2 [6]. Using trial and error, the place of 9° was located within a 10° space, and then carried around the circle, making 19°, 29°, 39°, etc. by reading from every preceding 10° space with the microscopes. But when reading 9° forwards from each of these irregular places, one could locate the degrees 18°, 28°, 38° etc. and from them, in turn, 17°, 27°, 37°, until one had divided down to 360 individual degrees. If half degrees were required, a 15° space was bisected and the resulting $7\frac{1}{2}°$ used to fill in the fractions [7].

Each degree was subdivided by a process outstanding in its novelty, but fraught with many hazards. It exploited the time-honoured relationship between the tangent and radius of a circle, and required the operator to take a board about 7 ft long, which was to be divided into 12 equal parts.

At the top of the arbor that carried the circle undergoing division was fitted a telescope set in a horizontal position and firmly secured so that circle, arbor and telescope rotated as one. The board, with its divisions, was next set up at such a distance from the telescope that its ends corresponded exactly to one of the degree spaces on the circle when viewed through the telescope. Each of its 12 parts thus subtended 5′ on the circle. The sightings of the board through the telescope were not used to scribe the circle direct, but onto a brass 'pattern plate' which in turn was used in conjunction with the microscopes, and applied to each full degree. Its divisions were scribed off with the same pointril built into the frame of the apparatus that had been used to engrave the previous degrees from their wax pieces.

Compared with the rest of his method, the subdividing technique seems singularly crude. As he was not a professional instrument maker, however, one cannot expect him to have displayed the same awareness of the destructive effects of very small errors that could enter into the work through faulty technique. Had he had this, one feels he would have adopted an alternative method of subdividing.

Before it subtends an angle of 1°, a 7-ft board must be removed from the observer to a distance of approximately 400 ft. At this range, it is not easy to ensure a perfect tangential alignment with the radius and centre of the circle upon which the telescope rotates, and without such an alignment, accuracy is vitiated. Furthermore, any person who is accustomed to the use of a theodolite can vouch for the difficulty experienced in making the cross-wires cover exactly a thin mark at this distance. Wind, haze and shimmering air currents all contribute to an image that is too indistinct to be used as the basis for an engraved scale. The use of survey techniques to test an already engraved scale, such as those used by the Académiciens on the pack ice of Tornea in 1736, is far less decisive in its consequences, for it acts merely as a repeatable check, and does not condemn a future scale to the immediate vagaries of the weather and a surveyor's chain.

The use of the above technique to produce a 'pattern plate', which would then be copied into every degree space on the circle, made the final graduations no more than a third-hand copy of a straight rod of unattested accuracy, viewed through 400 ft of atmosphere. Only after all the subdivisions had been engraved could their positions be accurately tested with the microscopes, and by this time it was too late. In the light of these considerations it is obvious that the method could never have attained that critical accuracy which the astronomers of 1768 were expecting as a matter of course.

Original and forward-looking as the duc du Chaulnes' method was in so many respects, it failed to take into account several factors of importance that were already well established in the repertoire of the best English craftsmen. No adequate allowances were made for temperature changes during the process of graduation, although the effects of expansion between the various parts must have been significant when one considers the large amount of direct manipulation involved as the operator constantly repositioned the wax piece with his fingers. As the method worked on trial and error, it must have been tedious to perform, placing great stress on the operator's patience and attention as the circle's expansions and contractions continued unheeded over the days taken to divide it. There was no attempt to lay off the principal points before temperature changes could occur, as was Bird's practice, nor can the placing of warm wax onto the scale have contributed to its thermal stability.

Cross-checking was very variable, both in quality and range. It was at its best when the main divisions were being made, when original use was made of the microscopes, but was virtually non-existent when subdividing. No adequate safeguards were to be found against possible errors arising from eccentricities of the central axis, upon which the circle was reversed.

As a scientific gentleman of the *ancien régime* it is unlikely that the duc du Chaulnes was familiar with the latest techniques of the dividing trade, especially as they were almost exclusively a London preserve. But in this respect, one must consider how widely known were the refined techniques of Bird and Sisson even amongst the rank and file of the London trade itself. The London craftsmen had many levels of competence and receptivity, and even as late as 1809, Edward Troughton knew jobbing craftsmen who 'generally suppose the expansion of metals to be a trifle which need not be regarded in practice'. Judged by the standards of the middle of the eighteenth century, therefore the duc du Chaulnes' contributions were not without significance [8].

But whether his ideas ever penetrated the London instrument-making world, or whether the principles behind his method were independently re-discovered, cannot be reliably ascertained because of documentary omissions, though it was within the competitive workshops of Fleet Street that the art of circular division was to grow to maturity.

JESSE RAMSDEN (1735–1800)

No other instrument maker of the eighteenth century drew such lustre to the science of practical mechanics as Jesse Ramsden. Like Graham and Bird before him, and Troughton after, Ramsden won both official and commercial success, along with academic honours as a scientist in his own right. As a Board of Longitude prizewinner, F.R.S., and St Petersburg Académicien, Ramsden and his patrons, Sir George Shuckburgh and General William Roy, produced a succession of accounts of the instruments which his skill had contributed to the advancement of science. Rich as they are, however, in the technical details of use and adjustment, they are wholly silent upon the crucial issue of how Ramsden executed the circular divisions which made them unique.

Ramsden was never to divulge his method in print, though it appears from Troughton's comments that it was known and practised by 'all the best dividers' in London by *c.* 1800 [9]. Its principles may be ascertained from a paper by Pearson, written within a dozen years of Ramsden's death while, no doubt, the oral tradition was still extant, in some comments in Ramsden's own writings, and in several adverse remarks made by Troughton in 1809.

It is in the writings of Ramsden and Troughton that one best senses the perfect blend of intellectual and manual accomplishment that was the hallmark of eighteenth-century positional astronomy. They were imbued with the spirit of Newtonian exactitude in the Heavens, which they strove to reproduce in brass, in the workshop and observatory. One shares with them the satisfaction they must have often experienced when a complicated machine was made to delineate, over and again, the positions of the stars to within a fraction of a second of arc, and the delicately engraved scales which always returned to zero, no matter how exacting the test.

At the outset of his career, Ramsden had used a scale of equal parts like Bird, but having found the method unsatisfactory, set out to develop his own independent technique. When he first brought it into operation is not recorded, and by the time of Pearson's writing it was 'perhaps known to no-one except Mr. Berge', Ramsden's old foreman [10]. The date was probably in the early 1770s, when Ramsden's inventive skills were at their peak. Ramsden perfected the first commercially viable method of dividing astronomical circles, which was capable of attaining a standard of accuracy superior to the best quadrants, and contained elements from many sources.

From the English school of quadrant dividers, Ramsden continued to use the beam compasses to obtain his primary points, but conjoined them with the principle of *adjustable* dots, microscopes, and reversing the circle, which lay at the foundations of the duc du Chaulnes' technique. In spite of Ramsden's reluctance to pay intellectual homage, Pearson was no doubt correct in suggesting that certain elements of his technique were derived from the duc du Chaulnes [11].

Ramsden laid off his first sequences of primary dots around the circle with beam compasses, using a technique that may have been influenced by Bird, but as he was aware that errors would be produced, he endeavoured to assess and correct them. Two microscopes were next set up across the diameter of the circle, similar to those used by the duc du Chaulnes, and the circle reversed until the operator was satisfied that every dot, or pair of dots, stood exactly at 180°. If any deviations were found to occur, corrections were applied. Dispensing with the duc du Chaulnes' wax pieces, Ramsden endeavoured to physically shift each erroneous dot with a pointed instrument, until part of it was 'coaxed' beneath the desired cross-wire. Hence the name 'coaxing' by which the method came to be known.

As up to two-thirds of the primary dots were found to be erroneously placed when examined microscopically, a considerable amount of coaxing was necessary to obtain the desired accuracy, and these 'doubtful or bad points' produced a somewhat rough appearance on the finished scale [12].

Though the displacing of a dot may seem a crude expedient in precision workmanship, one must remember that the original beam compass dots were little more than guides to the microscopes, and once the true place for the intended division was visible in the cross-wires, the original dot was quite expendable and could be deformed at will. Inelegant as it may have been, when compared with Troughton's improved technique of correcting the primary circle, it was less prone to displacement errors than the duc du Chaulnes' wax pieces, and was capable of achieving a degree of accuracy quite beyond that of a conventionally divided quadrant. This was made possible by seizing upon the unique reversing properties of the circle, which, when used in conjunction with microscopes, afforded a check more stringent than anything hitherto devised.

When he tried the Ramsden method at the outset of his own career, Troughton found it 'tedious in the extreme', requiring 150 days to graduate a full circle [13]. This was occasioned by the large amount of trial and error necessary to re-adjust the dots.

Whether consciously or not, Ramsden had contributed two important features to the duc du Chaulnes' method. He had reduced the trial and error substantially by first marking out close approximations of the eventual places of the true dots with the beam compasses. Secondly, he took careful precautions against temperature-based errors, and though their precise nature is not known, it is likely that they were modelled on Bird's [14].

Instruments carrying circles divided by Ramsden's method had come to be installed at a variety of observatories between Scotland and Sicily by 1800. One of the finest of these was the 4-ft equatorial, built for Sir George Shuckburgh in 1793, and although its circles were graduated by Matthew Berge, the work was executed under Ramsden's direction. After setting up the instrument in his private observatory in Warwickshire, Sir George presented a paper to the Royal Society in which its accuracy was examined.

The 'Shuckburgh Equatorial' had right ascension and declination circles, and neither were found to have centre-errors that amounted to more than a single second. Though some of the 'coaxed' dots were inelegant, many of them were quite round, subtending an average angle of $21''$-wide in the microscope crosswires [15]. Dividing errors were very small, amounting to $0''.53$ on the equatorial circle and $0''.57$ in declination. To read the scales, either in observation or examination, one viewed them through each of the six micrometer microscopes that stood every 60° around the circle.

An observation made with one microscope in one quadrant produced a probable error of $1\frac{1}{2}''$, but when all six were used, and the corrections applied, they fell to below $0''.5$.

Early in his paper, Shuckburgh stressed that one of the circle's chief advantages was the ease with which it could be checked by the astronomer himself, thus enabling him to ascertain, tabulate, and correct every error to obtain critical accuracy. This stemmed from the instrument's reversing properties, absent in the quadrant. This principle was to be of the utmost significance in instrumentation, and was later to lead William Lax to suggest that critical work was even possible on an indifferently graduated circle, for the astronomer could tabulate every error with micrometer microscopes, and apply corrections at leisure after each observation [16].

One might indeed suggest that the instrument makers' skills had surpassed themselves, and now threatened to make them redundant.

EDWARD TROUGHTON (1753–1835)

> For many years previous to the publication of the following method by Troughton, the art of graduation had been carried on in secrecy and silence; every artist had, or pretended to have, a method of his own [17].

Troughton's monograph, which won him the Royal Society's Copley Medal in 1809, not only contained a method of circular division that established new parameters in astronomical accuracy, but provided a rare glimpse into the instrument-making community and its cherished secrets. Reading his treatise with hindsight, one sees the English tradition of instrument making reach full maturity.

The secret of his technique lay in 'taking short measures with instruments which cannot themselves err to any sensible degree' [18]. The technique that enshrined this method first occurred to Troughton in 1778, after he experienced dissatisfaction with conventional methods, though it was not until 1785 that his brother John, to whom he was apprenticed, would permit him to put it to the test [19]. Convinced that beam-compasses and dividers were 'little better than so many sources of mischief', he resorted instead to what was then considered the most perfect branch of mechanics — metal turning [20].

Troughton set a carefully turned metal roller to rotate on a radial arm, so that it described a track around the circumference of the circle to be divided. Although after running its course he discovered that a mark upon the roller rarely coincided with its departure mark upon the circle — which resulted from the varying porosities of the two metals — its course was nonetheless found to be remarkably constant. The respective circumferences of the circle and roller were carefully adjusted, so that 16 turns of the roller were required to go once around the circle. As the head of the roller was itself divided into 16 parts, one revolution thus divided the circle into 256 parts of 1°24'22".5 each — a number chosen because of its bisectional properties.

Before commencing division, the marks on the roller and circle were brought together and viewed through the microscope set above them. As every subsequent graduation of the roller made contact with the circle, as seen through the microscope, a small round dot was incised with a special punch until the circle had been divided into 256 equal parts [21]. The primary circle of dots, which the duc du Chaulnes had obtained by laborious trial and error and Ramsden with beam compasses, Troughton was able to strike off with speed and ease from his roller. Furthermore, once the original roller and mounting had been made, it could be used to divide any number of circles with an enormous saving of time.

But as the primary circle of dots was not expected to be any more accurate than Ramsden's beam compass points before they had been coaxed, the circle was next set up between two facing microscopes to ascertain the deviations from 180° of each pair of dots [22]. When dots were found to vary, instead of coaxing them, Troughton simply measured their deviation with an eyepiece micrometer in the microscope, and compiled a table of errors until the exact place of every dot was known. Once these points had been fixed with certainty, their interval spaces could be broken into degrees and fractions with a 'sub-dividing sector', which fitted as an extreme extension radius and scale onto the roller [23]. The sector's own scale was used in conjunction with a micrometer microscope that could be made to yield the correct ratio of minutes between the primary dots. When Troughton was satisfied that the place of a division was correct, it was incised into the metal as a fine line by a special cutter.

For the last, most delicate stage of dividing, when he engraved the degree marks into the final scale, Troughton abandoned the use of dots in favour of lines, for while dots were easy to bisect with a micrometer wire in the early stages, they were sometimes deflected from their true places by inequalities in the metal, whereas lines, even when temporarily deflected, always resumed their true course and were thus preferable in the critical stages [24].

The entire process was finely regulated, the coarser stages preceding the more delicate, and everything being scrupulously checked. At the first stage of primary division the motion of the roller was checked by its own microscope, and when its dots had been laid down, their places were observed, corrected, and tabulated with micrometer microscopes. At the last and most critical stage of subdivision, the table of corrected dots was checked by the subdividing sector, the scale of which would not return to zero unless the pair of corrected main-scale dots between which it operated were perfectly equidistant. In this way, errors were localized, detected, and checked before they could accumulate in other parts of the circle. The scale of the subdividing sector received its own divisions from Troughton's dividing engine [25], which was itself another mutually cross-checking machine that will be discussed presently.

Troughton's method was wholly visual in operation, depending as it did on micrometer microscopes at all stages, and as such, renders complete the severance from the tactile tradition of English quadrant dividing. Ramsden's use of the compasses at the primary stage of dividing still preserved his affinity with the tradition, although his use of microscopes at the more critical stages made his a mixed tactile and visual method. But it was not until 1790 that Troughton first used the micrometer microscope, after the idea had suggested itself from General Roy's description of that accessory on the new 36-in. Ramsden theodolite built for the triangulation survey. Before this time, Troughton had made the measurements by viewing a micrometer through a single lens of short focus, and though he reduced the collimation error by observing it through a small hole in the top of a 4-in viewing tube, he could not prevent dust from falling onto the exposed wire, and the arrangement was inferior to a micrometer microscope [26]. With his improved microscopes, Troughton claimed to measure down to 1/50000 of an inch, and took issue against Smeaton who had claimed similar accuracies for the faculty of touch in 1785 [27].

At all stages of the work, minute attention was paid to temperature stability, 'for it is absolutely necessary that . . . the whole circle should be of the same temperature exactly'. Troughton discovered by experiments that when one half of the circle was 1°F warmer than the other, 'the upper semicircle will actually exceed the lower by 2 seconds', irrespective of the mechanical accuracy of the technique [28]. Along with temperature control, Troughton endeavoured to optimize the sensitivity of his own vision during graduation and preferred to work in a shuttered room by the controlled light of a special lantern.

In one of his invaluable contemporary insights into the instrument world, Troughton compares the time taken to divide a circle by his own method with those of its closest rivals. Bird's method would have taken 52 days, and Ramsden's 'method of adjustment' an incredible 150 days, assuming two-thirds of the dots had to be corrected. Troughton's own method, however, needed no more 'than 13 days of eight hours each' which, even allowing for slight exaggeration, represents a time-saving factor of 11 against its only serious competitor.

As a judicious entrepreneur as well as a man of science, Troughton was aware of the commercial prospects of the new pressures that were coming to bear upon the trade, which demanded both increased quantity and improved quality in instruments. His dividing engine was already busily engaged in what, by 1809, had become the routine graduation of nautical instruments, and it was his boast that roller division now made it possible for any ordinary artisan to graduate astronomical circles with a precision hitherto beyond the skill of the most subtle compass dividers [29]. Using conventional dividing techniques, it had required at least 'twice seven years [before] a man could hardly become a workman in this difficult art', but it was now possible for a man of only mediocre skill to obtain critical accuracies in graduation. What had once demanded a rare skill of hand could now be performed faster and better by an operative who was merely careful and conscientious in the use of the roller and accessories.

Troughton's own work with the roller and micrometer microscopes transformed the art of dividing, setting it upon new theoretical principles, and producing a re-appraisal of the concept of accuracy in astronomy. Numerous contemporary mono-graphs and articles refer to the description and use of instruments divided by Troughton, and their observatory performance will be examined subsequently [30]. For his contributions to both the science and art of instrument making, Troughton deserved his Copley Medal and the profits that accrued to him.

After its presentation in *Philosophical Transactions*, Troughton's method was taken up by other makers, including Thomas Jones, who, after experimenting with the roller, soon discarded Ramsden's 'coaxing' technique 'which I learned in the course of my instruction, and practised . . . with patience and perseverance, for it requires much of both' [31].

But its success did not prevent Cavendish from launching a rearguard action to restore the beam compasses to their former place. Cavendish proposed combining the compass with a sliding micrometer microscope that could be used to measure computed chords across the circle, and hence produce its graduations. Though his proposed method was ingenious, it was 'altogether inconsistent with practice and inelegant in design', and as it never appears to have been used, need be pursued no further [32].

Allusion has already been made to William Lax's suggested method of correcting a circle's divisions after construction. Both from its publication date and drift of argument, Lax's method was clearly influenced by that of Troughton. Yet in spite of its ingenuity — and the aspersions it cast against the instrument-making profession — the 98 hours which it required to correct an indifferent circle represented a saving of only six hours against the time taken by Troughton to graduate a 'perfect' one [33]. Captain Kater also published a method, but there is no evidence of its being used in practice. A demonstration of the impracticability of these, and other 'gentleman amateur' methods of the early nineteenth century, can be found in Pearson [34].

THE CONSTRUCTION OF CIRCULAR INSTRUMENTS AND THEIR APPLICATION TO ASTRONOMICAL RESEARCH

The successful utilization of the circle demanded the solution of problems in instrument design that had been absent in the structurally simpler quadrant. A quadrant consisted of a single limb, securely anchored to its mural support, and traversed by a telescopic sight. But to exploit the reversing properties of the circle, it was necessary to make the entire limb and telescopic sight rotate around a centre pivot, and this presented structural problems in the mounting. The very nature of the circle, mounted like a wheel upon an axle, afforded a more even weight distribution, and disposed of the need for elaborate counterpoises, which had been sources of mischief on many quadrants [35]. Once a satisfactory mount that combined strength with lightness had been evolved, the advantages of the circle were manifest.

Improvements in the optics of the refracting telescope and the development of achromatic lenses were also invaluable in contributing to the success of the astronomical circle. Though telescopic optics are outside the scope of the present work, the colour-free, corrected lenses fitted to the new circles permitted a visual accuracy much superior to that with the single-glass quadrant telescope [36].

Jesse Ramsden had been one of the first to devise a successful mount, by bracing his circles with spokes that comprised hollow brass cones set with their bases upon the axle, and their apexes girdering the graduated limb [37]. Clearly, the method was derived from the conical bearings of transit instruments, and was to provide the structural framework for the subsequent astronomical circles of Ramsden, Jones, Troughton and Simms.

To make the astronomical circle perform to advantage, both its graduations and the means whereby they were read had to be established upon new principles. It was not enough to graduate a circle as though it were four separate quadrants, like the 4-ft circle, described by Bugge, in which each quadrant carried the traditional 90- and 96-part scales and was read by verniers [38]. A similar approach is seen in the early nautical circles of Mayer and Borda.

Microscopes had already been used to read the divisions of circular scales by Römer and the duc du Chaulnes, but both had been restricted by other technical factors. Römer's graduations had not been in themselves good enough to utilize microscopes to advantage, and the duc du Chaulnes never records having used the microscope on anything other than a dividing engine. It was Ramsden who, having first produced superior graduations by means of microscopes, used the same to read his divisions to best effect [39]. Microscopes, in conjunction with eyepiece micrometers, gave much greater certainty when used to read scales, making it possible to discern fractions of a single second of arc. But not before the late eighteenth century had techniques of circular dividing made microscopic reading really worthwhile. The microscope and circle complemented each other.

One of the earliest instruments to bear superior circular divisions, conical spoke bracings, and microscopes was the 36-in theodolite built by Ramsden for General Roy's triangulation in 1787. Though this was not the first full-circular instrument commenced by Ramsden, it was the first to become operational and be described. It was built to survey with critical accuracy the longitudes between the Greenwich and Paris Observatories. Its main circle, braced with conical spokes, lay horizontal, and its 15' spaces were read with a pair of 180° microscopes [40].

In each microscope field was a metal plate indented with 15 equally spaced notches that represented minutes of arc. Two vertical wires also stood in the field, one fixed, the other movable by a fine micrometer screw. To make a reading, both wires were first made to coincide, and if they fell between a pair of 15' graduations, the movable wire was turned from the fixed one across the notched plate, until it encountered the nearest 15' division on the limb, which it was made to bisect. By simply counting the interval notches between the wires, the residual number of minutes was found, which, after being added to the angle on the limb, gave the total reading. As the micrometer head governing the screw was divided into 60 parts, it was possible to ascertain the individual seconds. Though the success of the survey cannot be wholly ascribed to the quality of the theodolite, the instrument was of great importance in establishing a revised Greenwich–Paris longitude value of 2° 19'51"

[41]. The angles for Roy's 16 triangles were found to be accurate to within just over a second. Ramsden's theodolite remained in use from 1787 to 1853 [42].

As Ramsden never indicated a date at which his improved method of division first became feasible, it is difficult to establish a chronology of development. Yet by the time he had completed the Roy theodolite, he had long been engaged upon two astronomical circles: the Shuckburgh and the Palermo circles.

The equatorial acquired by Shuckburgh in 1793 was probably similar to the instrument originally ordered by, and intended for, the Royal Observatory in 1778 [43]. In January 1781, however, Maskelyne wrote to the Royal Society complaining that Shuckburgh had offered Ramsden an extra £50 on top of the Ordnance Board's £500 for the instrument, and that Ramsden was on the verge of accepting, as he needed the money urgently because of a lawsuit [44]. How Ramsden avoided a second lawsuit by this conduct is difficult to say, for the instrument went to the highest bidder, though it took another decade to complete. Shuckburgh's comments on the quality of its graduations have already been discussed [45].

The Shuckburgh equatorial shows all the signs of an experimental design, for after its presentation to the Royal Observatory by Shuckburgh's heirs in 1811, it was found to be too weak and shaky to support the long polar axis. Pearson suggested that its place at Greenwich reflected more upon 'its former proprietor's munificence rather than its maker's success in the strength and stability of its essential parts' [46], and by 1858, Airy considered it but 'a small indifferent telescope on a weak frame' [47]. In Appendix 3, I discuss the development of the Equatorial as a measuring instrument.

Ramsden's altazimuth instrument, built for Piazzi's Palermo Observatory, was the first really important astronomical circle. By its completion in 1789, Ramsden had evolved a much stronger mount, bracing the limb with ten conical spokes, in a way that was reminiscent of the Great Theodolite. To facilitate ease of observation, Ramsden placed a small mirror at the foot of each microscope to illuminate the divisions. The eyepiece wires of the main telescope were illuminated by shining light through the hollow axis of the instrument, and into the tube [48].

The divisions of the vertical circle were found to have a maximum error of 3″, and the azimuth circle 6″. As these were errors in straight division, corrections could be applied, although when exposed to direct sunlight an additional error of 4″ or 5″ could develop, through the expansion of parts [49] (Plate 37).

Its graduation and design made the Palermo circle the finest of its day, and Piazzi used it to establish the places of the 7646 stars of his 1814 catalogue, as well as for his asteroid work [50]. It became a prototype instrument and a second was ordered for Trinity College Dublin, though this was completed after Ramsden's death by Matthew Berge, who took over Ramsden's business [51].

Though 60 workmen were employed in Ramsden's business [52], he had a total disregard for production deadlines, and instruments were often years in arrears. But this may be forgiven when it is remembered what he was trying to achieve: the pioneering of original designs while maintaining the highest quality in current production. He wanted his experimental designs to be perfect first time, and with this in mind, we may regard his 20-year delays more charitably than did his exasperated customers.

Troughton incorporated the principal Ramsden features into his own circles, but aimed to overcome the inherent instability of so many Ramsden instruments.

According to Pearson, he entertained a strong dislike for mounting azimuth circles so that their vertical supports were anchored into an overhead bearing, as Ramsden had done on the Palermo circle. Because the overhead bearing would bask constantly in the sunlight when the dome was open, yet the lower bearing remain in shadow, problems of unequal expansion would inevitably ensue. Troughton thus secured his instruments on a single lower bearing of great strength [53].

Though he had divided several instruments already, Troughton produced his own prototype in the 30-in Westbury Circle constructed for Pond's private observatory in Somerset. It combined Troughton's superior roller graduations with a greatly improved overall design that overcame the weaknesses of many earlier circles. When first examined in London through the two 180° microscopes, the divisions were found to have a maximum error of 1″.25 and a mean of 0″.7. But during its journey to Somerset a suspected alteration of the collimation took place, for on its arrival a regular 3″ error was found evenly distributed about the circle [54].

In 1806, Pond published a set of reduced observations in which he compared this Westbury instrument with the Palermo circle, a Troughton circle at Armagh, and the old Bird quadrant at Greenwich. A discrepancy of 10″ to 12″ was thus detected in the Greenwich instrument, and Pond affirmed that, by 1806, the quadrant was finally obsolete [55].

Maskelyne had requested a meridian circle as early as 1792, but not until the shock of Pond's publication were the Commissioners jolted into action, and in 1807 an order was placed with Troughton for a 6-ft meridian circle, to replace the Graham and Bird quadrants [56].

As a meridian circle was required to move only in declination, Troughton obtained maximum stability by securing it to a stone wall and thus making it a mural circle. No astronomical circle had been hitherto mounted this way, and the Royal Society was suspicious of the design, although after proving itself in practice the 'Mural Circle' became a prototype for many other English instruments [57].

The 6-ft 'cartwheel' turned around an axis set deep in masonry, and its divisions, engraved on a platinum strip, were read by six microscopes. For many years after becoming operational in 1812, Pond (who had succeeded Maskelyne as Astronomer Royal) found it unnecessary to effect any adjustments, for when all six microscopes were used together, 'the errors of division became almost insensible' [58]. The use of six microscopes to read an observation, moreover, could make even an indifferent circle perform satisfactorily, as was demonstrated in the error analysis of the Cape of Good Hope circle in 1833 [59].

A second circle by Thomas Jones, almost identical to Troughton's, was set up at Greenwich in 1824, so that comparative readings could be made [60]. To employ them to best advantage, a method of observing by reflection was devised. At any given observation, one of the circles would be used to observe the star's declination in the normal way, and the other depressed so as to observe the star's image as reflected from a trough of mercury [61]. The complementary readings acted as a stringent check, and remained in use until the method was rendered obsolete in 1850.

Great progress in instrumental accuracy had taken place between 1780 and 1810. In the 1790s the 'ceiling of accuracy' had passed beyond the 1″ of arc barrier, and by 1820, Pond's observing books displayed consistent readings to places of 1/10″ [62].

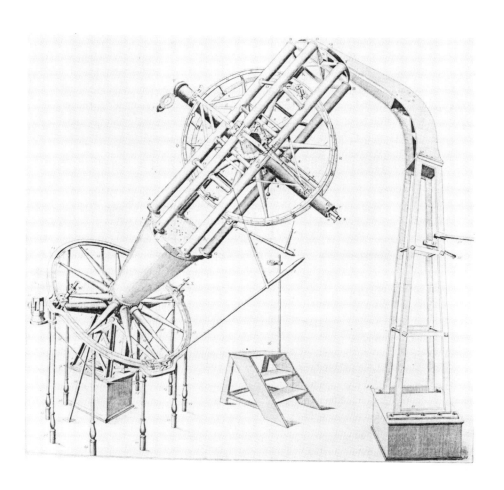

Plate 33 — The 'Shuckburgh' Equatorial, built by Jesse Ramsden, 1793. The original instrument is still preserved in the Science Museum, London. Its circles were graduated by Ramsden's 'original graduation' technique, although the declination circle was re-divided in 1838. G. Shuckburgh 'An Account of an Equatorial Instrument', *Philosophical Transactions*, **83** (1793).

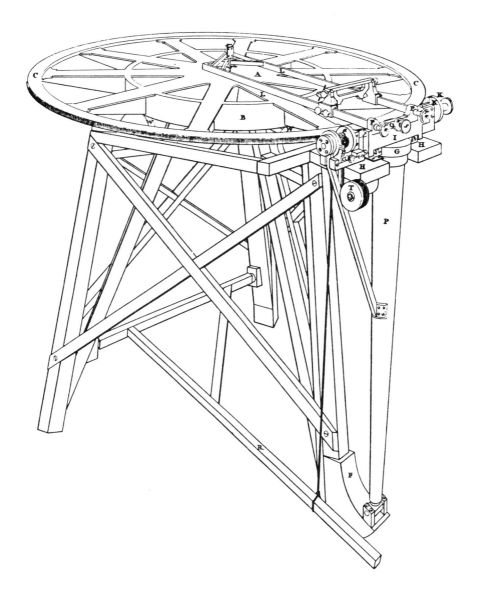

Plate 34 — Jesse Ramsden's circular dividing engine of *c.* 1775. The work to be divided was placed upon the centre of the large wheel. When the treadle was depressed, it rotated the wheel through a prescribed angle, ready for the scriber to engrave the division. J. Ramsden, *Description of an engine for dividing mathematical instruments* (London, 1777). Fold-out plate.

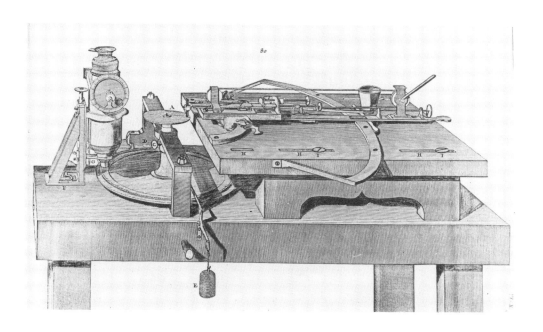

Plate 35 — The duc du Chaulnes' circular dividing engine of *c.* 1768. The microscope was used to critically align the 'master circle', so that its divisions could be copied and engraved onto the work, placed on the shaft above it. Duc du Chaulnes, *Nouvelle méthode pour diviser* (Paris, 1768), 'Plate V'.

Plate 36 — Airy's Transit Circle, 1850, built by Troughton and Simms. The great telescope was placed exactly on the meridian rotating upon precision trunnions. Declinations were read off against a 6-foot-diameter graduated circle. The man on the extreme right reads the scale with six micrometer microscopes placed at 60° apart, set into the stone pier. Edwin Dunkin, *The Midnight Sky* (1891), p. 156.

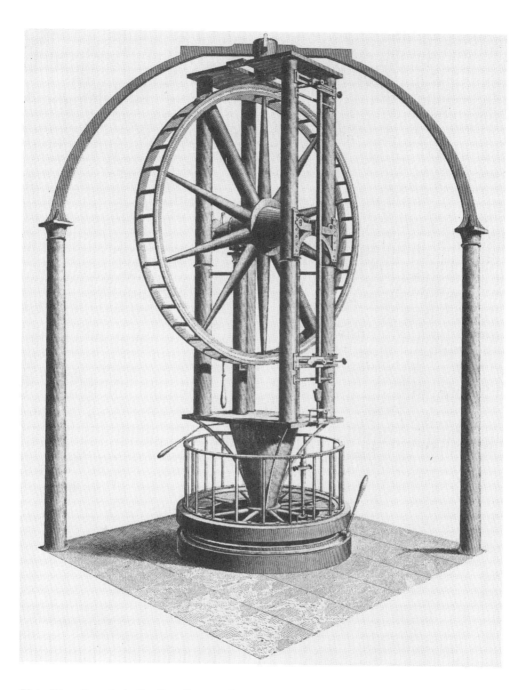

Plate 37 — Ramsden's five-foot diameter circle for the Palmero Observatory, 1789. Its vertical and horizontal circles gave their readings through pairs of micrometer microscopes. This was the first major circular instrument to come into use in any European observatory, and provided the coordinates for Piazzi's 1814 Catalogue. (W. Pearson, *Practical Astronomy*, 1829, Plates vol., XXVIII.

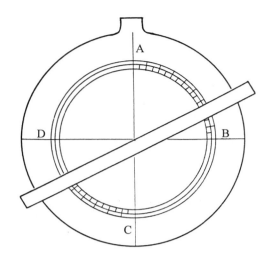

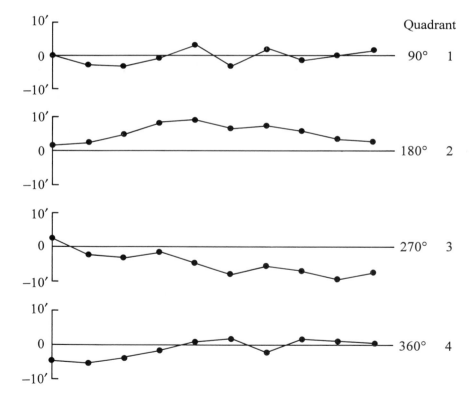

Plate 38 — (A) Scribing an astrolabe or circle by copying the divisions of the quadrant A–B across the centre onto quadrant C–D, resulting in an error distribution with a two-fold-rotational symmetry. (B) The four quadrants of the instrument are plotted in four graphs, 1, 2, 3, and 4. Note the way in which the error curves of the quadrants 1–3, 2–4, 'reflect' each other. (Astrolabe c. 1450, of 10.6 inches diameter. Item no. 10 listed on page 154).

Plate 39 — (A) A Victorian 'Garret Master's' or jobbing craftsman's dividing engine? The graduated wheel with its inside denticulations was turned by the knurled head to bring the divisions against the pointer. The cutter, on the horizontal bar, was then used to incise the divisions into the work secured onto the spokes of the wheel. (B) Detail of the graduations on the main wheel. Note the redundant graduations and fine gear teeth from an earlier instrument, now used as a base plate beneath it. (Appendix 2, page 160).

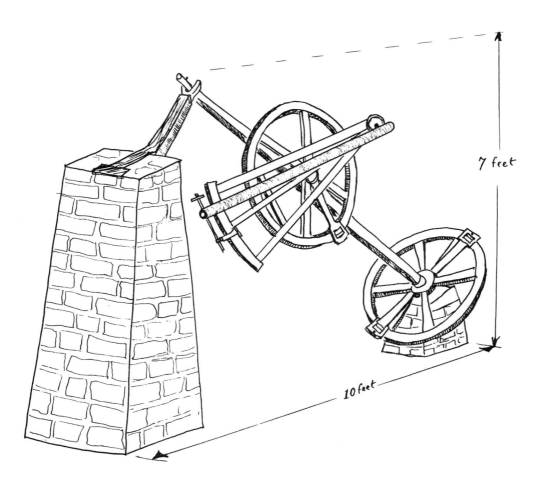

Plate 40 — John Bird's Equatorial Sector for the Radcliffe Observatory, Oxford. The 36-inch diameter circles, dated 1775, are the only circles that Bird is known to have graduated for a major instrument. They were used to guide the five-foot radius Sector arm and telescope which was mounted on the Declination Circle on the polar Axis. (Appendix 3, page 162) (Original drawing by A. Chapman).

Circular instruments, however, were confined almost exclusively to declination measurements; even when located murally on the meridian, the right ascensions were taken in the usual manner with the ungraduated transit.

Francis Wollaston had been amongst the first to secure simultaneous right ascension and declination readings at a single observation by using a transit circle of his own design, built by Cary in 1793 [63]. It comprised a 2-ft meridian circle, rotating between vertical pillars and read with microscopes the same as General Roy's theodolite. That Wollaston had only learned the use of such microscopes from a remark by Ramsden in 1787 indicates their novelty. Wollaston published a catalogue of circumpolar stars observed with the circle in 1800, along with a discussion of the circle's special merits [64], but its overall design was somewhat shaky.

Troughton endeavoured to overcome its shortcomings in the transit circle he built for Groombridge in 1806. Mounted between two stone pillars like an ordinary transit, the Groombridge instrument carried two graduated circles of 4-ft diameter, one each side of the telescope, and the whole being rigidly braced. Twelve microscopes in all were used to make the readings, six on each side of the circle. It was indeed an advanced instrument for its time, and enabled Groombridge to make the 30 000 observations that formed the basis of his Board of Longitude catalogue, as well as to accomplish his work on stellar proper motions [65]. Like a conventional transit, the Groombridge circle could be lifted out of its axial bearings and reversed, thus allowing its index error to be determined by the six microscopes [66]. A constant index and collimation error of 7″ or 8″ was detected, but they were ascribed to various mechanical eccentricities, and Troughton's graduations were considered well-nigh flawless. Index errors presented little problem, for after their determination they could be eliminated by routine correction by a similar procedure to that used in June 1811. By using six microscopes on each side of the circle, it was possible to 'diminish any errors that may have been occasioned by wear or temperature', thus ensuring accuracy by multiple readings.

The transit circle, however, was slow in winning popularity in England, and astronomers preferred to observe their right ascension transits and declinations with separate instruments. Troughton himself entertained a distinct suspicion of the transit circle and broke up a second model, half completed, because he did not consider it 'a good kind of instrument' [67].

As the Royal Observatory had only one assistant in 1800, the authorities were disappointed to discover that the Troughton 6-ft mural circle did not also perform well as a transit after its installation in 1812, but as this had never been intended in its original specifications, the inventor was censured unjustly [68].

English astronomers restricted their use of the improved circular instruments to declination and azimuth work for over 40 years after the Groombridge transit. It was on the Continent that the transit circle was realized in research with the superlative instruments of Reichenbach and Ertel [69]. Not until 1850 did the instrument reappear in England, with the Greenwich transit, designed by Sir George Airy.

The Airy transit embodied many features of great originality, and in its fabrication the English precision instrument-making tradition reached it high water mark. It is manifestly a piece of heavy engineering, in which Airy aimed at maximum stability and balance both to mount the 6-ft divided circle and to guarantee a perfect, regular motion of the telescope on its trunnions. All the 'massive parts' were the work of Messrs Ransome and May, Engineers, of Ipswich, whilst Troughton and Simms were entrusted with the optical and graduated work [70] (Plate 36).

To avoid the loosening of screws and the weakening of parts that had so bedevilled earlier circular instruments, all components that were not required to move were cast solid. Six microscopes were required to read its divisions, but the circle itself was remarkable in having been graduated on 'Mr. Simms' admirable dividing engine' instead of being produced by original division [71]. By 1850, it had become possible to dispense with the elaborate procedure of manual circular dividing, and obtain yet more critical accuracies by mechanical action. As the graduation of the Airy transit belongs really to the history of the dividing engine, greater attention will be paid to it under that heading in the next chapter.

Suffice it to say, that with this circle, Airy could read meridian declinations to hundredths of a second of arc, whilst the eyepiece micrometer enabled him to take right ascensions to a small fraction of a second of time at one and the same observation.

Special collimator telescopes were used to guarantee exact meridian adjustment, without recourse to distant markers, along with an elaborate system of cross-checks devised to eliminate error. An eight-inch-aperture telescope, working at a magnification of ×195, was employed to observe celestial transits [72].

So successful was Airy's instrument that it remained in use from 1851 to 1954, and after 1884 came to designate the International Greenwich Meridian line as the standard for G.M.T. It still remains in full working order, and having made observations with the instrument myself, I feel competent to vouch for the facility of its operations.

The Airy transit may be regarded as a point of confluence in the history of circular division. With its completion, the astronomical circle achieved maturity as a piece of precision optical and mechanical engineering. The very success of its engine-divided scales, furthermore, finally rendered obsolete the ancient art of original graduation by which a succession of practitioners from Sharp to Troughton had risen to distinction.

By the late nineteenth century, the 'ceiling' of accuracy had risen as high as could be effectively utilized by ordinary human faculties, and further improvements were only possible after the introduction of electrical, photographic, and finally electronic techniques had assigned the critical stages of measurement to mechanisms more exact than the human nervous system. This had been attempted by Airy as early as 1854, when he introduced an electric Chronograph micrometer to reduce personal errors when observing transits [73].

With the above innovations, the art of celestial measurement moves into a realm beyond the scope of the present book.

8

Dividing by machine

I have long been of the opinion, that to copy the divisions of a circle of large diameter, which had been graduated with extraordinary care, upon work of smaller dimensions, would be more satisfactory than Original Graduation.

William Simms [1]

The treatment of the art of graduation has so far been concerned with what its practitioners styled as *original* division. It constituted the most important branch of the art, being concerned with the primary graduation of observatory and other instruments intended for astronomical research. But for centuries there was also the art of copy or *secondary* graduation, which existed to produce scales in quantity by dividing them from a master template. The practice of this art in the late Middle Ages has already been discussed under the construction of cross-staffs, astrolabes, and similar small instruments, and more refined 'dividing plates' were known to the craftsmen of Restoration London.

These dividing plates were of simple construction, comprising a centre pivot set within the master circle of degrees. The work to be divided was located on the pivot, and a radial arm made to extend from the centre to the circumference of the circle. Upon bringing the fiducial edge of the radius against the appropriate division on the circle, a line was struck with the dividing knife along the radial arm and into the work. The operator proceeded thus until the work had received all its requisite graduation marks. As a copy process, being at all times dependent upon the quality of the master circle, it was clearly unsuitable for the graduation of research instruments, and was gradually reserved for the trade production of protractors, clinometers and geometrical instrument scales [2].

Flamsteed had a dividing plate on loan from the Royal Society — presumably to make his own instruments — for he complained of its being taken away in 1679, and four years previously, Robert Hooke had recommended the use of 'a very large quadrantal dividing plate of 10 feet radius' to set out the places of the teeth in making his screw edge quadrant [3].

Though the dividing plate continued to be used in the production of simple instruments until well into the nineteenth century [4], the incentive to make really accurate copy division was a strong influence on the trade, and encouraged the development of a machine that would be capable of working to far higher tolerances than even the biggest dividing plates. The perfecting of the dividing engine casts an important sidelight onto the economics of eighteenth-century science, for as the machine was invented to produce scales in quantity, its very existence implied market pressure. To possess an accurate engine offered the prospect of cornering the market in the lucrative production of navigational and astronomical scales.

The 'pre-historic' phase of the dividing-engine is obscure, yet between 1670 and 1740 it is possible to discern three significant influences on the development of the machine: Robert Hooke, the clockmaking trade, and the invention of Hadley's reflecting quadrant. The earliest recognizable engines were not built to graduate scales, but to produce horological gear-work [5]. But with the invention of a reliable nautical instrument by Hadley in 1731, an incentive was created to produce cheap, plentiful scales, engraved to *astronomical* standards of accuracy.

THE HOROLOGICAL ENGINE AND ROBERT HOOKE

Brief references to devices aimed at simplifying horological gear cutting occur in the sixteenth century, but one of the earliest contributors to mechanical dividing was Hooke. Several references to a dividing machine occur in the *Diary*, for 1672, and though no mechanical details are given, it was probably intended to divide horological gears [6].

By the late seventeenth century, however, a 'Hooke'-type horological engine seems to have come into use, and the Science Museum, South Kensington, possesses a specimen allegedly made between 1668 and 1672, the dates of which correspond with Hooke's *Diary* entries [7]. The engine comprised a vertical arbor, set to rotate in an arm frame, on the lower part of which was mounted a circular plate. The plate was scribed with a set of concentric circles, divided into equal parts, each digit being represented by a hole drilled through the plate. The several number of holes in the plate corresponded to the tooth ratios commonly used in clockwork, so that when a pin was inserted into a chosen sequence of holes, the rotation of the plate and arbor could be stopped at prescribed intervals.

If a blank gearwheel was mounted into the top of the arbor it only required the application of a cutter to its edge to copy as many teeth into the wheel as there were holes in the plate. Such engines were common by the eighteenth century [8], and three are currently on display in the Museum of the History of Science, Oxford.

Although the horological engine was too crude to be used to graduate scales, and the digital nature of the plate divisions made it impossible to subdivide, the mounting of the work upon a vertical arbor, the motion of which was governed by the rotation of a master plate, contributed several important features to the eventual success of the dividing engine [9].

In his method of original division, presented in *Animadversions*, Hooke suggested incising his quadrant with gear-teeth, so that angles could be read by the rotation of a wormwheel [10]. Though it had been a failure as a method of original division, its basic principle reappeared 70 years later, when Henry Hindley of York used a wormwheel to rotate the denticulated dividing plate of what became the first moderately efficient dividing engine.

HENRY HINDLEY (1701–1771)

The only surviving documents concerning Hindley and dividing consist of two long letters sent to John Smeaton in 1740–1741, and reprinted by the latter in *Philosophical Transactions* some 45 years later. They describe how Hindley constructed his engine and set out the tooth divisions on its plate. No mention is made of Hooke, or any other inventor, and though the whole system could well have been an independent fruit of Hindley's intellect, its basic principles bear a close resemblance to those of Hooke's screw-quadrant. Hooke's posthumous reputation as a mechanic and horologist was considerable in the early eighteenth century, his biography having been published in 1705 [11], and his *Philosophical Experiments* edited by Derham in 1726 [12]. It is not unlikely that a literate and intelligent clockmaker like Hindley was familiar with Hooke's mechanical corpus, especially when one considers that he was working in the 1730s. Thomas Reid later considered that Hindley's attentions were first drawn towards the use of screw division on his dividing engine from a knowledge of Hooke, and even suggested that Hooke in his turn had come upon the idea during his youthful experiments to perfect a screw-governed engine to cut fusee barrels for watches [13].

Whereas Hooke had applied the screw and wormwheel to a quadrant, Hindley applied it to a full circle, and substituted the same in place of the perforated plate of a common horological engine. Its denticulated plate could be turned through any fraction of a turn one chose with the micrometer wormwheel, and was not restricted to a fixed course of divisions. Such an engine had promise for true scale division, provided that its teeth could be cut with requisite accuracy [14].

In 1741, the description of an horological engine devised by Pierre Fardoils was published in Paris. Like the Hindley machine its dividing plate was also denticulated and rotated by a tangent screw, after Hooke's quadrant, but while Fardoils' machine may have been made before Hindley's, the Englishman does not appear to have been aware of it. Fardoils' engine was intended only for gear-cutting, and was too rough in its overall construction to graduate scales successfully [15].

At all stages in its development, the dividing engine utilized the properties of circles, rather than part-circles, to bear the graduations of the main plate. Full circles possessed the advantage that, in operation, they could be turned around continuously in one direction, thus giving equal wear to all parts of the circle. On Hooke's arcs, conversely, the screw had been racked back and forth across those degrees most commonly used, causing uneven friction on the teeth.

Hindley's method of graduating his plate was novel, and aspired to combine the simplicity of linear division with the certainties of a circular scale. Unlike all the other circular techniques to be described in this book it was tactile in operation and made no use of lenses, microscopes or other aids of vision.

Intending to make an engine plate of about 13-in diameter, Hindley took a brass strip, the approximate length of the circumference, and carefully divided it into 360 equally spaced holes, by clamping the strip between a pair of prepared jaws. The

jaws were drilled through with two small holes, the separation of which corresponded to one degree of the intending circle, so that after inserting a fine drill
through each hole in turn and progressing along the brass strip, one eventually
produced the 360 holes. Upon finishing, the strip was joined up into a hoop, and
carefully fitted into a wooden mandrel [16], which was used to graduate the dividing
wheel proper, though Hindley did not reveal how this was done. Like Troughton's
method of roller graduation, perfected 50 years later, it depended in operation upon
the accurate lathe-turning of the mandrel and wheel.

Hindley made no allowances for temperature changes within the parts, and his
stepping process appeared to Troughton as no more than a 'train of violent operations
performed with blunt tools' [17]. Yet these conclusions were drawn across 60 years
of hindsight, when even the improvements to the Hindley technique brought about by
Smeaton and Stancliffe had been themselves superseded [18].

It may have been Hindley's interest in fusee cutting and precision lathe work that
first encouraged him to consider seriously the division of circles by screws, and fit his
engine with an hourglass worm [19]. Such a worm had to be curved to correspond
with a segment of the circle it was intended to engage, and had to be lathe-turned in
the manner of a double fusee. Whereas a common cylindrical worm could only
engage four or five teeth of a dividing plate, Hindley's hourglass worm could
encompass 15, thereby reducing play in their meshing [20]. Smeaton says that the
action of the hourglass worm was completely sweet and smooth, but this feature was
omitted from Ramsden's engine.

Hindley's other original contribution to the dividing engine was the invention of a
cutter, set to move parallel to the radius of the dividing wheel, to incise the divisions
into his work. Its principal feature was the elimination of lateral movement, achieved
by making the cutter carriage travel between a pair of radial bars, thus preventing
lateral play which could ruin the eventual divisions [21]. This feature was later
incorporated into the engines of Ramsden, Troughton, and Simms.

From these features of Hindley's engine, one may reconstruct its operation.
After placing the work to be divided upon the arbor, the workman would advance
the hourglass wormwheel through whatever angular interval he wished to scribe, as
denoted on the dial-plate. The sliding cutter would then be advanced, incising the
divisions into the work, and the task repeated until the requisite number of divisions
had been cut.

Hindley's engine was originally intended both for horological and scale division,
and was one of the few dual-function engines. In a letter to Nairne, Smeaton related
that it was possible to fit a conventional dividing plate onto the engine's arbor when
cutting clockwork in common tooth ratios, for the screw-edged wheel and ordinary
horological plate seem to have been interchangeable on the same arbor [22].

Smeaton relates that it had been one of Hindley's hopes that the engine would be
sufficiently trustworthy for the graduation of the new Hadley octants to merit an
official reward [23]. With the £20 000 Board of Longitude prize still unclaimed, it was
quite conceivable that Hindley imagined his right to a part-share, if his machine
reduced the price and raised the accuracy of the Hadley instrument, which it was
hoped would enable navigators to measure lunar distances.

When Smeaton eventually came into possession of the engine in the 1770s, he
found it to be still capable of dividing small instruments, and informed Nairne that he

would soon be able to divide a Hadley quadrant 'more closely than the best hand in town can do it by hand' [24]. But Hindley had never used it 'in the graduation of a capital instrument' and Smeaton doubted its reliability when working to critical accuracies, being best suited to clockwork [25]. The engine failed to win any rewards.

In designing his machine, Hindley had incorporated the best features of the horological engine with the principle of screw division — both of which had been known to Hooke as separate devices. To these, he added his own division cutter, which came to be incorporated into most subsequent English engines, and the hourglass worm — which was neglected.

As a prototype engine, it seems to have been remarkably successful if after 30 years of heavy usage it could still compete with good hand-division. But its failure, commercially, stemmed from several features of its design. The diameter of the engine plate was much too small to produce high accuracy, considering the prevailing technical limitations of 1740. A ratio of one tooth per degree was far too coarse for critical work intended to denote seconds. For a machine to scribe 1′, each tooth would have had to be capable of being read to 1/60th part, which, even considering the safeguard of an hourglass worm, was too much. Smeaton's recommendations for improving the engine centred upon increasing the size of the dividing plate, but to provide more teeth and to render division more certain. It is indeed surprising that Hindley did not divide the wheel into at least 720 teeth, for on a 13-in. plate, each tooth would have occupied 1/8 in. on the limb, a pitch somewhat coarser than that used on the winding-barrels of common long case clocks [26].

Because of the small size of Hindley's dividing plate, he was greatly restricted in the size of instruments he was capable of dividing upon it. Subsequent engine division was to be a *reduction* process, where a plate 3 or 4 ft in diameter scribed divisions onto an instrument of 8 or 12 in., thus operating with great accuracy. Early Hadley quadrants were large instruments, quite often of 18- or 20-in. radius, and if such instruments were divided upon the Hindley engine, as Smeaton claimed, their limbs must have overhung the dividing plate by a foot or more. Instead of working by reduction, it would have become division by extension, from a smaller circle to a greater, and would inevitably have magnified errors.

But in addition to these shortcomings, which prevented Hindley's engine from receiving the acclaim which Smeaton thought it deserved, other points must be considered. Hindley himself was no failure, being a Freeman of the City of York, a leading provincial clockmaker, and a respected citizen [27]. Though his occasional ventures into intrument making were not crowned with much commercial success, it must be remembered that, within the increasingly specialized world of the eighteenth century, he was not an instrument maker, but a clockmaker, and as he was the craftsman commissioned to build the new Minister clock [28], one assumes that his skill was highly regarded. Hindley, furthermore, seems to have made no attempt to establish himself as an instrument graduator — and this is an eminently simple explanation for his not succeeding. With the exception of enlisting Smeaton in the attempt to sell one of his equatorial telescopes, Hindley made no effort to break into the London trade [29]. As a maker of fine clocks in Yorkshire, his market was quite different from that of the mathematical instrument makers of Fleet Street.

Some comment must be made, however, upon the relationship between Hindley and Smeaton, along with their acquaintances Holmes and Stancliffe. The greatest incongruity in the early history of the dividing engine is that Hindley, a successful provincial craftsman in his 40th year, should have so willingly divulged the secrets of his potentially lucrative engine to an unknown lawyer's son of 17 as Smeaton was at the time. Even allowing for Hindley's 'most communicative disposition, and ... fertile genius', the confidence seems inexplicably great [30]. It is inadequate to argue that Hindley was innocent of business acumen, for this is precluded by his success as a clockmaker, although an answer might be found amongst the social and family connections between the two men. By eighteenth-century standards, Hindley, with his flourishing business and new invention, was an artisan on the way up, whilst Smeaton, a failed law clerk whose father had allowed to 'sink' to trade as a way of earning his living, seemed to be a gentleman on the way down. Not until Smeaton's later career vindicated his birthright, and established the new profession of gentleman civil engineer, was the anomaly righted. One must also remember that Smeaton remains the sole reporter of Hindley's work, and was to write down his impressions as an elderly man, recording a friendship of his youth, over 40 years before.

It is interesting to note that John Holmes, who wrote a short biography of Smeaton, first met the engineer in 1742 while still an apprentice to Hindley [31]. Holmes, no doubt, would have been acquainted with the dividing engine, though no mention of it is made in the biography. It is also likely that he knew John Stancliffe, who had once been apprenticed to Hindley before migrating to London and entering Ramsden's employ [32]. Though little documentation has survived about Stancliffe, he seems to have provided the link between Hindley's work, and the 'perfected' engine of Jesse Ramsden.

THE DIVIDING ENGINE OF THE DUC DU CHAULNES

Though the duc du Chaulnes' work falls chronologically between that of Hindley and Ramsden, he stood outside the English tradition, and his contributions to the art are somewhat tangential. The principles on which his method was grounded differed radically from those of the English school, depending on optical alignments that made his engine a logical development from his techniques of circular division. In this respect, the duc's technique was more 'pure' than that of the English school, using as it did only one faculty — vision — for all types of division, whereas the English adopted vision only in their original graduation, retaining the time-honoured faculty of touch as the basis of their engine work [33].

The basis of the English dividing engine resided in the motion of a precision worm screw, via a denticulated plate, working as an endless screw. But on the duc's engine there was no such screw, for whilst an endless screw acted as a fine adjustment on his linear dividing engine, the device was not part of his method of dividing circles [34] (Plate 35). Instead of the screwed dividing plate, he placed a master circle, divided into degrees and minutes (by his method described in Chapter 7), onto the vertical arbor of his engine. When commencing to divide, he would turn the master circle until the first division fell beneath the cross-wires of a vertical microscope set above it. A special scribing tool would then be actuated to cut a division into the limb [35]. In common with the English engines, the limb to be divided was carried on the same arbor as the master circle, and after the division had been cut, the circle was advanced beneath the microscope, and the operation repeated. In this way, one proceeded until each of the divisions had been transferred from the master to the copy circles [36].

Though the faculty of vision may have been more sensitive than touch in original circular division, it was unnecessarily laborious when used for copy work. On the English engines, however, relying as they did on contact, it was necessary only to rotate a wormwheel through a prescribed turn to obtain exact angles automatically [37].

This potential, which eventually made the English dividing engine self-acting, was entirely lacking in the duc's optical method, where the cutting of each division had to be preceded by a critical microscope observation. It required an operator of greater skill to make several hundred critical microscope observations per circle — any of which could be rendered erroneous through fatigue or distraction —, was less certain, and demanded almost as much care as did his method of original graduation.

To incise his divisions into the limb, du Chaulnes used a mechanical tracer, similar to the one he used for original graduation, to draw a line of a prescribed length, although this device was over-complicated and lacked the certainty of the English radial cutter [38]. Moreover, from the disposition of parts when shown ready for use, the duc's engine probably required two operatives: one to align the microscope, the other to actuate the scriber, for the two were 3 ft apart [39]. If it were operated by one man, he would have had to walk from the eyepiece and around the machine to work the scriber, which cannot have conduced to accurate workmanship. None of the English engines needed more than one operative, and he remained stationary throughout.

Finally, the duc's engine was too small to be really effective in the graduation of astronomical instruments. Its main dividing plate was of under 11-in diameter, which would have made it unsuitable for the graduation of instruments of much above 5-in radius without the risk of compounding the errors by enlarging them [40]. Even assuming all constructional details of the machine had been faultless, the size factor alone would have restricted the machine's capacities.

In his assessment of the above method of graduation, Brewster stated that it was not known 'that any small instruments were ever graduated on the Duke's engine, or that any large ones were done according to the original method by which it was graduated' [41]. Though the duc contributed several important techniques to the art of original circular division, his work on mechanical dividing produced no instruments of consequence.

JESSE RAMSDEN (1735–1800)

'It is . . . to the ingenuity of the late Mr Ramsden that the world is indebted for engine dividing in its full effect' [42]. By adopting the endless screw method of division, Ramsden succeeded in combining the best Hindley features with his own contributions, to produce an engine of outstanding design. This machine was capable of executing the most delicate of nautical scales, with speed and consistent accuracy, and won for its inventor the first public reward to be granted for a method of mechanical graduation.

Little documentary evidence can be produced to prove a line of descent back to Hindley, though it will soon become apparent that the debt to him was substantial. Though Ramsden was neither apprenticed nor worked in the precision trades whilst resident in Yorkshire, he was nonetheless a native of Halifax and was probably aware of the work of his elder contemporary at York. But a more positive connection can be established through John Stancliffe, who first worked for Hindley in York before entering Ramsden's employ following his migration to London [43]. It was Stancliffe, no less, who is alleged to have revealed to Ramsden the principle of the Hindley cutter and maybe other features as well. In 1788, Stancliffe was said to have built his own engine, though nothing is known of its performance [44].

Ramsden's first dividing engine, intended for the graduation of Hadley octants, had a plate of 30-in. diameter, its edge denticulated and rotated by a precision wormwheel. Completed in 1767, before the duc du Chaulnes made public the details of his machine, it was found to be good for the division of theodolites and similar instruments [45]. But Ramsden was not wholly satisfied with its performance for nautical and astronomical instruments, and set about the construction of a more refined machine.

Ramsden's engine came at a crucial time in English maritime history. Based on the tables of Mayer, the first reliable longitude-finding method using 'lunars' had just been placed at the disposal of sailors by Maskelyne in the *Nautical Almanac* (1767). To find the longitude in this way it was first necessary to take the place of the Moon against certain stars to within 1'. Though such observations could be made with the Hadley quadrant, the full potential of the 'lunars' method was restricted by the expense and slow production of these hand-graduated instruments. Machine gradua-tion offered the prospect not only of cheaper, more plentiful instruments, but of easily attested accuracy that was free from the personal errors of even the best craftsmen. Whilst it was true that the errors of the dividing engine descended upon each scale it engraved, once these errors had been ascertained, they could be eliminated by routine correction in a way that was impossible with the varied errors of hand-made scales.

It was Ramsden's engine which won the accolade that had first inspired Hindley — a government reward [46]. Though its total sum of £615 was substantially less than the original longitude prize, it must be remembered that Ramsden's contribution was not so much a method of finding the longitude, as a way of simplifying a *part* of the method, and as recently as 1773 John Harrison had been awarded the full £20 000 prize for his separate chronometer method [47]. Indeed it says much for the rapidly advancing state of mechanics that not only was the longitude solved by two independent methods in the decade preceding 1775, but that an essential instrument — the sextant — had become capable of relatively rapid production [48].

Ramsden's second prizewinning engine became operational about 1775 and was described by him in the monograph of 1777, the publication of which was one of the conditions of the official reward (Plate 34). Its purpose was to 'enable any intelligent workman to construct and use engines of the same kind', and between October 1775 and 1777, Ramsden was entrusted with training official apprentices in its operations [49] (Plate 34).

Similar in form to his first machine, Ramsden's second engine was bigger and more exact; its principal feature was a denticulated bell-metal plate, of 45-in. diameter and braced with 12 spokes to combine strength with lightness [50]. Its circumference carried 2160 teeth, one every 10′, and was an immediate improvement upon the Hindley machine with its one tooth per degree. To determine the place of each tooth, Ramsden first divided the wheel into five equal sectors. Each sector was then trisected into three parts and each resulting sector into four. The division of each sector was continued until the wheel had been divided into 240 equal parts, each of which was destined to contain nine teeth on the eventual dividing plate [51].

As Ramsden was apprehensive about making so many trisections, he described a second circle 1/10 in less than the first, and divided it by continuous bisection to act as a check. A silver wire mounted upon a frame that moved around the circumference was then brought above every pair of dots on the two circles, and their agreement examined through a powerful magnifier. The two sets of marks were found to be in satisfactory agreement [52].

Ramsden does not relate whether he used a 'coaxing' technique to divide his engine plate, but as the plate was divided twice, and there is no mention of reversing microscopes, it is unlikely. The graduations were no doubt obtained by straight compass work, checking the trisected against the bisected scale, in the manner of Graham and Bird. Yet the whole procedure was superior to Hindley's brass-strip, and derives straight from the English school of beam compass graduation within which Ramsden had been trained.

Smeaton had been silent regarding Hindley's method of incising the teeth into his engine plate, and one is left to assume that he used a file. Ramsden, conversely, produced his teeth by a regulated 'hobbing' technique, using a rotary cutter that incised several teeth at once. This formed a continuous cross-check and ensured the homogeneity of the teeth, as the wormwheel cutter with notched spirals was applied to each of the 240 segments of the circle in turn. With nine rotary cuts to each segment, the full 2160 were incised into the wheel [53]. 'To make the impression of the screw deeper', the cutter was applied to each segment three times, after which Ramsden . . . 'ratched the wheel around continually in the same direction . . . about 300 times' until all the teeth had been rendered equal.

After cutting and equalizing the teeth, the dividing wheel made ready to receive the wormwheel proper, which was to be of the same pitch as the cutter, but with a smooth thread. It was cut, however, from a cylindrical piece of steel and did not possess an 'hourglass' section, for the larger diameter of Ramsden's engine plate presented a flatter surface to the wormwheel, thereby making it possible for a straight screw to engage several teeth with perfect facility. The use of large-diameter wheels fitted with several thousand small teeth dispensed with the need for hourglass worms.

Ramsden took great care in the cutting of his main wormscrew, performing the task upon a special lathe that was similar in operation to a horological fusee lathe. Its main component was a lead-screw of untempered steel, and while he did not reveal how it was cut, Ramsden probably used the spiral line and file method discussed above [54]. In the screw-cutting lathe, the rotation of the lead screw governed the cutting tool, thus incising duplicate threads in the tempered steel blank of the intended engine wormwheel. Ramsden's lathe was a versatile machine and could either make straight duplicates of the lead screw, or screws of differing pitch, by the insertion of change gears into the transmission.

Two years after describing his circular dividing engine, Ramsden published details of his machine for dividing straight-line scales, along with an improved screw-cutting lathe to fashion the lead screw [55]. Because the worm screws governed the motion of the dividing wheel and controlled the accuracy of the engine, great care was taken in their cutting. Indeed, by the early nineteenth century, a separate craft of precision screw making was beginning to arise, the leading English exponent of which was Samuel Rhee [56].

To simplify the operation of his engine, Ramsden endeavoured to render its action semi-automatic, by connecting its worm shaft to a treadle mechanism, thereby advancing the plate through a prescribed angle by simple foot pressure [57]. Once the operative had thus rotated the dividing plate, he cut the graduation with a manually operated Hindley-type cutter, to produce standardized work, for little skill and no experience was demanded of him after the machine had been initially adjusted [58].

Such engines threatened redundancy to the skilled hand-dividers of nautical instruments, for when a sextant graduated upon Ramsden's engine was sent for examination to John Bird in 1774, the master returned a favourable report on the quality of its divisions [59]. In this respect, the dividing engine was an early portent of the Industrial Revolution, when traditional skills would be displaced by a child or labourer operating a complex machine.

Almost certainly, the dividing engine was produced in response to the problem of the longitude and the need to graduate the newly invented Hadley octants with sufficient accuracy to enable them to take lunars. Once the principle of a hand-held instrument reading critical accuracies by reflection had been realized, a joint technical and market pressure was created to improve the instrument. The solution lay in machine graduation, for not only could an engine produce scales of attested accuracy, but the principle of reduction inherent in machine graduation meant that reliable scales of 6- or 8-in radius could be produced. The dividing engine in its turn also occasioned the transformation of the 90° octant into the lightweight sextant of 120°. The new compact sextants of Ramsden and Troughton became universal astronomical instruments, capable of shooting a lunar two-thirds way across the sky in a way that would have been impossible with a large hand-divided octant.

Of the total reward of £615 made over to Ramsden by the government, only £300 was paid for the invention itself. The remaining money was to purchase the engine on behalf of the nation and to compensate Ramsden for training an official apprentice. He was also permitted to use the engine — which remained in his custody — to divide for 'the trade', charging 3s for octants and 6s for sextants, when engraving scales down to half minutes on instrument bodies made by other craftsmen [60].

Though he brought major changes both to astronomical instrumentation, and the organization of 'the trade' itself, Ramsden seems to have possessed little flair for business as such. He was notoriously slow both in his engine work [61] and the production of his observatory instruments [62], although he was capable of sharp dealing when pressed for cash, as his conduct over the Shuckburgh equatorial indicates.

Having perfected the dividing engine, he failed to extract its full commercial potential, with the result that competitors began to interlope into the graduation business, the foremost of whom were the brothers Troughton.

JOHN AND EDWARD TROUGHTON

The subsequent history of the mature dividing engine is closely associated with the premises at 136, Fleet Street, London, and the firm of instrument makers that traded under 'The Sign of the Orrery' [63]. In the hands of the brothers Troughton, and later William Simms, these premises were to become the centre of one of instrument making's most successful firms, revolutionizing both parts of original circular and mechanical division, and profiting accordingly.

During the mid-1770s, when Ramsden's second engine was beginning to win acclaim, John Troughton was practising as a hand-divider of Hadley quadrants and in this occupation was 'justly considered the rival of Ramsden' [64]. But the latter's imputed inefficiency in executing division work sent to him by the trade was the cause of both annoyance and financial loss. John Troughton, therefore, undertook the construction of a dividing engine of his own 'which at the full stretch of his pecuniary means had occupied him for three years' [65]. But as this machine, finished in 1778, was basically the same as Ramsden's, one must assume that Troughton was allowed access to the original as early as 1775. This was before the published description, and the trade privileges it conferred, and was too early in the machine's history to have been of much use to anybody as an economic tool. In spite of alleged trade disgruntlement, therefore, it appears that John Troughton was quick to change from hand to machine division, as soon as there was a machine in London worth copying and an inventor sufficiently generous to give him access to it. Whilst this was not exactly a case of industrial espionage, Troughton does not appear to have been a man to miss a good idea. This was later borne out in the statement that John and Edward made more money by overcharging the trade for a quick dividing service on their engine than Ramsden made from his rewards [66].

It has been suggested that Troughton was originally inspired by Ramsden's *first* dividing engine, rather than his second. Though I would not doubt that his curiosity, along with that of many other craftsmen, may have been fired by Ramsden, it is unlikely that this engine was ever a prototype for Troughton's own machine, for by 1775, Ramsden II was operational, and its maker so satisfied with its performance that he could confidently sell the superfluous number I.

If, as Edward Troughton admitted, it was possible for his brother to make what was essentially a copy of Ramsden's engine in the three years before 1778, one assumes that it must have taken Ramsden considerably longer than three years to diagnose the faults of number I, embody the modifications into a new machine, and be so confident of its accuracy as to be able to sell the original. This would suggest that Ramsden had been aware of the faults of number I not long after completing it, around 1767 or 1768.

Even if John Troughton had been aware of the overall design of Ramsden I, it is unlikely that he would have modelled his own machine upon it, knowing that its inventor considered it imperfect. Almost certainly, Ramsden II was the prototype machine, being the only one with the chronology, design features, and overall accuracy able to match the forthcoming Troughton engine.

The significance of Ramsden II upon the subsequent history of mechanical dividing was, moreover, indicated by Brewster, when he stated that the 10 or 12 engines currently operational in London around 1815 were 'generally copies of Ramsden's second engine'. Two of these engines indeed were in the Troughton shops.

The *Edinburgh Encyclopaedia* [67] states that, even before the details of Ramsden's engine were generally known (presumably in the early 1770s), Messrs Dollond had already completed a dividing machine. Though no details of this engine, except the fact that it existed, seem to have survived, the *Edinburgh Encyclopaedia* states that its design differed materially from Ramsden's, and that 'It was never used except in the graduation of instruments by them', namely, the Dollonds. As the Dollonds were optical rather than mathematical instrument makers, the machine might well have been used to graduate the setting circles on the stands of their telescopes [68].

No details of the construction of the Dollond machine are given in the *Edinburgh Encyclopaedia*, and by 1815, it seems to have been little more than a trade memory. Most probably, it was a form of horological engine, with fixed courses of divisions. Simple types of dividing engines were not uncommon, for when Thomas Bugge visited Richmond in 1777, Dr Demainbray showed him a 'dividing instrument' with which 'it was possible to divide up a circle with a radius up to $3\frac{1}{2}$ ft very accurately' [69]. But neither of these machines seem to have made much impression upon the subsequent history of the dividing engine.

It is sometimes incorrectly stated that John Troughton died in 1784, and Edward thus assumed control of the business, whereas in truth, his death occurred in 1807 [70]. Practising originally in Surrey Street, John moved to 136, Fleet Street in 1782, succeeding to the premises formerly occupied by Benjamin Cole. After working alone under his own name, he entered into partnership with Edward in 1788, and directories continued to list the premises under 'J. and E. Troughton' until 1804, which was, therefore, probably the date of John's retirement [71].

John Troughton's original engine had a dividing wheel 4 ft in diameter, but this necessitated the operative working in such a posture 'that it had done no good to either his health or my own', recorded Edward, 'and had materially injured that of a young man then my assistant' [72]. Upon entering into partnership with his brother in 1788, Edward set about the construction of a second engine, smaller than the first, and 'contriving the parts with more simplicity . . . [to] get the work done at less than two thirds the labour and expense' [73]. It was completed in 1793, and described by the inventor in an article published in Brewster's *Edinburgh Encyclopaedia*.

Many features of this engine were derived from the machines of Ramsden and John Troughton, and Edward's main contribution lay in his improved way of graduating the circle and cutting its teeth. Like Ramsden's engine, Edward intended his dividing wheel to carry 2160 teeth, governed by the action of a worm-wheel of 20 threads to the inch, so that one revolution advanced the wheel through $10'$. Having computed beforehand the correct tooth ratio for a wheel of given circumference, Troughton proceeded to divide it into 256 segments, with moving rollers and microscopes, as in his method of original circular division, which afforded greater certainty than beam compasses [74]. To obtain the individual tooth positions from the 256 marks, Troughton used a precision worm-screw, producing 2160 fine scratches on the engine wheel, to act as guides to the cutter. This accomplished, the same screw had cutting edges filed into its threads, and again advanced around the circle, to incise the teeth into the metal.

By giving his screw a dual scribing and cutting function, Troughton combined accuracy with economy. The course of 2160 scratches made with the blank worm provided a guide that had been unavailable to Ramsden, and thus avoided incongruities of pitch that could have arisen from the use of two screws.

Ramsden had made no reference to the problems of actually cutting the teeth, though when Troughton reached this stage of construction, he declared the process to be 'one of the most troublesome I was ever engaged in', demanding months of tedious labour. Troughton ascribed the difficulty to the slight variations in sharpness of the cutting screw, which gave an unequal 'bite' and occasioned errors of 7″ or 8″ in the places of the resulting teeth. The work was at last brought to perfection, however, and checked with microscopes against the 256 construction points.

This experience in cutting the teeth had taught Troughton to regard with scepticism all 'self-correcting' methods of racking an engine plate, such as the one that earned a Society of Arts medal for James Allen in 1810, for 'in mechanical matters at least, faith is a poor substitute for good works and ought never to supersede the use of the senses' [75].

The cutter faces, which Troughton filed into the threads of his screw, were arranged in the form of overlapping spirals, or zigzags, to overcome the irregular motion which resulted when the cutter faces were arranged in straight notches, as in the case of Ramsden's cutting screw [76]. Troughton demonstrated that with Ramsden's notches, the whole of the cutting face was brought into operation against the metal with a sudden abrasion, producing a jerky, uneven motion of the cutter. But each individual space on Troughton's *spiral* cutter came into action by degrees, thus affecting a smooth ingress and egress. By the time of the completion of the second Troughton engine in 1793, one assumes that Edward's business had become sufficiently lucrative to make it unnecessary to use the new machine to divide for 'the trade'. It was never Edward's intention for 'this engine to divide any other instruments than those of my own construction', and it lacked an interchangeable centre pin, thereby making it difficult to centre other craftsmen's work upon it. When adjusted for use, it was possible to engrave up to 30 divisions per minute on a blank sextant, by operating the treadle and Hindley-type cutter in sequence [77].

The exact operations of this engine allowed scales of great accuracy to be drawn upon instruments of small radius, thus paving the way towards the modern marine sextant. Using a vernier, or diagonal scale, the early Hadley octants could scarce be trusted within a minute of arc in 1760, whilst by the 1800s Troughton was producing brass sextants of 8 in that could be read to 5″ by a practised eye [78].

Within the space of 40 years, the accuracy of nautical instruments had improved a dozenfold, and a labourer could accomplish in a couple of hours a feat of division that would have been beyond the capacities of the most skilled hand-craftsman.

WILLIAM SIMMS (1793–1860)

Troughton's success at both original and engine division had depended on his attempts to eliminate human error from all aspects of the graduation process, which he had accomplished by reducing reliance upon the skill of the operative and placing it instead on the untiring vigilance of the machine. His method of original graduation, though tedious, had demanded little real skill in execution, whilst the dividing engine itself could be worked by a raw apprentice [79].

By 1835, when William Simms assumed control of the Troughton business (into which he had entered as a partner in 1826), the prospects of combining the original and mechanical departments of graduation had become a distinct possibility. Since the time of Troughton's own innovations in the 1790s, toolmaking, casting and the whole of mechanical engineering had undergone major improvements that opened up new vistas of accuracy [80]. Simms therefore considered that to 'copy the divisions of a circle of large diameter, which had been graduated with extraordinary care ... would be more satisfactory than original graduation' [81].

With Simms, the art of graduation reached its greatest simplicity, and highest accuracy. By combining Troughton's technique of original circular division with the principle of the dividing engine, Simms built a machine capable of operating to within a fraction of a second of arc, thus producing the most delicate astronomical graduations. Troughton had brought original division within the capacities of a diligent workman: Simms' self-acting machine finally relinquished the task to a steam engine [82].

It was Simms' invention to eliminate error by making the whole graduation process mechanical, to produce circles of attested accuracy. Recognizing that the chief drawback of earlier engines had been the 'hobbing' technique used to derive the places of the individual teeth within each segment of the wheel, Simms proposed to obtain the place of all 4320 teeth on his wheel by original division. A precision cutter then incised each individual tooth, to avoid the potentially dangerous 'hobbing' procedure [83]. Taking advantage of the new casting techniques of Messrs Maudsley and Field, Simms had his engine wheel cast from a solid piece of gunmetal, 46 in. across. A silver strip let into the edge of the circle was then divided into single 5′ spaces by Troughton's roller graduation technique to designate the 4320 teeth into which the plate was to be divided. The precision cutter was adjusted with microscopes to coincide with each 5′ dot and the tooth cut. 'It is not without hope', stated Simms, 'that the teeth upon the edge would by this means be cut so truly as the original divisions themselves, and this expectation has, I believe, been fully realised.' The process was simple, direct, and needed no trial-and-error coaxing. Reliable tools and abundant patience were all that it needed to produce critical accuracies.

Simms' engine was an industrial machine and continued the English dividing engine 'tradition' by aiming to 'lessen the labour of the artist, and increase the accuracy of the graduated instrument'. Earlier machines had been semi-automatic, requiring a labourer to actuate the treadle and cutter, but Simms' engine was self-acting and could work 'independently of any personal exertion or superintendence' [84]. Though the cutter differed 'in no respect from Hindley's of York, which was adopted by Ramsden and Troughton', it now moved in an automatic sequence with the endless worm-screw, so that when power was applied to the main drive shaft, it produced regular divisions until disengaging itself after completing 360°.

Sometime after 1843, one assumes, Edward Troughton's 1793 engine was also converted to automatic action, for as it now stands in the possession of the South Kensington Science Museum, its worm-shaft and scribing tool are both geared to a pulley drive, so as to render their motions automatic [85].

William Simms junior, the inventor's nephew, was entrusted with most of the firm's routine graduation work in the late 1830s, and having mastered the Troughton roller technique of original division, which he had practised on a variety of large instruments, was glad to be relieved of the task when his uncle's self-acting engine came into operation [86]. Yet irksome as young Simms had found the roller technique, it was infinitely less demanding than the earlier 'craftsman' methods of Bird and the Graham school, which had required at least 'twice seven years' before one could even aspire to competence [87].

Simms junior provided an impressive list of major instruments that he had graduated originally as a young man, followed by a list of further instruments divided on the new engine. These include the principal instruments in many of the world's leading observatories, but undoubtedly the most famous and long-serving of them all was the 'Airy transit circle' supplied to the Royal Observatory in 1850 [88]. Although described in detail in the previous chapter, this circle represented a new kind of instrument, not only in its design as produced by Airy, but in being one of the first important research instruments to be engine-graduated. Indeed, the very fact that its 6-ft circles were specimens of extension rather than reduction engine graduation (the engine plate being just under 4 ft in diameter) gives splendid testimony to the quality of Simms' machine.

Simms was not responsible for the overall fabric of the transit, only the graduated circle and optics, both of which were rigorously tested by Airy. When finished and mounted, Airy examined the circle in a series of segments of diminishing amplitude, first examining with the six microscopes the 'Cardinal divisions' of 60°, and then proceeding downwards through 20°, 10°, 5° and 1° spaces. From the table of errors printed for every degree of the circle, one observes that the deviations spread through a range extending from $0''.100$ to $0''.029$, with the majority falling around $0.''065$ [89].

After attaining these levels of accuracy, all earlier methods of original graduation were rendered obsolete, and the dividing engine came of age as a tool of primary scientific research [90].

Copy division had begun as a cheap way of dividing astrolabes and geometrical instruments, until in the late eighteenth century it became sufficiently accurate to be entrusted with the graduation of nautical instruments. But by 1850, it had merged with, rivalled, and finally superseded original division, allowing Simms to achieve in a few hours of unsupervised mechanical operation what had taken Ramsden five months of painstaking 'coaxing', with the additional bonus of nearly a 100-fold improvement in the accuracy of his astronomical circles.

9

The London scientific instrument-making trade

John Bennet, at the Globe in Crown Court between St. Annes Soho and Golden Square, London, Makes & Sells all sorts of Mathematical, Philosophical and Optical Instruments of Various Materials, According to the Newest Improvements, and Globes from the Latest Discoveries, with books of their uses, at Moderate Prices.

John Bennet's trade card, *c.* 1750 [1].

Hitherto in this book, attention has been paid predominantly to the craftsmen of London. Although it is obvious that the practitioners of other nations, such as Tycho or Römer, pioneered developments of great importance, it was London that came to be recognized as the abode of the finest optical and mathematical craftsmen by the early eighteenth century. This primacy was attested by the numerous foreign visitors, including Uffenbach, Bernoulli and Van Marum who purchased instruments from the London workshops [2].

Several factors conspired to produce this English predominance in applied mechanics, but one of the most important was the strongly empirical character that had been assumed by British science. The philosophy of Francis Bacon, as enshrined and institutionalized within the Royal Society, gave stress to the manipulative aspects of natural enquiry, along with a recognition of the value of instruments. This recognition, moreover, was greatly assisted by the fame of Robert Hooke, whose researches consolidated the mechanical arts and fashioned them into a respectable department of scientific enquiry.

While it is true that physical astronomers had been striving to perfect accurate instruments long before the seventeenth century, England came to provide especially favourable conditions for their advancement. In addition to the conduciveness of the scientific atmosphere that prevailed by 1700, England also enjoyed unique facilities of patronage, which derived from a highly favourable set of economic conditions. These conditions were associated with a relatively unfettered social system, in which talent could win money, and money could buy social place, even for the low-born [3]. The tenor of English life in the early eighteenth century, which, following from the 'Glorious Revolution', placed the initiative upon the private gentleman, gave an openness to society that is best mirrored in the controversies and low literature of the period [4]. This emphasis upon individualism and free exchange is seen at its best in the coffee-house life of the age, although it is also evident even in formal institutions like the Royal Society, College of Physicians, and Society of Antiquaries, all of which were intensely proud of their essentially 'private' status. The rich self-confidence of mercantile London provided the ideal mixture of intellectual stimulation, encouragement for talent, and the prospect of public and private acclaim that the profession of instrument making demanded.

In its organization, the trade developed into three branches, containing the makers of *mathematical* (graduated), *optical*, and *philosophical* (demonstration) instruments, although it is with the first of these groups that the present work has been almost exclusively concerned. But the three-fold division was more a product of the mid-eighteenth century, and for a hundred years previously, instruments had been manufactured by men who were often clock or spectacle makers by designation. Mathematical instrument-making went back to Tudor times.

Thomas Tompion and George Graham are best remembered as pioneers of English watch and clockmaking, and the construction of instruments was really a side interest to them. But an apprenticeship in clockmaking gave the best overall training in fine metalwork, so that it was frequently to clockmakers that resort was made for graduated scales.

But such recourse was by no means a unique procedure, for in the early days when precision scales were required, it was customary to engage any man who seemed competent to execute them. Abraham Sharp, the graduator of Flamsteed's mural arc, had received no specific training for any craft, whilst John Bird started life as a weaver [5]. It was not until the late eighteenth century that more precise lines of demarcation began to appear, although it still remained possible for outsiders to win success, as did William Herschel.

Once a regular demand for instruments had come into existence, the trade soon began to diversify and specialize, so that by 1770, the omnicompetence of the horologists had become quite superseded. Indeed, the precision trades had always enjoyed a high degree of division of labour in their internal organization — especially in the quantity production of watch movements [6] — and it might be argued that had Adam Smith resided in London, he might have chosen some aspect of instrument rather than pin making, to illustrate the advantages of specialized industrial processes.

John Cuff made little other than microscopes, whilst James Short was to designate himself an 'Optician, solely for Reflecting Telescopes' [7]. It is probably true, however, that the optical side of the trade became more rigidly specialized than the mechanical, for with Ramsden and Troughton one finds the emergence of virtuoso engineers who would tackle anything from a barometer to a mural circle.

It is also interesting to note the division of labour that was required to make a mural quadrant. In his correspondence with Hornsby in 1771, Bird related how the brass bars for the framework of the Oxford quadrants had to be imported from Holland, the fine steelwork from Sheffield, the optics from Dollond, and other items from elsewhere. The problems of international trade and the labour difficulties which occasioned some delay in their completion lend a surprisingly modern ring to the account [8].

The prosperity of London trade was safeguarded by the generally benevolent if somewhat loose arrangement of City Companies. Most instrument makers belonged to some Company or other, although there were exceptions, such as John Bird. Partly because instrument makers had no specific Company of their own, one finds them belonging to a wide variety of Companies, including Spectacle-Makers, Grocers, Blacksmiths, and Clockmakers.

Tompion, Graham, and the Sissons were made free of the Clockmakers' Company, but as instrument making diversified away from horological work, later craftsmen conveyed their corporate allegiances elsewhere [9].

Edward Troughton was bound apprentice to his brother John, and both were made free of the Grocers' Company, along with numerous lesser makers who appear in the Grocers' Rolls as 'Rulemaker', 'Mathematical instrument-maker', 'Shagreen-case maker' and so forth [10].

Although it was possible for a man possessing the right talents to become rich and successful without having undergone any formal indenture, as was the case with Bird, Short and the elder Dollond, it was customary to enter the trade by apprenticeship. This normally meant that apprentices were made free of the same company as their masters, and one tends to find the more successful makers belonging to prestigious companies, such as the Grocers'.

Apprenticeship premiums could vary considerably, depending upon the status of the master and the background of the apprentice. John Troughton senior (1716–1788), uncle to John junior (1739–1807), was bound apprentice to Thomas Heath in the Strand in 1734 at a premium of £10-10-0 [11]. John junior later bound his own brother, Edward Troughton (1753–1836), upon a consideration of 'love and affection' [12]. Premiums up to £30 are not uncommon in the Grocers' Rolls, and in 1747, Campbell stated that between £20 and £50 was normal [13]. Such a sum would have been equivalent to the total annual income of a modest yeoman farmer, or *seven* times the income of an agricultural labourer [14]. Perhaps the largest apprenticeship premium to be recorded was that paid to George Adams in 1777, who bound Christopher Steadman for an incredible £280 [15].

Before commencing apprenticeship, it was necessary for the aspiring youth to possess a 'mathematically turned head', a solid education and obvious practical gifts. After seven years' diligent application, journeymen could expect to earn at least a guinea a week and more, 'according as they are accurate in their Trade' [16].

Instrument making was a curious occupation inasmuch as it amalgamated economic, manual, and intellectual elements. The successful practitioner required a 'professional' education, an artist's touch and a merchant's shrewdness. To set up in business, he required between £100 and £1000, so that he occupied a social position roughly equivalent to that of a surgeon or attorney at law [17].

One invaluable possession in the Clockmakers' library, in Guildhall, is a workshop commonplace book covering the years 1693–1727 that *may* have belonged to the Coventry clockmaker, Samuel Watson. Though it contains nothing on scale graduation, it is rich in the workshop-lore of the period. It contains a description of a horological gear-cutting engine and refers to the writings of Thomas Streete, William Whiston, and Vincent Wing [18]. Surprisingly, the clockmaker possessed a substantial knowledge of the lunar theory of Jeremiah Horrox, 'a diligent sercher (*sic*) after y^e. moon's motions' [19], and devoted a page to the orbital eccentricity. It also contains occasional medical tips and a formula for the removal of aching human teeth, using a poultice of calcined earthworms. The book provides an interesting insight into the world of an intelligent, well-read, but undistinguished craftsman of Queen Anne's day.

It would be absurd, of course, to claim that all makers were so diligent or alert, and there must have been many jobbing workmen, like the one who charged David Brewster an extra 6d for making a special Gunter's rule because 'the little order had put him out of his common track' [20]. The majority of makers were no doubt uninspired jobbing artisans who made rulers and ground lenses, being employed by masters who, though skilled and successful, survive only as names in the Trade Directories. The recent study of Miss Joyce Brown into the structure of the instrument-making trade reveals whole 'dynasties' of craftsmen who served the routine trade and never rose to any distinction [21]. Although difficult to substantiate in detail because of the absence of documentation, it is likely that many artisans were engaged on the routine production of brass tubes, stands, and other components supplied to master craftsmen. It is possible that James Short made little other than mirrors, which he fitted into telescope bodies supplied by anonymous makers [22].

Yet for those men who did possess the right gifts and energy, both profits and honours could ensue. In addition to the empirical, instrument-based tradition of British science, a set of economic and political conditions prevailed in the eighteenth century that provided abundant patronage and encouragement to ingenious mathematical practitioners. This patronage came from two directions: the exigencies of a rapidly expanding seaborne empire, which made the problems of navigation a matter of urgent *public* concern, and an abundance of *private* leisured wealth within England itself.

By the late seventeenth century, the uncertainties of the longitude determination had become a matter of national importance. Already, the Royal Observatory had been built in the hope of finding a solution, but even by the end of Flamsteed's long life the difficulties were scarcely any less intractable. If was fully understood that the longitude could be found, theoretically, by two methods, lunars and chronometer, but both of them required instruments of a much higher order of accuracy than was available in the first quarter of the century. These two theoretical 'carrots' were therefore hung before the next three generations of instrument makers, until by the last quarter of the eighteenth century, the required ceiling of accuracy had been reached and the longitude successfully found.

But the things which gave these 'carrots' their flavour was money. By setting up the Board of Longitude in 1714, with the statutory power to administer a £20 000 prize, a legislative precedent of state interest in practical science was established [23]. This financial incentive system was to be of primary importance in encouraging craftsmen to overstretch themselves, although it is true to say that the total prize money paid out between 1714 and 1828 (when the Board was abolished) was but sparse recompense for the efforts put in by aspiring craftsmen. Apart from the awards paid to Harrison, Bird, Ramsden, and Arnold, relatively little money was won out of the Board of Longitude — and even that was won painfully [24], although the striving undoubtedly led to an enormous increase in instrument standards that redounded to the advantage of the London trade. Official parsimony had its desired effects.

A much more positive form of official encouragement were the contracts given by the government to supply instruments to the Royal Observatory and Admiralty. Large cash grants were paid to Graham and Bird for their quadrants and transits along with sums to lesser makers for the supply of lenses, levels, thermometers and the like [25]. Though none of these commissions were sufficiently frequent to maintain an instrument maker, they demanded the very highest standards, and lent great prestige to the craftsmen involved that could be useful in other aspects of business. It is not without significance to note that the quadrant techniques of the Graham school and Bird's dividing were both perfected in response to the pressure of Royal Observatory contracts.

Besides public patronage, there was also the private sector, and while the former may have given lustre to a man's name, it was the latter that put most of the money into his pocket. But in some respects, private patronage was almost indistinguishable from public, as when a craftsman was commissioned to supply instruments to a university observatory. The instruments supplied by Bird to the Radcliffe Observatory between 1771 and 1774 were identical in design with those supplied to Greenwich, with the exception that he was now charging a higher price. Whereas his original quadrant to Bradley had cost £300 in 1750, its replica to Hornsby cost £380 [26]. Such was the price of fame.

Nor, indeed, does it seem from his correspondence that Bird was innocent of the precise way in which to apply pressure to a wavering customer, for he constantly reminded Hornsby that Maskelyne was about to place a large order and 'unless you determine soon, the Astronomer Royal will be before you' [27]. This had the desired effect, for less than a fortnight later, Bird was writing back to Oxford to confirm receipt of the order for two quadrants, and congratulating Hornsby in having pipped Maskelyne at the post. In this way, Bird secured total contracts amounting to over £1300 from the Radcliffe Trustees [28]. (See also Appendix 3.)

Though in the above correspondence Bird spoke of the need to engage more workmen to finish the instruments, he does not say how many, nor what was the normal size of his London establishment. It is very difficult to ascertain the size of the labour force, even for the workshops of a prominent practitioner, for mention of such things was rarely made. We do know, however, that even working on his own, John Cuff could make a seven-guinea microscope in two weeks [29], whereas at the other end of the scale, Ramsden had 60 men on his books when at work on General Roy's large theodolite [30].

When William Ruat, the London agent for Glasgow University, was instructed to purchase instruments in 1754, a correspondence ensued that casts much light on the mid-eighteenth-century trade. Like all observatories of the period, Glasgow desired a Bird quadrant, and Ruat reported back that a $2\frac{1}{2}$-ft instrument cost £100, while a 2-ft one cost £80. After suitable bargains had been struck, an order was placed with Bird for a $2\frac{1}{2}$-ft quadrant, which was considered a convenient size for a portable instrument [31]. Along with the wall brackets to turn it into a mural quadrant, its total cost came to £107-8-4. Bird was asking £30 for a 4-ft transit, but the order went to Sisson, who offered the same thing for £22 [32]. A 2-ft reflector was also ordered from Short at 35 guineas, and a divided object-glass micrometer for the same at 14 guineas [33]. Although it was protested that for the purchase of a regulator clock 'Mr. Dickie at Edinburgh will serve you as well & much cheaper than anybody here', they decided to go for a prestigious London piece and ordered a 60-guinea clock from Shelton [34].

What also emerges from the correspondence is that while Bird and other makers produced standard lines, they carried relatively little stock-in-trade, because of the delay that occurred between placing an order and receiving the commodity. Ruat ordered the Bird quadrant towards the end of March 1754, but it was not until November 9th that he, accompanied by James Short, went to inspect and approve the new instrument [35].

The safest conveyance to Glasgow was considered as being by sea, and Ruat gives details of the sailings of ships bearing the new instruments. The Bird quadrant was shipped with Captain McUun aboard the *Greenock* on December 14th 1754, although it was not until four months later that he had word of its safe arrival in Scotland [36]. Probably because of the rigours of the winter passage, the Shelton regulator, which had been ready in February 1755, was not dispatched until August of that year [37]. Bird's own charge for 'posterage' on the quadrant, which was so heavy that two men were needed to lift it, and was packed into four crates, was 8s 4d [38].

An interesting light is cast upon the times, when it is remembered that Ruat, who moved with such apparent ease amongst scientists and instrument makers, was himself Professor of Oriental Languages and Ecclesiastical History at Glasgow.

Precision instruments were also supplied to large private observatories, such as the one belonging to the Earl of Macclesfield, and by mid-century a steady foreign demand was building up. English craftsmen were supplying instruments to Russia, America, Holland, Germany, France, Italy and almost every country possessed of scientific aspirations.

Though the production of a few great instruments may have contributed to the general fame which won Graham a tomb in Westminster Abbey, they were not the foundation of his economic success. His financial security derived from the bread-and-butter trade in watches, clocks, and minor scientific instruments. This was indeed the case throughout the trade, for it was the sale of sextants, opera-glasses, orreries, and popular demonstration equipment that made a business buoyant and gave enterprising masters both the money and leisure to develop a great instrument that would be of primary value in scientific research.

The buoyancy of the trade derived in its turn from the general prosperity of the nation at large. In a century of low inflation, good harvests, thriving East India shares, and an expanding merchant marine, there was a growing class of persons in England with an abundance of wealth and leisure [39]. Because one of the chief fashions of the time was natural philosophy, a brisk trade was guaranteed in minor paraphernalia as the genteel classes affected Newtonianism in the days before they took to 'sensibility'. The rise of popular lecturers like Desaguliers, Benjamin Martin, and Adam Walker in the metropolis and spa towns helped to foster a demand that found an outlet in the instrument shops of the Strand [40]. Several prints and paintings of the period depict the landed classes residing on their broad acres, proudly displaying airpumps and microscopes amongst the family treasures [41]. It was not for nothing that the great age of English instrument making coincided with the golden age of the country house.

Yet much of the success of English craftsmen derived not only from the wealth, but also the openness and ease of English society. With its small aristocracy and large, independent gentry, England was fortunately free from the stultifying effects of many of the European caste systems, and this was reflected in institutions like the Royal Society which opened its ranks to successful instrument makers in a way inconceivable for the French Académie. Though the quality of Royal Society personnel was very variable, its essentially democratic atmosphere made it more akin to a private club than a department of state. This was only possible in a country enjoying both security and a high degree of social mobility, where a person from the commercial classes could become a gentleman fit to be received by his sovereign [42].

Although Tompion frequented the Royal Society and made a fortune that enabled him to retire to Bath [43], it was his successor, George Graham, who became the first craftsman to succeed both scientifically and socially. His growing reputation as an experimental scientist and astronomer won him a Fellowship of the Royal Society and the admiration of the scientific world. In spite of his accomplishments, however, he continued to designate himself, even at the Royal Society, as a 'watchmaker', for this was the foundation of his success [44].

While never actually elected F.R.S., John Bird's superlative instruments won him public rewards and the acclaim of the European scientific world. James Short was even tipped — unsuccessfully — for the post of Astronomer Royal. But when Short died, in 1768, while a member of the Royal Society's Transit of Venus Committee, he bequeathed a £20000 fortune that was greater than that of any incumbent of the Royal Observatory [45].

With Ramsden and Troughton, the status of the craftsman-scientist became secure. Both were Fellows and Copley medal winners of the Royal Society, as well as being heads of established commercial houses. Ramsden was even elected Fellow of the St. Petersburg Academy [46].

The status of French craftsmen was very inferior by comparison. They were both socially and financially oppressed and sometimes seemed to be scarcely literate [47]. Instead of the loose network of prosperous City Companies and learned societies as existed in London, they subsisted within a tyrannical guild system that supressed ingenuity. Even the foundation of a corps of certificated royal engineers, just before the Revolution, did little other than reveal the pitiable ignorance of the candidates, in its elementary examinations in physics and geometry [48]. These men, moreover, were the cream of French practical mechanics.

Just as the success of English craftsmen derived directly from the buoyancy of the nation at large, so the reverse applied in France. Whereas English patronage was diffuse and came essentially from the pockets of private gentlemen, in France it was centred very largely upon the Court, and when it encouraged skills at all, they tended to be those of the decorator or 'toy maker', rather than the scientific mechanician.

At a time when Ramsden's profits enabled him to make capital investment in his second, prizewinning dividing engine, it was necessary for Lenoir to beg a cash advance to buy the metal, even before he could begin a commissioned instrument [49].

After a visit to England in the 1780s, J. D. Cassini was impressed not only with English standards of craftsmanship, but also with the status of men like Ramsden and Dollond, and informed the duc de Breteuil accordingly. In his subsequent correspondence with Ramsden, Cassini spoke to him as an equal — a convention that would have been quite inconceivable when addressing French artisans [50]. Not until after the Revolution did the status of French instrument makers begin to improve significantly, as they came to be more integrated into the scientific body, to give encouragement to men like Breuget.

One may also observe how few successful English craftsmen of the period were indeed London-born, and the attraction of talent towards the metropolis says much for the mobility of English society in the eighteenth century. Most craftsmen came to London to seek their fortunes, and many of the most renowned originated from the North of England. The Troughtons were a Cumberland family, as was Graham. Bird was a native of Durham, whilst Sharp and Ramsden were Yorkshiremen. It is not without interest to note that so much of the talent that helped revolutionize precision mechanics came from the same regions of England as were later to produce the Industrial Revolution.

The practical exigencies of British astronomy in the eighteenth century, concerned as it was with navigation and Newtonian dynamics, found admirable complement in the social and financial conditions then prevailing in the country. Without this fertile balance of demand, supply and the nurturing of native skills, there would have been no trade in instruments, and subsequent science would have assumed a very different complexion.

10

The technical frontier: astronomical instruments and the cosmological framework

At all times in this work, the concern has been to show the close relation between instruments, ideas, and the frontiers of accuracy that prevailed at different times. In this chapter these themes will be highlighted to illustrate their process of interaction in the context of cosmological understanding.

It has been my argument throughout that this interaction constitutes three 'ages' of instrument technology between 1500 and 1850, in which a specific invention allowed a new level of research for two or three generations, until a new technical breakthrough became necessary. There were the Tychonic improvements in scale division; the Restoration discovery of the telescopic sight, micrometer and pendulum clock; and the late-eighteenth-century development of the astronomical circle. Each one represented a barrier beyond which scientific verification could not have advanced without innovation at the workshop level, thus indicating how, at so many turns, the theoretical astronomer was in the artisan's pocket.

Without the instrumental innovations of Tycho Brahe, which rendered a single minute of arc a sensible quantity, it is unlikely either that the work of Kepler would have been possible, or, conversely, that Copernicanism would have acquired such a strong rival in the alternative Tychonic scheme.

The whole force of Kepler's work which made possible his demonstration of the elliptical shape of planetary orbits, and his two other laws that followed from it, was derived from a discrepancy of 8′ in the observed motions of Mars that could not be accounted for by orthodox circular orbits. Yet to any astronomer other than Tycho, 8′ would have simply been ascribed to instrumental error in the late sixteenth century, for, as Tycho discovered when examining Copernicus' triquetrum, there was an 8′ error in its pinnule sights alone, not to mention further errors in its division and elsewhere [1]. It is thus possible to evaluate, with some exactitude in this case, how the derivation of what later proved to be the first three laws of celestial mechanics was grounded upon a technological breakthrough. But over the course of the ensuing 80 years one detects a feedback process in action, in which the new Tychonic accuracy provided data upon which original interpretive minds could work, until by the late seventeenth century, the ideas of Newton could only be demonstrated after another succession of technical innovations that built upon those of Tycho.

Tycho's inability to measure a stellar parallax with what by 1590 were the finest instruments in the world naturally provided observational ammunition to the anti-Copernicans. In the period before the Galilean telescope provided an alternative set of analogies in favour of the moving Earth, the foremost stumbling-block to Copernicanism lay in the inability of its advocates to supply what was acknowledged as the acid-test evidence of a stellar parallax. If the Earth moved, the stars should show a periodic shift, and from the supernova of 1572 onwards, Tycho had been unsuccessfuly trying to find one [2].

This failure was followed by his proposal of his own geocentric world-system, which provided a very serious rival to the Copernican hypothesis. The strength of the Tychonic scheme derived from its being the only theory current in 1600 that could satisfactorily account for most of the available observational evidence. It explained the retrograde motions of the planets just as well as Copernicanism, yet it avoided the problems of the infinite void and gave a good justification for why a parallax could not be found with the Uraniborg instruments. Moreover, it still retained the necessary explanatory devices of Aristotelian physics, which accounted for the movement of falling bodies. Even the Galilean telescopic discoveries could be incorporated within the Tychonic scheme with little difficulty [3].

The Tychonic observations thus substantiated two contrary themes in seventeenth-century cosmology, the fixed Earth and the Earth moving in an elliptical orbit, though the final solution was not to come until yet better observational data became available. Though we now acknowledge the originality of Kepler's work, and its transmission via Horrox to Newton, the Tychonic cosmology was especially cogent, and provided for almost a century a very viable alternative to *De Revolutionibus*. This alternative, in turn, hinged upon the quality of interpretive data available to contemporary cosmologists, and placed the unavoidable onus of proof upon the accuracy of the instruments and their graduations.

Although the decisive parallax was not to be successfully measured until 1838, the idea of the moving Earth came to be accepted into cosmological currency by way of supplementary arguments that drew their weight from observations that were within the accuracy compass of contemporary instruments. Most significant in this respect was the substantiation of Newtonian dynamics, which predicated a moving Earth, and drew its strength from instruments that measured things other than the direct stellar parallax.

While it is a truism amongst philosophers of science that the intellectual apparatus of Newtonianism derived from Kepler, it is my argument that Newtonianism could not have existed without the *second* technological breakthrough that was contemporaneous with the Restoration. Without the great improvement in data-collection made possible after the invention of the telescopic sight, micrometer, and pendulum clock, Newton would have lacked the observational bedrock upon which the consequences of *Principia* could be developed.

The explication of Kepler's system, upon which Newton built, demanded more accurate values for the elements of the elliptical orbits in which the planets moved. One way in which these elements could be established was by measuring the seasonal variations in the solar diameter, for to a Copernican astronomer, the apparent motion of the Sun was but a reversal of the Earth's true motion. This goes a long way to explaining Horrox's persistent concern with the solar diameter, and the ingenious techniques he devised to measure the same. But a proper understanding of the solar theory was not possible until the filar micrometer provided a technique that was superior to Horrox's 'foramen'.

Newton's debt to Flamsteed at the Royal Observatory will probably never be fully acknowledged, although it was from the Astronomer Royal that many of the astronomical quantities relevant to gravity theory were first obtained. Newton's work on cometary orbits drew substantially upon Flamsteed's sextant observations. In September 1685, he wrote to Flamsteed saying that if he could get three observations, accurate to a minute, he could compute the parabolic orbit of a comet [4]. Flamsteed obliged with a set of distances observed for the 1681 comet, to which Newton kindly replied ' ... Your observations of ye comet, being so exact ... will save me a great deale of pains. I shall have no need to give you further trouble at present . . .' [5]. Yet the observations that were to prove of greatest utility to Newton were those of the Moon, and became the subject of much correspondence [6].

Mention was made in Chapter 3 of the large number of lunar observations that Flamsteed supplied to Newton in the 1690s, when the latter was working out the intricacies of the lunar theory, but Flamsteed was correct in feeling that he had been slighted when he wrote

> Mr. Newton frequently called upon me for new observations of the Moon: whilst some of his creatures in town cried up his success in correcting the lunar theory: but said not one word of his obligations or debt to the Royal Observatory [7].

What is of particular interest is the date, both of Flamsteed's complaints and Newton's assiduity — the 1690s. This was the very decade in which the new mural arc was beginning to yield results. Flamsteed complained in 1696 that he had '. . . sat here [Greenwich] now 19 years, but for the 14 first I have not had such instruments for my work' [8]. After the first few hours' observation with the new arc, however, it so proved its worth that it rendered all his previous observations 'Arena sine calce' [9].

The 1690s were a decade of great confluence for the Royal Observatory: Flamsteed had recently demonstrated the Earth's isochronal axial rotation, and completed the first, unpublished, star catalogue with the now largely discarded Tompion sextant. In addition to the mural arc, the degree clock (1691) had just come into operation. It will be recalled from the treatment of these instruments in Chapter 3 that they allowed right ascension and declination angles to be read not only simultaneously by a new technique, but also to a much higher degree of accuracy. The lunar values given to Newton were the most accurate determinations for the motion of that body observed to date. The mural arc's 10–12″ error was a six-fold improvement upon Tycho. While the earlier sextant and micrometer observations had no doubt been sufficiently accurate to justify the implications of *Principia* in 1687, Newton could not afford to ignore the superior data made possible by the mural arc.

It is not the intention to minimize in any way Sir Isaac's achievement, for the penetration of his intellect succeeded in forming new and imaginative links between so many hitherto disparate aspects of natural philosophy. The present purpose is rather to demonstrate the extent to which he realized the need to keep his work within the boundaries of the *evidence*, and how in turn this evidence was limited by the quality of the instruments available to determine the essential orbital elements. Though it would be ridiculous to argue that Tompion, Sharp and Flamsteed formed the basis of Newtonianism, it is well to remember Newton's 'debt to the Royal Observatory', and reflect why the new system of natural philosophy was a product of the same culture that bred the craftsmen treated of elsewhere in this book.

If the original instrumental breakthrough at the Restoration had provided the impetus that made Newtonianism possible, it was also through the realm of instrumentation that the 'Newtonian cosmos' became substantiated in the eighteenth century. Without the initial pendulum experiments by Richer, or the Lapland observations of the Académiciens, Newton's theoretical postulates about the shape of the Earth could never have been demonstrated. Without the zenith sector observations of Bradley, aberration and nutation would have remained unquantified, and without Maskelyne's Schahallion experiment, the universal character of gravity would have continued unproven. It is true that all of these attributes of nature were mathematically derivable from the first edition of *Principia*, but it was due to a research project that spanned more than a century that the theoretical implications of Newtonianism came to be articulated as a statement about the *real* cosmos, and not just a mathematical phenomenon-saving device. Just as Newton himself had been indirectly indebted to the skills of Restoration instrument makers, so the subsequent consolidation of the Newtonian cosmos into a *real* cosmos proceeded at a speed that related directly to the development of the skills of Graham, Bird, and Ramsden.

By the mid-eighteenth century, astronomical research had developed a momentum of its own that contained a feedback process of innovation, discovery, and further innovation. The theoretical and practical demands had become thoroughly intertwined, and this had developed very largely as a result of the two long-term projects that had become parts of astronomical research: the quest for a stellar parallax and the vindication of Newtonianism.

It is also interesting to view the essentially instrumental character of eighteenth-century science as related to the prevailing theories of knowledge and the empirical psychology of Locke, which was then so much in vogue. To an age that conceived of the universe as a mathematically demonstrable self-acting machine, the essentially mechanical mode of enquiry in astronomical research found a perfect justification in the philosophy of Locke, with its emphasis upon the primacy of sense knowledge as lying at the root of all natural enquiry. Because the mind was a blank at birth, and knowledge built up from mental images of objects that entered via the five senses, one found a ready justification for an instrumental approach to science, for the instruments were but devices that rendered our sensual apparatus more precise [10]. But to Locke, as amongst the eighteenth-century astronomers, the eventual quality of knowledge was governed by the empirical data that could be examined in the outside world. In this respect, the prevailing concern amongst scientists to see the world measured with ever-increasing accuracy was in complete accord with prevailing philosophical beliefs.

The final vindication of Newtonianism demanded yet greater accuracies than were feasible with even the best zenith sector or quadrant, and the passing of this 'frontier' was made possible with the development of the astronomical circle in the late eighteenth century. Without the fine circular instruments that were available by the early nineteenth century, it is unlikely that the orbital data that allowed Adams and Leverrier to predict the place of the unknown planet Neptune from the perturbations of Uranus would have been possible [11].

It had been due to little more than good luck that Herschel discovered the planet Uranus in 1781, but over the next 60 years, it refused to move in accordance with the *Newtonian* orbit calculated for it by Euler. It was from these orbital discrepancies that Adams and Leverrier deduced the place of Neptune, the disturbing agent, in 1846 [12].

Although both astronomers independently calculated the place of 'planet X' in accordance with Newtonian theory, the *precision* of their prediction would not have been possible without very accurate values for the place of the disturbed planet Uranus. In this respect, they were dependent upon measurements made over the previous half-century with circular instruments in England and on the Continent. The best quadrants had got down to tolerances of about 2″ by 1775, but by about 1820, the circles were measuring down to fractions of a single second. The achievement of this 'next decimal' was of the utmost importance to the discovery of Neptune, where the angular quantities of the perturbations were very small indeed.

The eventual discovery of 'planet X' in the place predicted for it was a singular proof of the validity of Newtonian dynamics, if not of Bode's law. It caught Airy, the Astronomer Royal, by surprise for he had been sceptical of the validity of Adams's mathematical method. But it was not Airy's job to search for the planet at Greenwich, and he welcomed news of the discovery from Berlin [13].

The astronomical circle was itself invaluable to the measuring of the first stellar parallax in 1838. Although it was with a heliometer that Bessel detected the parallax, it would have been futile attempting to measure the seasonal shift of 61 Cygni without an accurate star-chart against which to select guide points from which to triangulate its suspected movement. Potential 'parallax stars' were chosen on account of large proper motions or brightness, being considered closest to the Earth and hence the most likely to exhibit parallaxes. It was the circle which provided this necessary background knowledge of positions and proper motions against which Bessel measured his first parallax.

It is indeed interesting to note that three parallaxes were independently discovered within a few months of each other in 1838–1839, by Struve at Dorpat, and Henderson at the Cape [14]. It indicates how remarkably even astronomical discovery tends to be: once a given technical barrier is breached, corroboratory discoveries often follow in rapid succession, emphasizing once again the dependence of cosmological frameworks upon the contemporary capacity of instruments.

The whole of this book has been concerned with the interaction between discovery, the cosmological framework, and research undertaken with graduated instruments. Yet while the graduated instrument, with its scale, micrometer, and telescopic sights, was fundamental to the cosmological pattern of the period between 1500 and 1850, it is probably true to say that this whole concept of instrumentation had become obsolete by 1860.

Airy's Greenwich transit of 1850, which in so many ways represented a point of confluence in instrument making as the first major instrument to be graduated on a dividing engine and fabricated as a piece of precision heavy engineering, was capable of delineating hundredths of a second on its scale. But the unaided human nervous system is not capable of utilizing such small quantities to the best effect, and in this respect, one encounters yet another research frontier. While it falls chronologically outside the scope of this present study, this perceptual barrier came to be of great importance to the future of instrumentation in the late nineteenth century, and helped to accelerate the demise of the conventional graduated circle as the chief instrument of astronomical enquiry. Therefore, before one could improve significantly upon the great transit of Airy, it was first necessary to invent observational aids that would assist and regularize the erratic elements in the perceptual equipment of each observer.

When observing right ascensions, James Bradley had been capable of timing a star's passage across the wires to $\frac{1}{6}$ s but an instrument of the Airy transit proportions was capable of greater mechanical accuracy, if only the observer's nervous reactions could be made to match it [15]. It was in pursuit of greater regularity in this respect that the instrument was fitted, in 1854, with the galvanic chronograph and, in 1915, with the 'impersonal micrometer', which registered the transits electrically on to a sheet of paper passing through a recorder. In this way an automatic comparison was possible between the star and the standard timekeeper, which relieved the observer of his traditional need to 'keep the clock' by estimating time intervals between the eyepiece wires, and standardized the 'personal equation' differences between observers [16].

By the addition of electrical and other devices that lessened the demands made on the personal judgement of the observer, it was possible for the Airy transit to remain in service for just over a century. But the very fact that the circle was able to remain in service for so long — nearly twice as long as the Bird quadrant, the next longest surviving graduated instrument at Greenwich — at a time of rapid astronomical progress, clearly indicates that by the twentieth century the real initiative in research had shifted from conventional divided instruments.

By 1900, the precision scale was no longer the principal arbiter in cosmological interpretation, and was coming to be relegated to routine work and timekeeping. Research in positional astronomy had lost its ancient primacy, having yielded ground to the new physical astronomy, the principal tools of which were the spectroscope and photographic plate. This development lies outside my present terms of reference, for with the 'exhaustion' of the graduated scale for cosmological research by the late nineteenth century, the surmounting of this fourth frontier came via an optical rather than a mechanical solution. Astronomy now moved away from traditional celestial mechanics into a wider realm of physics. Advancement was now a matter of bigger object glasses, higher resolving powers, and photographic plates possessing greater sensitivity.

Measurements were now more likely to be made from a photographic plate than by an observer at the transit circle, as was the procedure with the international *Carte du Ciel* from 1887. The 13-in astrograph set up at Greenwich in 1890 was built to partake in this project, and made photographic measurements of stellar proper motions. The resulting plates, on which 1' corresponded to 1 mm, were measured with a duplex micrometer [17]. Astrographic techniques allowed a much greater certainty than the old visual transit circle method when it came to cataloguing. Instead of having to work and read the scales by lamplight in a freezing observatory, the photographic plates could be measured at leisure with the duplex micrometer.

But this last technical frontier appears to have been less urgent and more gradual than the three frontiers discussed elsewhere in this book, for physical astronomy had been developing independently since the days of the elder Herschel. The disposition of stars in the Galaxy, the possible solution to Olber's paradox and the resolution of nebulae into individual stars could never be solved by celestial geometry, and were beginning to create a new type of astronomical research by 1850. The new cosmological picture created by Herschel, Huggins, and Lockyer owed relatively little to the circle dividers, whilst Lord Rosse's assaults upon the internal structure of spiral nebulae demanded optical resolution, not equal graduations. It was the opticians who were to become the master-craftsmen of physical astronomy [18].

Positional astronomy performed with graduated instruments became gradually obsolete, as the rising astronomical talent moved naturally into physical work by 1880. There was no sense of an urgent technical barrier to be surmounted, however, as one senses there must have been at the Restoration, when astronomers were striving to improve on the accuracies of Tycho. Research was not coming to a halt, but rather changing track.

Just as Hevelius had been the last major figure to distinguish himself as a naked-eye astronomer, so Sir George Airy's conservative interpretation of the 'staple and standard work' of the Royal Observatory made him what was probably the last great positional astronomer [12].

It may be added, for the sake of completeness, that as physical astronomy has grown and diversified in the twentieth century, so it has in turn encountered a new technological barrier in its attempts to construct a deep-space science of astrophysics. Before any settlement between the rival 'big bang' and 'steady state' cosmologies could be decided upon, it was necessary to study data other than light, especially considering the large amount of light-obscuring dust that was encountered in space. The new breakthrough came with the development of radio astronomy after World War II, and, in consequence of the study of radio sources by Ryle and Lovell in the 1960s, the weight of observational evidence came to favour the expanding universe model [20].

One may offer an observation concerning the enduring value of each technical breakthrough, and how much fresh research was possible with each new 'ceiling' of accuracy. Each breakthrough seems to have fallen within the third quarter of each century, and provided a development potential that lasted about 90 or 100 years. Thus the Tychonic ideas developed around 1570, the telescopic sight in the 1660s, the astronomical circle in the 1770s, physical astronomy in the 1860s, and radio in the 1950s.

The impression which emerges most clearly is the way in which viable ideas about the universe over the past five centuries have been limited by the contemporary exigencies of practical measurement. Little would have been accomplished but for fundamental innovations in the craft of instrument making, and the rise of a generation of astronomers who recognized that the price of perfection was eternal vigilance [21].

11

The archaeology of the graduated scale

Most of what we know about the art of graduation is derived from contemporary documentation, left either by the craftsmen who made the instruments or by the astronomers who used them. Such written evidence tends very often to be subjective, being limited as it is by the technology and concepts of accuracy of a given historical period. It was because of these limitations that I began to look for alternative sources of evidence, in a attempt to make a more comprehensive evaluation of the precision skills of the past. The problem of how accurate an instrument or technique *really* was becomes more acute the further one proceeds back in time, and for anything dating from much before the middle of the sixteenth century, it is beset with conjecture.

There is, however, no shortage of actual instruments that have survived, and it became clear some years ago that many of these pieces, preserved in museum collections, might be subjected to 'archaeological' investigation. For nearly a thousand years, the astrolabe had been a universally used astronomical instrument, and in Oxford alone there are excellently preserved specimens dating back to the tenth century A.D.

Many of the earliest surviving astrolabes, though, are Islamic in origin, and as I am concerned primarily with the art of dividing in the West, I selected for study 12 astrolabes and circles with a total of 22 scales, engraved in Europe between *c.* 1450 and 1659. All of them were in the Museum of the History of Science, Oxford. Whilst the Museum had European astrolabes dating back before 1450, many of them did not appear to be well-divided, and did not warrant exact measurement. The eventual selection, therefore, was made on the grounds of a good state of preservation, and visual fineness of engraving [1].

To perform the examination, the instruments were placed upon a modern engineer's dividing engine, equipped with micrometer scales reading down to 1″. As all the instruments to be examined were of between 6- and 16-in diameter, an engine with a 12-in plate, or table, was found to be satisfactory. A low-powered microscope fitted with cross-wires was then fitted above the dividing engine plate, to provide a pointer against which the astrolabe scales could be read.

Each instrument to be measured was then placed upon the engine plate, its graduation facing upwards. After careful centring, the horizontal wire in the microscope field was made to follow the outer perimeter of the graduations, and the vertical wire set to bisect each radial degree mark in turn. Seen through the microscope, the instruments displayed beautifully deep divisions, easily bisected by the cross-wire. After adjusting the dividing engine's zero degree point to correspond with the individual instrument's zero, the scale was gradually rotated beneath the microscope, until the first degree line appeared. Its position was noted on the dividing engine micrometer, and its deviation from a perfect degree tabulated in minutes of arc. Each of the remaining degrees were measured in this way, their deviations recorded, and a table of errors built up for all 360 degrees of the instrument.

When the individual variations of the degrees had been compiled, two methods of analysis were attempted. Firstly, the spread of errors was plotted on a graph, and secondly, a computer analysis established the overall mean graduation error of the scale.

In plotting the graph, the zero axis was made to correspond to a zero-degree error on the scale. If a particular degree was found to be bigger than it should have been, i.e. 62°8′, instead of 62°, then it was plotted eight units above the axis line. Likewise, if the 'degree' was smaller than a whole degree, it was plotted beneath it.

An examination of the graph now made it possible to observe the spread or 'flow' of errors in the engraving, and where the original craftsman had cut erroneous graduations. By concentrating on the flow of errors at this stage, as opposed to the absolute deviations in minutes of arc, it was possible to even out random errors, and detect underlying patterns that indicated construction techniques.

Next, the 360° graph was cut into four 90° strips, and the four quadrants of the circle set out on a page, one above the other. What now became clear was the way in which the error flow in one quadrant sometimes produced a reflexion, or two-fold rotational symmetry in the facing quadrants, in the sequence that quadrant 1 would reflect in quadrant 3, and 2 in 4 [2]. I suggest that these error patterns had been produced by the craftsman graduating one half of the circle by compass division, and copy-dividing the opposite half, by passing a straight edge across the centre and transcribing the original divisions (Plate 38).

Other instruments examined revealed the repetition of one distinctive error flow on the graph, which suggested that the maker had employed some sort of master template or protractor of 180° or 90° and simply copied it off onto the circle, to produce the same errors in each quadrant [3]. Both of these above-mentioned techniques embodied important labour-saving elements, and suggest the use of commercial methods of production.

Moreover, it was also necessary to watch how systematic errors were distributed around the 'cardinal' divisions of 30° and 60°, which would have been the first to be laid off in original compass division.

Some of the instruments displayed distinct error flow cycles that focused on the 30° and 60° points, which strongly suggested that they had been laid off first, and used as guides for the integer graduations [4].

What came to be seen as a test for an originally graduated, as opposed to a copy circle, was the appearance of microscopic construction dots, incised into the metal on either the 10°, 30° or 60° graduation marks. One beautifully engraved astrolabe of *c*.

1450 not only showed a neat dot every 10°, but larger double dots on the 60° marks [5]. It seems that either two compasses had been used to divide this piece — each with its distinct point prick mark — or else the scale had been cross-checked by re-dividing it backwards with the 60° compass opening to produce secondary dots.

The 10° divisions on many instruments were placed with much greater accuracy than their corresponding integers, and focused, or localized, the errors of the scale, although in certain cases the nine integers themselves sometimes displayed their own flow patterns. It is suggested that these repeated interval errors could well have been caused by the graduator making a 10° template which he applied to each 10° space in turn, as a labour-saving device.

In addition to the graphical analysis of error distribution, the measured degree errors were also scanned by computer. This revealed the main-scale error for the entire instrument, thereby making it possible to compare the overall performance and consistency of one craftman's work against another's. What did indeed emerge was the wide range of accuracies contained in the specimens examined. Some scales showed remarkable consistency, with an average deviation as low as 0.48′ [6], while others fluctuated by as much as 8 or 9′. Yet as the scales were drawn on a wide variety of radii, it was necessary to apply corrections before one could ascertain the intrinsic skill of an individual graduator, as a greater 'clumsiness factor' is involved in dividing a 6-in as opposed to a 16-in radius circle.

A standard correction factor was developed which, in effect, adjusted all the diverse radii to one imaginary radius, and either enlarged or reduced the measured mean scale errors to correspond to it. What now emerged was an overall *homogeneity* of errors, for when compared in this way, all the scales corresponded to each other to within a very small number of minutes or less. Renaissance circle dividers, it seemed, were masters of a highly conservative craft, and capable of producing very uniform results amongst themselves. What also became clear from this study was the lack of apparent improvement in accuracy over the 200-year range of instruments examined, as the astrolabe of 1450 was not significantly inferior to later pieces. One might interpret this as the growth of a conservative craft to meet the demands of a stable market of satisfied customers.

The ultimate worth of any comparative archaeological technique, however, depends upon the breadth of its data base. No single museum contains more than a relatively small selection of available instruments, so that the full exploitation of methods such as the one outlined above makes it necessary to use other collections, both at home and abroad. But the physical business of obtaining such data presents problems, as museums are naturally reluctant to dispatch valuable pieces great distances, even for analytical purposes of this kind. Likewise, the dividing engine and apparatus with which they are measured is too heavy and delicate to be conveniently moved.

The solution, it was concluded, lay in photography. If carefully centred photographs could be taken of the instrument, on 5×4 in glass plates, then the plates could be conveyed to the machine and measured in the same manner as an actual instrument. When a stable, acetate-base cut film was found to be commercially available, the process was further simplified, while the large-size images on a 5 × 4 in plate occasioned little loss of accuracy through the photographic process itself.

The 12-in diameter Copernican Planetary Equatorium of *c.* 1600 in the Liverpool City Museum collection was photographed in this way, and the transparent negative plates measured on the dividing engine in Oxford [8]. To facilitate the business of measuring, the engine table was covered with reflecting tinfoil, and the plate secured upon a machined perspex stand, about 1 in above it. When light was shone onto the tinfoil, the graduations stood out in high contrast on being viewed through the microscope, thereby permitting the image to be measured like an ordinary astrolabe.

Shortly after having secured the photographic plates, it became possible to arrange for the actual Equatorium to be brought to Oxford, where its scales were measured in the normal way. It was pleasing to discover that the plotted scale errors for the directly measured instrument coincided exactly with the photographs, indicating thereby the feasibility of the photographic technique.

The success of the archaeological method of examining early circular instruments led to the consideration of how the method could be adapted to larger pieces that were too big to be placed on a dividing engine. Many museums, after all, possess large-radius astronomical instruments, such as quadrants and sextants, and many seem to have been well-divided. The Museum of the History of Science, Oxford, contains three large-radius instruments used by the seventeenth-century Savilian Professors of Astronomy, whilst the National Maritime Museum and Science Museum possess pieces from the early Astronomers Royal, and their contemporaries [9].

The analytical technique used on large-radius instruments derived from the geometry of the circle. It was first necessary to obtain the exact radius of the instrument, but as several pieces lacked their original centres, the chord 0°–60° was measured with a high-quality steel tape, as this length is always the same as the radius. From this length, it was easy to calculate the length in inches of the circumference of the entire circle, and when this was divided by 360, the *linear* extent of each degree resulted.

A specially adapted precision 'G' micrometer, of the type used by mechanical engineers, was then applied to each degree in turn. The anvil and stem of the micrometer were brought respectively to the precise left- and right-hand extremities of each degree division, and the critical alignment secured by viewing them through a magnifier. When the main-scale of the micrometer was read off, the *actual* extent of each degree space was obtained to within 1/1000 in. As the angular amplitude for a 1/1000-in chord had already been calculated for the individual radius beforehand, it was easy to establish how closely the measured degree spaces corresponded to the perfect degrees to which their engravers had aspired.

The degrees on the measured instrument were next plotted onto a histogram, to establish how many of them approached perfection, and in what ratio the craftsman had made errors.

The 6-ft radius instruments graduated by Elias Allen in 1637 [10] were found to be of very indifferent accuracy for their size, when examined in this way. Though superlative in execution, the quadrant scale showed an overall error of 2′17″, which is very large for a radius of 78 in. Furthermore, by examining the disposition of the preliminary construction dots on another 2-ft-radius quadrant, also believed to be by Allen [11], it was possible to reconstruct the steps through which the graduator had built up the diagonal sub-divisions (Plate 9).

Although the 7-ft mural arc, built for Flamsteed by Abraham Sharp at Greenwich, has been lost since the 1720s, the National Maritime Museum possesses a 5-ft-radius quadrant, also made by Sharp around 1710 [12]. It was hoped that it might be possible to make an appraisal of Sharp's skill as a graduator — and by inference, the quality of Flamsteed's arc — by measuring the degrees of this quadrant.

When the measurements were reduced, it became apparent that Sharp was, indeed, a highly skilled craftsman, for the scale displayed remarkable homogeneity, with an average error of 55″ and a 'best scale' accuracy, taken over the main 77° of the quadrant, of 27.9″. Having obtained this value, I re-computed it to see what the proportional error would have been when Sharp was working at a radius of 7-ft. Assuming a similarity of dividing technique, the reduction indicated that Flamsteed's 7-ft arc would have had a scale error of 16.8″. This, indeed, comes very close to the 15″ error ascribed to the instrument by Dr Pound. Pound claimed to have detected this error when reducing the mural arc's observations for publication in 1721/2, the information being contained in a letter sent by Joseph Crosthwait to Sharp himself, in January 1721/2. It is unusual, indeed, to find an independent literary reference substantiating so precisely an 'archaeological' find of this sort (see p. 173 ref. 126).

By using physical techniques of analysis, I believe that historians are capable of re-appraising the skills and abilities of past craftsmen and scientists. We are enabled thereby not only to reconstruct the explicit procedures by which they attempted to lift the accuracy 'ceilings' of their predecessors, but what is more, to evaluate the success of these efforts to an extent beyond that of which even they were aware.

Whilst it is true that these researches exist at present in a rudimentary condition, and the data base must be vastly extended before positive conclusions can be drawn, a potential area of investigation is available. The pieces preserved in the world's museums should be seen as containing within themselves the unwritten history of science, the extraction of which presents a new and fruitful avenue of archaeological investigation [13].

Appendix 1:
The practical operation of the dividing engine

Edward Troughton claimed that a man operating one of his dividing engines could produce 24 graduations per minute, working 'for many hours together' and including 'frequent intervals of rest'. In this way, it was possible to divide a 90° octant in 23 min, a sextant of 120° in 30 min, and a 360° theodolite in $1\frac{1}{2}$ h.

In January 1978, I graduated a replica sextant upon John Troughton's 1778 dividing engine, now in the Science Museum, London. This machine, which was closely modelled upon Ramsden's prize-winning engine, had been fully restored some years previously, and, with the exception of some of its fine adjustments, appeared to be in full working order.

The engine was mechanically simple to operate, and I found that Troughton's estimated working speed was reasonable. Working continuously, I was able to produce a measured course of 53 graduations in 1 min 35 s, and in 1 min, I could scribe 36 divisions, both of which were faster than Troughton's claim.

But frequent rest would have been essential when operating the machine commercially, for the action of the treadle which turned the lead screw necessitated the operative standing on one leg when working. As the right hand was required to actuate the scriber, it became difficult to maintain one's balance after a couple of minutes. To operate the scriber, one was obliged to reach across the 4-ft-diameter dividing wheel, which aggravated the already difficult working position of the machine.

The sextant upon which I worked had a radius of 12 in., which I considered to be an optimum size for a person of my height and reach. The height of the operative would have been important for a comfortable working position, and while an apprentice of 5 ft 2 in. might have managed to work at 20 in. radius, it would have needed a man well over 6 ft tall to have divided one of Troughton's famous 'snuff box' sextants.

Before attempting to graduate the sextant, I drew a set of concentric arcs onto the brass limb with a pair of beam compasses; these arcs were intended to contain the radial graduation strokes. In practice, however, it was very difficult to scribe the lines neatly so that they neither passed beyond nor fell short of the terminal lines. This difficulty was occasioned by the design of the scriber mechanism, which made it impossible to see the engraving tool in motion upon the instrument. As lines of irregular length are never seen on original instruments divided upon these machines, it is likely that banking blocks were incorporated, to provide a groove of fixed length in which the scriber moved.

To use the machine effectively, it was necessary for the operator to make allowances for these and other mechanical idiosyncrasies. It was essential to apply a uniform pressure to the treadle each time, for if one kicked too hard, the pulleys that fed the catgut line that turned the lead screw had a tendency to jam. On two occasions when graduating the sextant, I also found that the catgut overrode the spiral-grooved drum by which it imparted motion to the lead screw. Although the overall motion of this drum was stopped at both ends with banking pins, the overriding line did not always permit a full turn, and thus produced smaller graduations. To ensure homogeneous graduations, moreover, the treadle had to be depressed almost to the floor, and the spring rachet allowed to return it fully. Obvious as this operation may seem, it was often difficult to maintain when working in an out-of-balance position.

With practice, however, an operative would soon have gained the feel of the engine, and provided he could make the necessary reach, would have been able to produce high-quality work upon it.

Several other dividing engines were examined in this study, and in particular, the anonymous 'Ramsden type' machine with a 37-in dividing plate, currently in the Science Museum store, at Hayes, Middlesex [1]. This undated machine bears a strong resemblance to Ramsden's prototype of 1775, and I suggest that it may have been John Stancliffe's 1788 engine. When examined in September 1975, it was not in full working order, although after I had re-assembled the spring ratchet barrel and adjusted the lead screw it was made to perform very well. Its cutter, scriber, lead screw, and dividing plate worked together with little irregularity, and I was able to scribe 17 graduations in 30 seconds of time upon a metal plate fixed to its centre.

The working position of this machine was much more convenient than that of Troughton's, because the smaller diameter of the dividing plate — 37 in. rather than 48 in. — required fewer gymnastics to operate it. As a result of the difficulties in operating the large Troughton machine and the damage it occasioned to the health of his assistants, Edward Troughton constructed his smaller engine in 1793. This engine is likewise in the Science Museum store, although it is in need of restoration. At some stage in its working life, this engine had been converted from manual to mechanical action, so that by turning a drive shaft, the lead screw and cutter could work automatically. The conversion was probably performed by William Simms, who inherited the Troughton business and built a large automatic dividing engine in the 1840s.

Appendix 2:
A Victorian 'Garret Master's' dividing engine?

In August 1994, I was invited by a private collector to examine a small dividing engine that he had recently purchased in an antique shop in Scandinavia. Though purchased in Bergen, Norway, from a dealer who did not know what it was (and it has subsequently been re-sold), the machine had many parts which suggested manufacture in England. But, unlike the engines of Ramsden, Troughton, and Simms, this was not a specimen from the technological forefront, but suggested a machine that was built to graduate routine instruments of small radius, such as protractors or clinometers.

The operational heart of the machine was a wheel, in plate brass one-eighth inch thick, supported upon six lateral spokes, the whole being a foot in diameter. Unlike the other dividing engines that I have seen, however, its teeth had been cut into the *inner* edge of the wheel rim. The teeth were coarse (more like those of a small turret clock rather than a precision dividing machine), and engaged by a leafed pinion turned by a knurled head.

A simple brass pointer (a later addition, I suspect), which was screwed to the heavy wooden base board was used to line up the graduations on the 12-inch wheel. A beautifully made 'Ramsden' type cutter, which was adjustable along a pillar-mounted iron bar set horizontally above the wheel, could then be used to transfer divisions from the main wheel to a piece of work secured upon it. In this way, the mainscale divisions could be transferred to the work by the simple process of turning the wheel by the leafed pinion, aligning the divisions to the pointer by eye, and then operating the 'Ramsden' type cutter.

Everything suggested that this machine was a collage of parts brought into their present configuration to perform the task of routine copy division. The denticulated brass wheel carried a beautifully executed 360° scale, divided down to ½° fractions that were almost certainly of late eighteenth-century English manufacture. The spokes of this wheel, however, were riveted onto a circular brass base plate some 10 inches in diameter, which carried a 360° scale, and numerals which suggested eighteenth-century German engraving. But these numerals served no purpose, nor did the fine gear teeth cut into the outer edge of this plate engage any screw. Quite clearly, the builder of the dividing machine wanted this plate solely as a brass base, and one presumes that he cannibalized it from an earlier instrument. The 'Ramsden' type cutter, moreover, was most likely incorporated into its present arrangement from another machine in which it had originally been a designed part.

Most of the parts of the present engine suggest an eighteenth-century origin, yet it is my suspicion that they were put into their present ensemble in the nineteenth century. Perhaps the engine is the product of a Victorian jobbing artisan who wanted a useful bench tool for dividing simple draughtsmen's instruments, and hunted around various brass dealers and workshops for a compatible set of components. Steel screws securing the brass parts to the heavy softwood base board, and even some round-headed screws, suggest such a provenance. Cardboard packing-pieces and a new degree pointer in flimsy sheet brass indicate some further modelling in the twentieth century.

But the real significance of this instrument resides in the fact that it has survived at all. As an assembly from cannibalized parts from either the lowest rungs of the nineteenth-century commercial instrument-making trade, or from an amateur mechanic's workshop, it is lucky that no one has gone on to cannibalize it in turn. How many curiosities existed in the workshops of obscure 'garret masters' who put together their own dividing engines, we have no idea. But this machine, surviving in a complete and workable form, constitutes a unique specimen from the sub-culture of mechanical division (Plate 39).

Appendix 3:
The Radcliffe Equatorial Sector of 1775: John Bird's last instrument

John Bird took the quadrant to its peak of technical development, as discussed in Chapter 4, before angular accuracy passed a new watershed with Ramsden's and Troughton's reversible astronomical circles from the 1770s. No circles by Bird were known to exist, though in the summer of 1993, the signed and dated 36-inch-diameter Right Ascension and Declination circles from the Equatorial Sector which Bird made in 1775 for the new Radcliffe Observatory, Oxford, were identified in the University store housing some of the historical Radcliffe instruments [1].

The three-foot circles were exquisitely divided, with fine graduations that were stylistically identical to those on Bird's quadrants, and the 28° Sector arm of five-feet radius which had long been on display in the Museum of the History of Science. The R.A. circle is divided in 24 hours, I–XII; I–XII, down to five minutes of time. The Declination circle is graduated so as to form four 90° arcs, with the four 0° points aligned to the polar axis, and the four 90° points to the celestial equator. Each degree is directly divided into 15 equal parts, while a vernier scale could make the Declination circle read to single arc minutes. No construction marks are visible on the circles, and it is not possible to learn anything about the graduation procedure from physical examination. It is likely, however, that Bird laid off the points from his famous 'Scale of Equal Parts' with beam compasses, though it is very tempting to speculate whether he might have used a reversal procedure to cross-check their evenness across the circle, as Ramsden and the duc du Chaulnes did.

The circles themselves were fabricated from arcs and strips of plate brass, about one-eighth of an inch thick, that were brazed and bolted together. The flat circular surfaces upon which the scales were drawn were supported by a series of right-angles and girders, firmly bolted, to give them maximum rigidity. The support of the circles employed a bracing technology very similar to that which Bird had developed to stabilize his quadrants, and to maintain thermal homogeneity, all parts were made of brass, including the bolts.

The Equatorial Sector for the Radcliffe Observatory shows John Bird as an experimenter in instrument design, as well as in angle-division, for it was the first major and permanently mounted instrument since the days of Flamsteed to attempt to measure precise astronomical coordinates out of the meridian. Although George Graham had built a portable (and now lost) 30-inch-radius equatorially mounted 'astronomical sector' for James Bradley around 1735, one suspects that it was the newly topical interest in cometary orbits in the late 1760s, combined with opulent funding from the Radcliffe Trustees, which encouraged Bird to develop a design in which the two three-foot circles and a 28° Sector of five-feet radius promised to measure accurate coordinates in any part of the sky.

All of the principal parts for Bird's Radcliffe Sector are now preserved in the Museum of the History of Science, Oxford, though for reasons of space, they are not assembled. (A pair of equatorial sectors with two-foot-diameter circles was built by Sisson for Dr Maskelyne at Greenwich when Bird became occupied with the Radcliffe order, but they have not survived.) The 36-inch Right Ascension circle of Bird's Sector was originally set in a short brick or stone support below the heavy wrought iron polar axis of seven feet which rotated within its centre. This axis was held in a fork at its upper end to form an English Mount. Upon this polar axis was bolted the Declination circle, which could be made to describe a great circle in any part of the sky. But the purpose of the Declination circle was not to make the final measurements towards which the astronomer aspired; these were obtained from the five-foot radius Sector arm with its 28° scale, telescopic sights, verniers, and micrometer reading down to just under 2 arc seconds. This 28° Sector arm rotated upon the Declination circle. In fact, the Declination circle was intended as a very precise mode of guidance, accurate in the polar great circle to 1 arc minute by verniers, whereby the movable Sector arm that it carried could be brought to bear upon any new objects that appeared in familiar star fields.

The principal use of the Equatorial Sector was to measure the positions of new objects, such as comets (or, in 1781, Herschel's Uranus), with relation to stars of established position upon extra-meridional great circles. Although Dr Thomas Hornsby was the Radcliffe Observer whose enthusiasm and funding pioneered the initial development of the Equatorial Sector, his Observing Ledgers suggest that he made relatively little use of the instrument after its completion. To some degree, perhaps, this was occasioned by the sporadic nature of comets and similar extra-meridional objects, though other evidence suggests that the design was found to be subject to a variety of mechanical stresses that may have made it less than wholly reliable when measuring small angles. Indeed, one can understand how the long iron polar axis with the heavy Declination circle and Sector bolted to one of its sides, could produce errors that would never have got into readings made by the more stable mural quadrant. But that, after all, was part of the price of using a new design and an untried technology.

Before the concept of measuring angles out of the meridian could be realized in practice, however, it was necessary for a revolution in engineering and in optics to have taken place. The Equatorial Circle formed the next stage of the development, when Ramsden's 'Shuckburgh' Circle (see page 114 and Plate 33) and Troughton's Armagh Equatorial produced much more stable though still imperfect designs.

But measurements out of the meridian could not become entirely reliable until one abandoned the large angular amplitude and stress problems of the circle and its

English Mount, and confined all operations within the field of view of a large-aperture object glass. Josef Fraunhofer's superb object glasses and precision micrometers, set upon stable German Mounts, provided the only reliable way of making measurements out of the meridian by 1830. And here, one was concerned with measuring very small angles indeed, such as the daily motions of minor planets, or the components of a stellar binary. Once again, the astronomer needed an accurate map of the background stars that had been made with a good meridian instrument before he could venture away from the meridian to observe the positions of new objects that were moving within familiar star fields.

But the first serious moves towards equatorial measurement were made when the last of the great quadrant dividers tried his hand at circular division in the year before his death in 1776 (Plate 40).

Notes and References

Abbreviations

Annals	*Annals of Science*
J.B.A.A.	*Journal of the British Astronautical Association*
J.H.A.	*Journal for the History of Astronomy*
M.N.R.A.S	*Monthly Notices of the Royal Astronomical Society*
Notes & Records	*Notes and Records of the Royal Society*
Phil. Trans.	*Philosophical Transactions of the Royal Society*
Q.J.R.A.S.	*Quarterly Journal of the Royal Astronomical Society*

John Flamsteed's *Historia Coelestis Britannica* (London, 1725) is now available in translation, as *The 'Preface' to John Flamsted's 'Historia Coelestis Britannica', 1725*, edited and introduced by Allan Chapman, based on a translation by Alison Dione Johnson (National Maritime Museum Monograph, No. 52, 1982). The principal references have been re-paginated to the translation, although some of the minor ones still relate to the Latin Edition. Where a reference is cited — Flamsteed *Historia* III — it indicates the reference to the Latin original. As the original pagination numbers are also included in the text of the English translation, it is simple to compare the two.

1   INSTRUMENTS AND HISTORY

[1] Robert Hooke, *Some Animadversions on the First Part of Hevelius, his 'Machina Coelestis'* (London, 1674). Hooke again argues for the primacy of instrumental evidence in his *An attempt to prove the motion of the earth* (London, 1674). See also, J.A. Bennett, 'Hooke's Instruments for Astronomy and Navigation', in *Robert Hooke, New Studies*, M. Hunter and S. Schaffer (editors), The Boydell Press (Woodbridge, 1989) pp. 21–32.

[2] A characteristic example is C.L. Prince, who devotes himself to a study of the

optics of Hevelius' long telescopes, while ignoring the much more significant sextants and quadrants in the Dantzig observatory, in *The illustrated account given by Hevelius in his 'Machina Celestis' of ... his telescopes* (Lewes, 1882).

[3] John Flamsteed, *The 'Preface' to John Flamsteed's 'Historia Coelestis Britannica', 1725*, edited and introduced by Allan Chapman (London, 1982). Flamsteed, *Gresham College Lectures*, edited by Eric G. Forbes (London, 1975).

[4] For a discussion of the changing instrumentation at the Greenwich Observatory over this period, see Allan Chapman, 'Astronomia Practica: the principal instruments and their uses at the Royal Observatory, 1675–1775, Vistas in Astronomy **20** (1976) 141–156.

For discussion of the relationship between instrument accuracy and the 'frontier' of research, see Allan Chapman, 'The accuracy of angular measuring instruments used in astronomy, 1500–1850', *J.H.A.* **XIV** (1988) 133.

[5] A good account of the development of the telescope is to be found in H. C. King, *A History of the Telescope* (London, 1955). A. Chapman, 'William Herschel and the Measurement of Space', *Q.J.R.A.S.* **30** (1980) 399–418.

[6] One exception is Nicolas Bion, *Traité de la Construction et Usages des Instruments de Mathématique* (Paris, 1714), and translated into English with a *Supplement* by Edmund Stone, 2nd edition (London, 1758).

[7] David Brewster, editor, *The Edinburgh Encyclopaedia*, x (Edinburgh, 1830), p. 370.

[8] John Bird, *The Method of Dividing Astronomical Instruments* (London, 1767).

[9] The paper presented by Edward Troughton was 'An account of a method of dividing astronomical instruments', *Philosophical Transactions*, **99** (1809) 105–143. For the letter to Maskelyne, dated 23 June, 1808, see Royal Society Library, Manuscript *MC 135*.

[10] Robert Smith, *A Complete System of Opticks* (Cambridge, 1738), pp. 332–340. The basic details of Graham's quadrant seem to have been known long before Smith's account was published. Samuel Cunn, in his *New Treatise on the Construction and Use of the Sector* (London, 1729), Chapter IV, discussed the principles of the 90- and 96-part scales, though he attributes them to Halley.

[11] James Bradley, 'A letter to Dr Halley giving account of a new discovered motion of the fixed stars', *Philosophical Transactions* **35** (1728) 637–661; 'A letter to the Earl of Macclesfield concerning an apparent motion ... of the fixed stars', *Philosophical Transactions* **45** (1748) 1–43.

For an account of Maskelyne's instrumental procedures, see his *Astronomical Observations made at the Royal Observatory, Greenwich, from MDCCLXV to MDCCLXXIV* (London, 1785). Derek Howse, *Nevil Maskelyne The Seaman's Astronomer*, Cambridge University Press Cambridge, 1989) pp. 62–74.

[12] Geoffrey Chaucer, *A Treatise on the Astolabe*, included in *The Complete Works of Geoffrey Chaucer*, edited by F.N. Robinson (Cambridge, Mass., 1957), pp. 544–563.

[13] Perhaps the best known and most definitive work in the taxonomic genre is R.T. Gunther, The *Astrolabes of the World* (Oxford, 1932). A recent example,

based on a major national collection, is Derek Howse, *Greenwich Observatory*, iii, 'The Buildings and Instruments' (London, 1975). Also, R. Torode, 'A Mathematical System for Identifying the Stars of an Astrolabe and finding its Age', *Astrolabica* **5** (1989) 53–76. (The reliability of Mr. Torode's technique is not universally accepted.)

[14] For a thought-provoking, if somewhat exaggerated view of medieval technology, see Jean Gimpel, *The medieval machine* (London, 1977). Also, Lynn White Jr, *Medieval technology and social change* (Oxford, 1962).

[15] Derek de Solla Price, *Gears from the Greeks: the Antikythera Mechanism — a Calendar Computer from ca.80 B.C.* (New York, 1975).

[16] J.A. Bennett, *The Divided Circle, A History of Instruments for Astronomy, Navigation and Surveying* (Oxford, 1987) gives a good representation of the range over which divided instruments were used, though he is not primarily concerned with construction techniques developing with relationship to specific problems.

2 THE TYCHONIC SCHOOL

[1] One Tychomic foot = 16.1 English inches, J. L. E. Dreyer, *Tycho Brahe, A Picture of Scientific Life and Work in the Sixteenth Century* (1890) reprinted (New York, 1963) p. 39 footnote. Hereafter cited as Dreyer.

[2] Tycho Brahe, *Astronomiae Instauratae Mechanica* (Wandesburgi, 1598) translated by H. Raeder, E. and B. Strömgren as *Tycho Brahe's Description of his Instruments and Scientific work* (Copenhagen, 1946) p. 89. Also, Dreyer [1] p. 31. Tycho Brahe, *Astronomiae Instauratae Progymnasmata*, i (Frankfurt, 1610) pp. 352–376.

[3] *Mechanica* [2] p. 90, also p. 46. H. T. Pledge, *Science since 1500* (London, 1966) p. 291. Allan Chapman, 'Tycho Brahe — Instrument designer, observer and mechanician', *Journal of the British Astronomical Association* **99**, 2 (1989) 70–77.

[4] *Mechanica* [2] p. 108. Also, Robert Hooke, *Some Animadversions on the First Part of Hevelius, his 'Machina Coelestis'* (London, 1674) p. 4. Also, Thomas Digges, *Alea Seu Scala Mathematicae* (London, 1573), see section 'Radii Astronomici Supplementa'. L. Digges, *Pantometria* (London, 1571) Ch. 4.

[5] Istituto e Museo di Storia della Scienza, Florence, No. 1096. See Bernard R. Goldstein, 'Levi Ben Gerson; On Instrumental Errors and the Transversal Scale' *J.H.A.* **8** (1977) 102–112.

[6] E. R. Kiely, *Surveying Instruments; Their History and Classroom Use* (New York, 1947) p. 178. A good example of a scale divided by continuous diagonal lines is the arc on the gunner's sector of c. 1600, in the Museum of the History of Science, Oxford, accession number 49–36.

[7] *Mechanica* [2], p. 141. Jost Burgi, mathematician to the Landgrave of Kassel, was acquainted with Tycho's method of drawing diagonals by Paul Wittich, in 1584; Tycho Brahe, *Epistolarum Astronomicarum* (Noribergae, 1601) p. 3.

[8] *Mechanica* [2], p. 46 and 142. Curt Roslund, 'Tycho Brahe's Innovations in Instrument Design', *Bulletin of the Scientific Instrument Society* **22** (1989) 2–

4. Victor E. Thoren, *The Lord of Uraniborg, A Biography of Tycho Brahe* (Cambridge, 1990) pp. 154–156.

[9] These instruments were of fundamentally different design from those of Regiomontanus and the Nuremberg school. See J. Schöner (editor) *Scripta Clarissima Mathematici M. Joannis Regiomontani* (Nuremberg, 1544). Also Donald de Beaver, 'Bernard Walther; Innovator in Astronomical Observation' *J.H.A.* **1** (1970) 39–45.

[10] *Mechanica* [2], p. 73, for the development of the sextants. Also, *Progymnasmata* [2], i, pp. 336, 342, 458–461.

[11] *Progymnasmata* [2], i, p. 204.

[12] *Mechanica* [2], pp. 52–67, for the development of the armillaries.

[13] *Ibid.*, pp. 12–19. *Progymnasmata* [2], ii (1610) pp. 461–464.

[14] Victor Thoren, 'New Light on Tycho's Instruments', *J.H.A* **4** (1973) 25–45. Also, V. Thoren, 'Tycho Brahe; Past and Future Research', *History of Science* **11** (1973) 270–282. Primarily a Tycho bibliographical study. Thoren, *Lord of Uraniborg* [8] pp. 144–191.

[15] Dreyer [1], p. 351, 357–358.

[16] G. L. Tupman, 'A comparison of Tycho Brahe's Meridian Observations of the Sun in "Leverrier's Tables"', *The Observatory* **23** (1900) 132–135, 165–171. See also, T. Brahe, *De Mundi Aetheri Recentioribus Phaenomensis, Liber Secundis*, being Part ii of the *Progymnasmata* (Frankfurt, 1610) Chapters 6 and 8. Also, T. Brahe (?), *Learned Tycho Brahae His Astronomicall Coniectur of His New and Much Admired * [star] Which Appered [sic] in the Year 1572*, (London, 1632). Most of the material in this tract was translated out of *Progymnasmata* [2], i.

[17] Walter G. Wesley, 'The Accuracy of Tycho Brahe's Instruments' *J.H.A.* **9** (1978) 42–53. See pp. 44–47 for a detailed breakdown of accuracies.

[18] This set of armillae, sextants and quadrants built by Ferdinand Verbiest for the Imperial Observatory, Pekin, between 1670 and 1674, appear to have been modelled in their technical details upon those in the *Mechanica*. The original instruments are still preserved in their mountings; see Joseph Needham, *Science and Civilisation in China*, iii (Cambridge, 1959), numerous references; see pp. 451–452, and Plates LXV–LXVIII. Verbiest described some of these instruments in *Astronomia Europaea* (Pekin, 1674) and (Dilengae, 1687) and produced a set of 117 woodcuts to illustrate the text, which were to be found only in the Pekin edition. A copy of the Pekin edition, containing the plates, is located in the School of Oriental and African Studies Library, London. The dimensions of these instruments, their adjustments and overall appearances correspond very closely with those in the *Mechanica* [2]. It is interesting to note that Plates 40, 52 and 56, depict the use of European-type beam compasses and drawing instruments to graduate circular scales. For Verbiest's association with the Pekin instruments, see Louis Le Comte, *Memoirs and Observations of a Journey Through China* (London, 1697) pp. 64–72. Also, H. Bosmans, 'Ferdinand Verbiest: Directeur de l'Observatoire Peking', *Revue des Questiones Scientifiques* **71** (1912) 195–273

In the autumn of 1980, I contributed a section to the BBC Television *Chronicle* documentary *China — Travellers in the Celestial Empire*, on

Verbiest and his work on instruments. See also, Allan Chapman, 'Tycho Brahe in China; the Jesuit Mission to Peking and the Iconography of European Instrument-Making Processes' *Annals of Science* **41** (1984) 417–443.

[19] T. Brahe (?), *Astronomicall Coniectur* [16] pp. 5–11. Dreyer [1] pp. 57–63. T. Brahe, *De Mundi* [16], Chapters 6 and 8.

[20] Christopher Hill, *Intellectual Origins of the English Revolution* (Oxford, 1965) p. 118. Johannes Kepler, *Astronomia Nova* (Heidelberg, 1609) ii, Chapter 19, translated M. Caspar, *Neue Astronomie* (1929) p. 166. A. Pannekoek, *A History of Astronomy* (London, 1961) p. 238.

[21] *Astronomia Nova* [20], cited from the English translation in Pannekoek, p. 238.

[22] Abraham Rees, *The Cyclopaedia, or Universal Dictionary of Arts, Sciences and Literature,* viii (London, 1819), see article 'Circle' by William Pearson p. 1.

[23] T. Brahe, *Epistolarum Astronomicarum* (Noribergae, 1601) p. 3.

[24] T. Brahe, *Historia Coelestis, Complectans Observationes Astronomicas,* edited by Lucius Barrettus (Augsburg, 1666) p. cxii. Dreyer [1] note, p. 372.

[25] Z. Horsky and O. Skopova, *Astronomy Gnomonics — a Catalogue of Instruments of the Fifteenth to Nineteenth Centuries, in the Collections of the National Museum, Prague* (Prague, 1968) pp. 28–29. The Museum of the History of Science, Oxford, also contains some Habermel pieces, but *not* ones associated with Tycho.

[26] Derek J. de Solla Price, *The Equatorie of the Planetis, edited from Peterhouse Ms. 75 1., with a Linguistic Analysis by R. M. Wilson* (Cambridge, 1955).

[27] Thomas Fale, *Horologiographia; The Art of Dialling* (London, 1593) p. 1. L. Digges, *Pantometria* (London, 1571) Ch. 7. Although Goldstein in his 'Levi Ben Gerson' article [5] discusses early methods of subdividing, there is virtually no mention of the workshop processes involved. The same silence in basic practical matters is also evident in the instrument extracts published in L. P. Rose, 'Jacomo Contarini (1536–1595), a Venetian Patron and Collector of Mathematical Instruments and Books', *Physis* **18** (1976) 117–130.

[28] Euclid, *Elements of Geometrie*, translated by Henry Billingsley (London, 1570) Bk. IV, Problem 15, Proposition 15.

[29] Pedro Nunez, *De Crepulis* (Lisbon, 1542) Prop. III, part 2. Also, Christopher Clavius, *Opera Mathematica*, ii (Manz, 1611) pp. 10–12.

[30] The details of this transition are outlined by E. R. Kiely, *Surveying Instruments* [6], pp. 169–177.

[31] *Mechanica* [2], p. 15. T. Brahe, *Epistolarum Astronomicarum* [7], p. 62. For a representation of a Nonius quadrant, see R. Dudley, *Dell'Arcano del Mare*, 3 vols (Florence, 1646–1647).

[32] *Opera Mathematica* [29], ii, p. 13. For a discussion of these scales, see the Letter, Curtius/Brahe, *Mechanica*, f. G3. *Note*, this letter is cited only in the original Latin edition of 1598, and not in the 1946 translation. In the Bodleian Library copy, Oxford, reference Arch. *Bodl.D.c.*4, the page is numbered '36' in pencil. See also Clavius' letter on the previous page.

[33] *Opera Mathematica* [29], ii, p. 33. William Pearson discusses the methods of 'Clavius the Jesuit' in his 'Graduation' article in Rees, *Cyclopaedia*, xvi (1819)

Sig. 3Y 2. Clavius may also have inspired the Duc du Chaulnes in his method of dividing 10° spaces, as discussed in the Duc's *Nouvelle Méthode pour Diviser les Instruments de Mathématique et d' Astronomie*, (Paris, 1768) p. 35.

[34] Pierre Vernier, *La Construction, l'Usage et les Propriétéz de Quadrant Nouveau de Mathématique* (Brussels, 1631).

[35] Johannes Hevelius, *Machina Coelestis*, i (Dantzig, 1673) p. 309. Vernier scales did not become general on divided instruments until well into the eighteenth century. One very fine specimen of 1677 is to be found in the Museum of the History of Science, Oxford. It is a small quadrant of about 6-in radius, with clear, well-incised divisions and vernier, bearing the inscription 'Iacobus Lusuerg Mutinensis, Faciebat Romae A° 1677, accession number not known, 1995. A similar Lusuerg quadrant is in the Science Museum, London, No. 1880/200, although instruments carrying verniers from this period — especially small radius instruments — are rare.

[36] John Bird, *The Method of Dividing Astronomical Instruments* (London, 1767) pp. 6–7. See also, John Smeaton, 'On the Graduations of Astronomical Instruments', *Philosophical Transactions*, **76** (1786) 12.

[37] For material on the geometrical square, see J. Schöner (editor) *Scripta Clarissima* [9], pp. 61–62, Sigs. r–riii. Peter Apian, *Instrument-Buch durch Petrum Apianum* (Ingolstadt, 1533) Sigs. L–Lii, r.v. R. T. Gunther, *Early Science in Oxford*, ii (Oxford, 1923) p. 339. *Mechanica* [2], p. 37.

[38] William IV, Landgrave of Hesse Kassel, *Coeli et Siderium in eo Errantium Observationes Hassicae* (Leiden, 1618) pp. 45 v., 48 v.

[39] *Mechanica* [2], p. 46. Tycho does not state whether he or Copernicus drew the equal divisions.

[40] *Ibid.*, p. 47, 49–51.

[41] *Tychonis Brahe Dani Thesaurus Observationum*, i, edited by J. L. E. Dreyer (Copenhagen, 1923) p. 236. Observation 26/12/1583.

[42] B. Goldstein, 'Levi Ben Gerson' [5], 102–112. Nicholas Bion, *Construction and Principal Uses of Mathematical Instruments*, edited by Edmund Stone (London, 1758) pp. 202–203.

[43] Peter Apian, *Cosmographicus* (Landshut, 1524) f. 30. Diagram f. 32. Sigs. C or Diii, and C or Diiii. *N.B.* In the British Library copy of this work, the signature marks are obscured, while there appears to be two sets of 'C' signatures. This reference relates to the second set. See also, M. Cortes, *Arte of Navigation*, translated by R. Eden (London, 1596) f. 69.

[44] Lucas Waghenaer, *The Mariner's Mirrour*, translated by Anthony Ashley (London, 1588) pp. 18–19. For a re-construction of the staff, or Radius of Pierre Gassendi, see A. Chapman, 'Reconstructing the Angle-Measuring Instruments of Pierre Gassendi', in *Learning, Language and Invention: Essays presented to Francis Maddison*, W.D. Hackmann and A.J. Turner (editors), Variorum and Société Internationale de I'Astrolabe (Aldershot & Paris, 1994) pp. 103–116.

[45] P. De Medina, *L'Art de Naviguer*, French translation from the original 1545 Valladolid Edition (Lyons, 1554) Bk. 5, Ch. 2, p. 83. See mention of the 'Arbaleste' at sea. William Bourne, *A Regiment for the Sea* (London, 1577) pp. 25–26 r, v and 27 for his account of using coloured glasses. Leonard Digges, *A Boke Named Tectonicon* (London, 1556), see the 'Profitable Staffe'. Edmund

Gunter, *A Description and Use of the Sector, Cross-Staffe, and Other Instruments* (London, 1624).

[46] John Davis, *The Seaman's Secrets* (London, 1595) Bk. 2, pp. 14 r, 15 r, v, 16 r.

[47] Thomas Harriot was one of the earliest practitioners to use, and correctly determine, the errors of the cross-staff. This work, and his suggestions for improving the accuracy of the instrument, however, were contained in his now lost *Articon*, only a part of which survives in the British Library Ms. *Add. MS. 6788*. It seems to have been directed more towards navigators than astromoners. See J. V. Pepper, 'Harriot's Earlier Work on Mathematical Navigation Theory and Practice' in J. W. Shirley, *Thomas Harriot, Renaissance Scientist* (Oxford, 1974) pp. 54–90. Also, E. G. R. Taylor and M. W. Richey, *The Geometrical Seaman, A Book of Early Nautical Instruments* (London, 1962) p. 40. E. G. R. Taylor, *The Haven-Finding Art; A History of Navigation from Odysseus to Captain Cook* (London, 1956) pp. 175, 188–189.

[48] *Coeli et Siderium* [38], p. 64. *Scripta Clarissima* [9], Sigs. Kii, Kiii r, v. John Dee, *Parallaticae Commentationis Praxeosque* (London, 1573), see sections 'Praefatio' and 'Radii Astronomici Supplementa'.

[49] *Mechanica* [2], p. 97.

[50] For sources dealing with cross-staff design and errors, see Peter Apian, *Instrument-Buch* [37], Sign. Niii; Gemma Frisius, *De Radio Astronomico* (Antwerp, 1545) Sigs. C to Ciiii; Edward Wright, *Certaine Errors in Navigation* (London, 1599) Bk. 5, Ch. 2, see 'Errors of the Crosse-Staffe'.

[51] For a detailed treatment of the cross-staff at sea, see D. W. Waters, *The Art of Navigation in England in Elizabethan and Early Stuart Times* (London, 1958). He indicates how the European cross-staff developed out of the Islamic 'Kamal', p. 53 onwards, and his Plate LXXI illustrates the evolution of the staff down to 1632. The connection between the cross-staff and the Kamal is also mentioned by F. R. Maddison, *Medieval Scientific Instruments and the development of Navigational Instruments in the XV and XVI Centuries* (Coimbra, 1969) pp. 46–51. Without doubt, the most definitive study of the cross-staff produced to date is by John Roche, 'The Radius Astronomicus in England', *Annals of Science* **38** (1981) 1–32. The 1563 Arsenius staff, or radius, is in the Museo Nacional de Ciencia y Tecnologia, Madrid, Inv. No. 85-4-478.

I have constructed a replica cross-staff to test its feasibility, and find that for angles beneath 45° it can be relied upon to $\frac{1}{4}°$ or $\frac{1}{2}°$ degree; Allan Chapman, 'The astronomical art — the reconstruction and use of some Renaissance instruments', *Journal of the British Astronomical Association* **96** 6 (1986) 253–257.

[52] Isaac Newton, *Principia Mathematica* (London, 1687) Bk. III Prop. xxxv, Scholium. See the English translation by Andrew Motte (1729), revised by Florian Cajori (Berkeley, 1962) ii, p. 475.

[53] Jeremiah Horrox, *Venus is Sole Visa, 1639*, translated and edited by Arundel B. Whatton, *The Transit of Venus Across the Sun, 1639* (London, 1859) p. 122.

[54] Jeremiah Horrox, *Opera Posthuma*, edited by John Wallis (London, 1672–1673) p. 247. Letter 25/7/1636; p. 250, Letter, 30/8/1636; p. 363.

[55] *Ibid.*, p. 298, Letter, 23/11/1637, refers to E. Wright's, *Errors of Navigation*.

[56] *Transit* [53], p. 363, p. 418, 2/12/1635; p. 408. Observation 5/9/1636.

[57] *Ibid.*, p. 181. Also, William Derham, 'Observations of the Spots that have been seen upon the Sun from the Years 1703–1711, with a Letter of Mr Crabtree, in the Year 1640, upon the same Subject', *Phil. Trans.* **27** (1711) 288, Letter, Crabtree/Gascoigne 7/8/1640.

[58] *Opera Posthuma* [54], p. 255, Letter 4/1/1637.

[59] *Ibid.*, p. 244.

[60] John Flamsteed, *Historia Coelestis Britannica*, i (London, 1725) Flamsteed commenced his Catalogue, by printing five pages of letters and observations from Horrox and his circle. See p. 4, Letters 26/5/1641, and 22/6/1641.

[61] These values are extracted from the Horrox correspondence printed in Flamsteed, *Historia* [60], i, and the *Opera Posthuma* [54], p. 268, Letter, 29/4/1637. Modern values are taken from the *Astronomical Ephemeris*.

[62] *Opera Posthuma* [54], p. 268, Letter, 29/4/1637.

[63] *Historia* [60], i, p. 4, Letter, 22/6/1641.
     Historia [60], i, p. 3.

[64] *Opera Posthuma* [54], p. 260, Letter 13/1/1637, for value obtained 32′–34′ of arc.

[65] *Ibid.*, p. 140, Letters, 2/12/1636 and p. 252, 15/11/1636.

[66] *Transit* [53], p. 146.

[67] Thomas Digges, *A Perfite Description of the Coelestiall Orbes* (London, 1576) f. 43, sometimes included with the later edition of Leonard Digges *Prognostication*. Also, F. R. Johnson, *Astronomical Thought in Renaissance England* (Johns Hopkins, 1937) p. 166. Alexander Koyre, *From the Closed World to the Infinite Universe* (Baltimore, 1968) p. 37.

[68] *Transit* [53], 198–199. While Kepler may have considered 2′ star diameters in the pre-telescopic part of his career, he later abandoned the idea, stating that in the telescope, star images were 'puncta mera': *Epitome Astronomiae Copernicanae* (Frankfurt, 1635) p. 498. Galileo in the *Siderius Nuncius* also considered the stars to be only points when seen telescopically; Stillman Drake, *Discoveries and Opinions of Galileo* (New York, 1957) p. 47. Horrox discussed the diameters of stars in *Opera Posthuma* [54], p. 61, where he admitted that Kepler had given up the idea of the stars exhibiting visible diameters. See also his letter to Crabtree, 28 September 1639, *Opera Posthuma* [54] 330.

[69] *Opera Posthuma* [54], p. 201. For a modern study of Horrox's transit work, see S. B. Gaythorpe, 'Horrock's [sic] Observations of the Transit of Venus, 1639, Novenber 24 (O.S.)' *J.B.A.A.* **47** (Dec. 1936) 60–68; and continued *J.B.A.A.* **64** (July, 1954) pp. 309–315.

[70] *Transit* [53], pp. 109–113 and pp. 161–186. Also, Allan Chapman, 'Jeremiah Horrocks, the Transit of Venus, and the "New Astronomy" in early seventeenth-century England', *Quarterly Journal of the Royal Astronomical Society*, forthcoming, **31**, 1990, 333–357.

[71] Pierre Gassendi, *Mercurio in Sole Visa* (Paris, 1632) p. 5.

[72] *Transit* [53], pp. 188–189. Also, *Opera Posthuma* [54], p. 331, Letter, 26/10/1639.

[73] *Transit* [53], p. 187.

[74] *Ibid.*, pp. 129–130.

[75] *Ibid.*, pp. 155, 212. Also, Arundel B. Whatton, *Memoir of the Life and Labours of the Reverend Jeremiah Horrox* (London, 1859) p. 83.

[76] B. M. Davis 'The Astronomical Work of Jeremiah Horrox', London University M.Sc Thesis (1967–1968) pp. 32–38.

[77] *Transit* [53], pp. 177, 111, 139.

[78] *Historia* [60], i, p. 3.

[79] J. Hevelius, *Machina Coelestis*, i (Dantzig, 1673) p. 308. Hevelius probably graduated his own scales for Plate 'T', which depicts them, bears the inscription 'J. Hevelius Inv. et Sculps', thus suggesting that he was a draughtsman and engraver of considerable skill. Though Plate 'T*' seems to be in the same hand, it carries no signature. Of the panoramic instrument plates in vol. i, eight are without signatures, while 19 is jointly inscribed 'A. Stek [Stech] del' and 'J. Saal Sculps'. In vol. ii, the frontispiece is signed 'A. Boy delineavit' and 'J. Falck Sculpscit', and the portrait, 'A. Stech Pinxit' and 'Lambertus Visscher Sculp'.

[80] *Machina Coelestis* [79], pp. 309–309.

[81] J. Delambre, *Histoire de l'Astronomie Moderne*, ii (Paris, 1821) p. 467. Also, Francis Baily, 'The Catalogues of Ptolemy, Ulugh Beigh, Tycho Brahe, Halley and Hevelius deduced From the Best Authorities', *M.R.A.S.* **13** (1843) 1–248.

[82] *Machina Coelestis* [79], i, p. 183, and Plate 'K'.

[83] *Ibid.*, p. 222, and Plate 'M'.

[84] Instead of tracking screws, Tycho steadied his sextant with iron rods, *Mechanica* [2], p. 74.

[85] See the early accuracy values in, G. Shuckburgh, 'An Account of an Equatorial Instrument', *Phil. Trans.* **83** (1793) 75.

[86] R. Hooke, *Animadversions* [4], p. 7.

[87] E. F. MacPike, *Hevelius, Flamsteed and Halley* (London, 1937) pp. 1–7.

[88] Hevelius is very much of an under-researched figure, and an important reason for his neglect could be his ponderous and difficult Latin style. Some of the optical sections in *Machina Coelestis* [79] were published in English by C. L. Prince. *The Illustrated Account Given by Hevelius in His 'Machina Celestis' of ... His Telescopes* (Lewes, 1882). For an authoritative treatment of Hevelius' instruments, see, J. A. Repsold, *Zur Geschichte der Astronomischen Messwerkzeuge, von Purbach bis Reichenbach*, 1450–1830 (Leipzig, 1908) pp. 36–41. A slender but useful contribution to Hevelius studies can be found in Ivan Volkoff, E. Franzgrote and A. D. Larsen, *Johannes Hevelius and his Catalogue of Stars* (Brigham Young University Press, 1971).

3 JOHN FLAMSTEED

[1] John Flamsteed, *The Gresham Lectures of John Flamsteed*, edited by Eric G. Forbes (London, 1975) Lecture 6, 28/10/1681 p. 147.

[2] Stillman Drake, *The Discoveries and Opinions of Galileo* (New York, 1957) pp. 30–31 for Galileo's proposed telescopic sight, *Siderius Nuncius* (1610). J.

Christmann, *Theora Lunae* (Heidelburg, 1611) p. 86.

The history of the telescopic sight has been the subject of several scholarly studies, one of the most comprehensive of which is; Robert McKeon, 'Les débuts de l'astronomie de précision: Histoire des instruments de l'astronomie et de géodesie munis d'appareils de visée optique', *Physis*, Year 14, 3 (1972) 217–242.

[3] Christopher Scheiner, *Rosa Ursina* (Bracciano, 1630), p. 132r, Col. 2, and p. 169.

[4] J. B. Morin, *Longitude Terrestrium nec non Coelestium* (Paris, 1643) pp. 18, 54–56. G. de Fouchy 'Sur la date de l'application des lunettes aux instruments . . .', *Histoire de l'Académie de Sciences* (1787) 385–392.

[5] S. B. Gaythorpe, 'A Galilean telescope made about 1640, by William Gascoigne, inventor of the filar micrometer', *J. B. A. A.* **39** 7 (June, 1929) 238–241. See also G. Albetti and V. Ronchi's article on Galileo's telescopes, translated by D. Baxandall, *Transactions of the Optical Society* **25** (1923–1924) 141.

[6] The only account of Gascoigne's sights surviving under his own hand was published by S. P. Rigaud, *Correspondence of Scientific Men in the Seventeenth Century*, i, (Oxford, 1841) pp. 33–59, for Gascoigne's letter to William Oughtred containing details of his instruments. Also. see Gaythorpe [5], p. 2.

[7] Rigaud [6], i, p. 46.

[8] William Derham published several Gascoigne and Crabtree letters in 'Extracts from Mr Gascoigne's and Mr Crabtree's letters, proving Mr Gascoigne to have been the Inventor of the Telescopick Sights of Mathematical Instruments, and not the French', *Phil. Trans.* **30** (1717); see letter 25/1/1640–42, p. 604.

[9] *Ibid.*, letter 12/12/1641, p. 605.

[10] *Ibid.*, letter 28/12/1640, p. 609.

[11] Rigaud [6], i, p. 47.

[12] *Phil. Trans.* (1717) [8], letter 30/10/1640, p. 608.

[13] *Ibid.*, undated letter *c.* 1640, p. 605.

[14] After the deaths of Gascoigne, Crabtree and Horrox, in the early 1640s, their papers were collected by the Towneleys, where they were examined by Flamsteed, at Towneley Hall, Lancashire, in 1672. See, Flamsteed to Molyneux, letter, 10/5/1690, MS. in Southampton Civic Record Office, *D/M. I/I. ff. 142–143.*

[15] *Phil. Trans.* (1717) [8], p. 605, Derham's text.

[16] G. Govi, 'Della invenzionne del micrometro', *Bulletin Boncompagni*, **20** (Dec. 1887) p. 59. Divini/Manzini (1663).

[17] Robert McKeon, 'Les débuts de l'astronomie de precision: Histoire de la réalisation du micrometre', *Physis* **13** (1971), 225–288, see pp. 235–236.

[18] McKeon [2], p. 228.

[19] C. Huygens *Oeuvres Complètes*, 5, published in 22 volumes (Hague, 1888–1950) p. 159. Letter, Moray-Huygens, 5/12/1664.

[20] Robert Hooke, *Some Animadversions on the First Part of Hevelius, his 'Machina Coelestis'* (London, 1674) p. 42.

[21] Robert Boyle, *The Works of the Honourable Robert Boyle*, VI, edited by Thomas Birch (London, 1772) p. 191. Letter, Oldenburg/Boyle, 24/8/1665.

[22] Letter, Flamsteed/Molyneux, 10/5/1690 [14].

[23] Flamsteed, *Gresham Lectures* [1], p. 39. Flamsteed claimed to have learned his basic optics from Gascoigne's papers.

[24] J. W. Olmsted, 'The application of telescopes to astronomical instruments, 1667–1669', *Isis* **40**, 3 (Aug. 1949) 213–225.

[25] *The Measure of the Earth . . . by Divers Members of the Academy of Sciences at Paris* (London, 1687) pp. 1–40. This work was based upon the geodesic observations of Jean Picard and others. It was sold bound up as a supplement to the English edition of Claude Perrault's *Memoir for a Natural History of Animals* (London, 1687).

[26] Robert Hooke, *An Attempt to Prove the Motion of the Earth* (London, 1674) p. 17.

[27] J. Hevelius, *Machina Coelestis*, i (Dantzig, 1673) p. 296.

[28] R. Hooke, *Animadversions* [20], pp. 1–7, 17.

[29] *Ibid.*, p. 7.

[30] R. Hooke, *Motion of the Earth* [26], p. 9.

[31] J. R. Baker, 'Experiments on the function of the eye in microscopy', *J.R.M.S.*, **85**, 3 (June, 1966) 231–254. Also, Sir Stewart William Duke-Elder, *A System of Ophthalmology*, vol. 5 (London, 1958) p. 148. Articles by Westheimer and Röhler are also cited.

[32] E.F. MacPike, *The Correspondence and Papers of Edmond Halley* (London, 1932) pp. 42–43, letter, 7/6/1679.

[33] William Molyneux, *Dioptrica Nova, a Treatise on Dioptrics* (London, 1692) p. 231.

[34] *Phil. Trans.* **7** (1672) p. 5119.

[35] Letter, Flamsteed/Oldenburg, 5/4/1677. Royal Society Library, MS. *L.B.C. Sup. 3. 360.*

[36] Flamsteed, *Gresham Lectures* [1] p. 5.

[37] Shuckburgh, 'An Account of an equatorial instrument' *Phil. Trans.* **83** (1793) 75.

[38] Francis Baily, *An account of the Revd. John Flamsteed* (London, 1835). For a full account of the instrumental work of Crabtree, Gascoigne and Horrocks, see Allan Chapman, *Three Northcountry Astromomers* (Manchester, 1982).

[39] Letter, Flamsteed/Molyneux, 10/5/1690 [14].

[40] *Phil. Trans.* (1717) [8], p. 604.

[41] *Ibid.*, p. 605.

[42] Richard Towneley, 'An extract of a letter written by Mr Richard Towneley to Dr Croon . . . touching the division of a foot into many thousand parts for mathematical purposes', *Phil. Trans.* **2** (1667) 458.
N.B. The above article was only intended to be Towneley's announcement on the micrometer. He followed it up with a fuller account and an engraving a few weeks later, entitled, 'A description of an instrument for dividing a foot into many thousand parts, and thereby measuring the diameters of planets to great exactness', *Phil. Trans.* **2** (1667) 541–544.

[43] Baily, *Account* [38], p. 32.

[44] J. Flamsteed, *The 'Preface' to John Flamsteed's 'Historia Coelestis Britannica', 1725*, edited by Allan Chapman (London, 1982) p. 104. See also, Allan Chapman, *Three Northcountry Astronomers* (Manchester, 1982), see Gascoigne.

[45] *Phil. Trans.* (1667) 543.

[46] Rigaud, *Correspondence* [6], i, p. 56, and ii, p. 123.

[47] *Phil. Trans.* (1667) 458.

[48] John Flamsteed, *Historia Coelestis Britannica*, i (London, 1725) p. 5.

[49] *Astronomical Ephemeris* 1976 (London, 1974) p. 547.

[50] The following planetary diameters were included in a letter from William Gascoigne to William Oughtred, undated, but probably written in February, 1641, printed in Rigaud, *Correspondence* [6], i, p. 52. The reductions to find the *computed* and *difference* value were undertaken by the Nautical Almanac Office, R.G.O., Herstmonceux, in 1973. I have constructed a replica of Gascoigne's micrometer, and tested it in the measurement of some standard astronomical angles: see, A. Chapman, 'Gauging angles in the 17th Century', *Sky and Telescope*, April (1987) 362–364.

[51] Rigaud, *Correspondence* [6], i, pp. 56–57.

[52] *Phil. Trans.* (1667) 457.

[53] *Ibid.*, p. 458.

[54] *Ibid.*, p. 458.

[55] Flamsteed, *Historia* [48], iii, pp. 94–95 (104 in translation). For Flamsteed's value for the 10″ of arc solar parallax, see his note on the parallax in *Phil. Trans.* **7** (1672), 5118–5119.

[56] C. Huygens, *Oeuvres Complétes*, vol. 15, edition in 22 volumes (Hague, 1888–1950) p. 350.

[57] *Ibid.*, p. 350, being *Systema Saturni* (1659) p. 52.

[58] The most comprehensive study of the early history of the micrometer, especially on the Continent, is to be found in Robert McKeon's 'Histoire de la réalisation du micrometre', *Physis* **13** (1971) 225–288. See also H. C. King, *A History of the Telescope* (London, 1955) Chapter 6, for a treatment of the Gascoigne/Crabtree contribution. Also, C. C. Malvasia, *Ephemerides Novissima* (Mutinae, 1662) p. 192, and *Journal des Savants*, 28/6/1667. J.A. Bennett 'A Study of *Parentalia*, with two unpublished letters of Sir Christopher Wren', *Annals of Science*, **30** (1973) 129–147, p. 147.

[59] Margaret 'Espinasse, *Robert Hooke* (London, 1956) pp. 92–93.

[60] Hooke, *Animadversions* [20], p. 48.

[61] *Ibid.*, p. 55.

[62] *Ibid.*, p. 58.

[63] *Ibid.*, pp. 70–71.

[64] Charles Holtzapffel, *Turning and Mechanical Manipulation*, ii (London, 1846) p. 635. Citation to the *Collected Mathematical Works of Pappus*, viii, Problem xviii. See also, Randall C. Brooks, 'Gleaning information from screw threads', *Bulletin of the Scientific Instrument Society* **22** (1989) 7–11.

[65] Maurice Daumas, 'Precision mechanics', in *A History of Technology*, iv, edited by Singer, Holmyard and others (Oxford, 1958) p. 387.

[66] Hooke, *Animadversions* [20], p. 54.

[67] Molyneux to Flamsteed, letter, 22/12/1685. MS, Southampton Civic Record Office, *D/M. 1/1, ff. 95, r.v., 96, r.v.*

[68] Hooke, *Animadversions* [20], p. 76–78.

[69] Richard Waller, *The Posthumous Works of Robert Hooke* (London, 1705)

pp. 506–507. Edmund Halley, 'Considerations on the change of the latitude of some of the principal fixed stars', *Phil. Trans.* **30** (1718) 736–738.

[70] Flamsteed to Oldenburg, letter, 5/4/1677. Royal Society Library, MS. *L.B.C. Sup. 3, 360.*

[71] James Bradley, *Miscellaneous Works and Correspondence of the Rev. James Bradley, D.D.*, edited by S. P. Rigaud (Oxford, 1832) p. lv.

[72] Robert Hooke, *A Description of Helioscopes* (London, 1676) pp. 4–5.

[73] Hooke, *Animadversions* [20], pp. 64–65.

[74] See a simple equatorial mount in, C. Scheiner, *Rosa Ursina . . .* (Bracciano, 1630) pp. 347–354.

[75] Hooke, *Animadversions* [20], p. 37.

[76] Hevelius is credited with a form of tracking device, *Animadversions* [20], p. 36. This probably derived from the tracking screws on some Hevelian instruments, i.e. Johannes Hevelius, *Machina Coelestis*, i (Dantzig, 1673) p. 222, Fig. M. But none of Hevelius's instruments lay in the equatorial plane.

[77] Eric G. Forbes, *Greenwich Observatory*, i, 'Origins and early history' (London, 1975), p. 22 for citation of Founding Warrant.

[78] Flamsteed, *Historia* [48], iii, p. 101 (p. 111 in translation). Forbes, *Greenwich Observatory*, i, pp. 18–21.

[79] Flamsteed, *Historia* [48], iii, pp. 102–103 (p. 113 in translation). Baily, *Account*, pp. 44–46.

[80] Baily, *Account* [38], p. 45.

[81] Derek Howse, 'The Tompion clocks at Greenwich, and the dead beat escapement', Part 1; *Antiquarian Horology* **7**, 1 (Dec. 1970) 21–22. See also the letter, Flamsteed to Moore, 20/12/1675.

[82] *Ibid.*, 21–22; letter, Flamsteed to Towneley, 22/9/1675. Flamsteed treated the equation in 'De Temporario Aequatione', included as part of Jeremiah Horrox's *Opera Posthuma*, edited by John Wallis (London, 1672/73).

[83] Howse, 'Tompion clocks at Greenwich', Part 2, *Antiquarian Horology* **7**, 2 (March, 1971) 114–115.

[84] Flamsteed, *Historia* [48], iii, pp. 103–107. Also, Derek Howse, *Francis Place and the Early History of the Greenwhich Observatory* (London, 1975) pp. 54–57, 59–61.

[85] Baily, *Account* [38], p. 41. Flamsteed, *Historia* [48], i, pp. 390–395, for Flamsteed's '"Revolves" table'.

[86] Baily, *Account* [38], p. 41.

[87] Letter, Flamsteed to Molyneux, 4/11/1686. MS. Southampton Civic Record Office, *D/M. 1/1. ff. 99, r.v. 100, r.v.*

[88] Flamsteed, *Historia* [48], iii, p. 103. Baily, [38], pp. 41, 42, 46.

[89] Letter, Flamsteed to Towneley, 3/7/1675, Royal Society Library, MS. *243. Fl.8.*

[90] Letter, Flamsteed to Molyneux, 4/11/1686 [87].

[91] *Ibid.*

[92] See the correspondence between John Aubrey and Francis Potter, in the Bodleian Library, Oxford, i.e., 29/4/1654, MS. *Aubrey 13, f. 148*; 29/11/1654, MS. *Aubrey 13, f. 149.*, and the undated letter of c. 1654, MS. *Wood, F. 39, f. 152.*

[93] J. Flamsteed, 'Brief History of the Observatory' (1710–1711), R.G.O. Library, MS. *Flamsteed 35*, p. 164. Also, Baily, *Account* [38], refers to Flamsteed's health, p. 57 footnote; p. 48, footnote.

[94] Baily, *Account* [38], p. 42.

[95] *Ibid.*, p. 46.

[96] R. Hooke, *The Diary of Robert Hooke, 1672–1680*, edited H. W. Robinson and W. Adams (London, 1935), see entry 6.5.1676. Howse, *Francis Place* [84], pp. 52–53, 59–61.

[97] Hooke, *Animadversions* [20], p. 14.

[98] Flamsteed, *Historia* [48], iii, p. 106. D. Howse, *Greenwich Observatory iii*, 'The Buildings and Instruments' (London, 1975) pp. 17–18.

[99] Baily, *Account* [38], p. 43.

[100] Letter, Flamsteed to Moore, 16/7/1678, R.G.O. MS. *36/62* (Flamsteed), in Baily p. 118. Flamsteed to Sherburne, 12/7/1682, R.G.O. *MS. 42.* (Flamsteed), in Baily, pp. 127–128.

[101] Flamsteed, *Historia* [48], iii, p. 107.

[102] Baily, *Account* [38], pp. 51–52.

[103] Baily, [38], p. 54.

[104] John Flamsteed, 'Foul Observations Book', R.G.O. Library MS. *Fl 1/188*, see entry 26/9/1679.

[105] Zacharias Conrad von Uffenbach, *London in 1710*, edited from his *Merkwurdige Reisen durch Niedersachsen Holland und Engelland* (Ulm, 1753), by W. H. Quarrell and Margaret Mare (London, 1734) p. 22.

[106] Baily, *Account* [38], pp. xxviii, xxix.

[107] Flamsteed, *Historia* [48], iii, p. 108.

[108] *Ibid.* Although the arc is now lost, another Sharp quadrant hangs at Greenwich; see N. S. Heineken, 'Relics of the mechanical productions of Abraham Sharp', *Philosophical Magazine* **30** (1847) 25–27. In 1977, I examined the graduations of this quadrant, measuring them with a precision engineer's micrometer and magnifier, and found that the average error of all the 90° on the scale came to 55″, whilst the 'best scale error', covering the most homogeneous 77° came to 27.9″. It is hoped that this may give some indication of the quality of Sharp's work. These measurements, along with measures of the accuracies of several other seventeenth and eighteenth century instruments, is currently being prepared for press; see Chapter 11 of the present book pp. 153–157.

An equatorial instrument, also made by Abraham Sharp, was acquired by the National Maritime Museum around 1975, and was also measured in the abovementioned study. For further details, see Chapter 11 of this book.

[109] Flamsteed, *Historia* [48], iii, pp. 109–110.

[110] William Cudworth, *The Life and Correspondence of Abraham Sharp, the Yorkshire Mathematician* ... (London, 1889). Letter, 2/2/1721–1722, pp. 16–18.

[111] Flamsteed, *Historia* [48], iii, p. 110.

[112] *Ibid.*, p. 110.

[113] *Ibid.*, p. 110.

[114] *Ibid.*, p. 132. Sinking of the wall. Also, J. Flamsteed, 'Coelum Brittanicum',

R.G.O. Library, MS. *Flamsteed 39*, pp. 101–103, and Baily, *Account* [38], pp. 55, 56.

[115] Baily, *Account* [38], p. 56.

[116] Uffenbach, *London in 1710* [105], p. 25.

[117] Flamsteed, *Historia* [48], iii, p. 113.

[118] Baily, *Account* [38], p. 56.

[119] Flamsteed, *Historia* [48], iii, p. 113.

[120] Tycho Brahe, *Epistolarum Astronomicorum* (Frankfurt, 1610) p. 269. Also, H. Alan Lloyd, *Some Outstanding Clocks over Seven Hundred Years, 1250–1950*, (London, 1958) p. 63.

[121] Baily, *Account* [38], p. 57.

[122] *Ibid.*, p. 52.

[123] For a full discussion of Tycho's use of Venus to determine the First Point of Aries, see, J. L. E. Dreyer, *Tycho Brahe* (1890) and (New York, 1963) pp. 349–351.

[124] Flamsteed, *Historia* [48], iii, pp. 125–152.

[125] *Ibid.*, p. 113.

[126] George Shuckburgh (Sir), 'An Account of an equatorial instrument', *Phil. Trans.* **83** (1793) 75, for Shuckburgh's estimates of the accuracy of his predecessors.

From an examination of Flamsteed's observations, James Pound concluded that the mural arc contained a graduation error of 15″; see Letter, Crosthwait to Sharp, in 'A Collection of Original Letters Addressed to Mr Abraham Sharp', Royal Society Library, MS. *Fl. Sh. xxiv d*. See letter, 27/1/1721–1722. The letters are bound in date order. Baily, *Account* [38], p. 346.

In 1977, I attempted to make an independent estimate of the accuracy of the 7-ft arc. Taking the measured accuracy of the surviving 5-ft Sharp arc (see [108]) and applying its known error distribution to a radius of 7 ft, the calculated error for the instrument came out at 16.8″, which accords very well with the error detected by Pound. My work on this field is now published in a separate fuller study entitled 'The Archaeology of the Graduated Scale'. For further details, see Chapter 11 of the present book.

[127] Baily, *Account* [38], p. 57. Issac Newton, *Correspondence*, iv, edited by H. W. Turnbull, (Cambridge, 1967), Letter, 16/12/1694–1695, p. 87.

[128] Baily, *Account* [38], p. 63.

[129] Flamsteed, *Historia* [48], iii, p. 113.

[130] On November 24th 1719, Flamsteed wrote to Abraham Sharp saying that he would have the *Prolegomena* ready for the press in one month's time; see 'A Collection of Original Letters Addressed to Mr Abraham Sharp', Royal Society Library, MS. *Fl. Sh. xxiv d*. Item 124. From the comment it would appear that he intended to publish the *Prolegomena* in English. Flamsteed died on December 31st 1719. R.S. MS. *Fl. Sh. xxiv d*. Item 126.

[131] It was probably Flamsteed's editors who decided to publish in Latin for the benefit of the international market. It was eventually translated by a Presbyterian minister referred to as Mr Anderson, who charged £2 per sheet for his work. 'Sharp Letters' [130], Items 161 and 168.

[132] R.G.O. MS. *Flamsteed 32c*. The suppressed section of this manuscript,

covering the pages 74 to 93 etc., was included in Francis Baily's *Account* [38], pp. 71–105.

[133] 'Sharp Letters' [130], Item 158. I have recently edited an English translation of Flamsteed's *Prolegomena*, for the National Maritime Museum, which incorporates all the suppressed manuscript sections, along with the translated Latin text. Allan Chapman, *The 'Preface' to John Flamsteed's "Historia Coelestis Britannica"*, National Maritime Museum Monograph No. 52 (Greenwich, 1982).

[134] Flamsteed had intended to include an account of his alleged discovery of the parallax of Polaris in the *Prolegomena*, for one appears in the 'Sharp Letters' [130], Item 158, p. 37. An account of this work had already been published as part of John Wallis's *Opera Mathematica*, iii (Oxford, 1699) p. 705.

[135] R.G.O. MS. *Flamsteed 32c*, pp. 74–75.

[136] *Ibid*. Elsewhere in his manuscripts, Flamsteed had stressed the importance of the mural arc to Newton's conclusions: 'What care I took to observe the moon, ever since the arc was finished, and with what success will appear from the large synopses of her places deduced from my observations and imparted to Mr Newton'. R.G.O. MS. *Flamsteed 39*, reprinted in Baily's *Account* [38], p. 57.

[137] R.G.O. MS. *Flamsteed 32c*. p. 75. Newton's particular debts to Flamsteed are discussed in pp. 74–77. Newton did feel obliged to offer some thanks, however, because 'If I do not make a handsome acknowledgement, they will reccon me an ungrateful clown', *Correspondence of Sir Isaac Newton*, iv, edited by H. W. Turnbull (Cambridge, 1968) p. 87. Also, Flamsteed, *Historia* iii, p. 113.

[138] R.G.O. MS. *Flamsteed 32c*, pp. 76–77.

[139] *Ibid*., p. 78 onwards.

[140] *Historia Coelestis in Libri Duo*, edited by Edmund Halley (London, 1712). The Preface is only six pages long. A modern English translation has been made by E. M. Barker, a stencil copy of which is pasted into the cover of the Bodleian Library copy of the *Historia*, ref. *Arch. Ab I*.

[141] R.G.O. MS. *Flamsteed 32c*, pp. 90–91.

[142] *Ibid*., p. 82.

[143] *Ibid*., p. 76.

[144] Nevil Maskelyne, 'An Account of Observations made at Schahallion for finding its Attraction', *Phil. Trans.* **65** (1775) 500, and Henry Cavendish, 'Experiments to Prove the Density of the Earth', *Phil. Trans.* **88** (1798) 469–526.

[145] Frank Manuel *A portrait of Isaac Newton* (Harvard, 1968) provides an interesting assessment of Newton's character and conduct, especially during his last years. Although Manuel's tendency to interpret a great many of Newton's actions in the light of Freudian psychology is suspect, he has made a close study of Newton's papers to produce a view of the man that is free from the traditional reverences. Chapter 14 is devoted to the relationship between Newton and Flamsteed. Also, R. S. Westfall *Never at Rest* (Cambridge, 1980).

[146] A useful bibliography of both primary and secondary sources on Römer accompanied Z. Kopal's article in the *Dictionary of Scientific Biography*, although Kopal omits A. V. Nielsen, 'Römer and his Meridian Circle', *Vistas*

in Astronomy, 10, edited by Arthur Beer (Oxford, 1968) pp. 105–112. The observations that survived after 1728 were published in the *Triduum*, edited by J. G. Galle (Berlin, 1845).

[147] Peter Horrebow, *Basis Astronomiae, sive Astronomiae pars Mechanica ...* (Copenhagen, 1735) Chapter 5, para. 54.

[148] *Ibid.*, para. 58.

[149] *Ibid.*, para. 54.

[150] *Ibid.*, para. 57.

[151] *Ibid.*, para. 59.

[152] John Smeaton, 'On the Graduation of Astronomical Instruments', *Phil. Trans.* **76** (1786) 9. There is also a discussion of Römer's instruments in David Brewster (editor) *The Edinburgh Encyclopaedia*, x (Edinburgh, 1830) p. 362.

[153] *Basis Astronomiae* [147], para. 60.

[154] *Ibid.*, para. 63.

[155] *Ibid.*, para. 65.

[156] G. Shuckburgh, 'Description', *Phil. Trans.* (1793) [126], p. 98, where Shuckburgh describes his own use of microscopes.

[157] J. Delambre, *Histoire de l'astronomie moderne*, ii (Paris, 1821) pp. 639, 632–661. R. Grant, *A History of Physical Astronomy* (London, 1852) pp. 461–467.

[158] *Miscellanea Berolinensia*, ii, pp. 277–278 in the seven-vol. series (1710–1743), Histoire de l'Académie Royale des Sciences et des belles-lettres de Berlin.

[159] *Ibid.*, p. 277.

[160] R. Grant, *Physical Astronomy* [157], p. 464. See also, *Ole Römer's Adversaria*, edited by T. Eibe and K. Meyer (Copenhagen, 1910), along with G. van Biesbroeck and A. Tiberghien, 'Etudes sur les notes astronomiques contenues les Adversaria d' Ole Römer', *Oversigt over det Kongelige Danske Videnskabernes Selskabs Forhandlinger*, vol. 4 (Copenhagen, 1913) pp. 213–273.

4 DIVIDING AS A HIGH ART

[1] John Smeaton, 'On the Graduation of Astronomical Instruments', *Phil. Trans.* 76 (1786) p. 1.

[2] Robert Smith, *A Compleat System of Opticks* ii, (1738) pp. 332–340.

[3] Graham was originally apprenticed to Henry Aske, but his indentures were later transferred to Tompion, who made him free of the Clockmakers' Company in 1695. A. Raistrick, *Quakers in Science and Industry* (1950) reprinted (Newton Abbott, 1968) p. 235.

[4] Francis Baily, *An Account of the Revd. John Flamsteed* (London, 1835) p. 359.

[5] Smith, *Opticks* [2], p. 333. Smith's account of the Graham quadrant forms the basis of the section 'Quart du Cercle; Instruments Mural' in Diderot's *Encyclopedie*, xiii (Neufechastel, 1765) pp. 667–671. The instruments and workshop scenes depicted in *Recuil des Planches*, 'Astronomie Instrumens', Plate XII, Fig. 9, are clearly based upon Smith, being artistically re-drawn copies of the simple line engraving, No. 593 etc., in the *Opticks*.

[6] William Ludlam, *An Introduction and Notes on Mr Bird's Method of Dividing*

Astronomical Instruments (London, 1786) paras 8 & 9. David Brewster (editor) *The Edinburgh Encyclopaedia*, x (Edinburgh, 1830) article 'Graduation', p. 364.

[7] Smith, *Opticks* [2], p. 334.

[8] *Edinburgh Encyclopaedia*, x, p. 363. Smith, *Opticks* pp. 335–336.

[9] *Edinburgh Encyclopaedia*, x, p. 349.

[10] Smith, *Opticks* [2], p. 335.

[11] Smith, *Opticks* [2], pp. 338–339.

[12] John Bird, *The Method of Dividing Astronomical Instruments* (London, 1767) pp. 9–10.

[13] Smith, *Opticks* [2], pp. 337–338.

[14] James Bradley, *Miscellaneous Works and Correspondence of the Rev. James Bradley, D. D.*, edited by S. P. Rigaud (Oxford, 1832) pp. xv–xvi. James Bradley, 'A letter to Dr Halley giving Account of a New Discovered Motion of the Fixed Stars', *Philosophical Transactions* **35** (1728) pp. 637–638.

[15] Bradley, *Works*, [14], p. iv.

[16] Smith, *Opticks* [2], pp. 332–333.

[17] *Ibid.*, p. 336.

[18] Abraham Rees, *The Cyclopaedia, or Universal Dictionary of Arts, Sciences and Literature*, xvi (London, 1819), article 'Graduation', by W. Pearson, Sig. 3, Yr.

[19] Bradley, *Works* [14], p.1v. Bradley attributed the error to pivot wear; also, John Bird, *The Method of Constructing Mural Quadrants* (London, 1768) p. 7, hereafter, Bird's *Quadrants*. Bird attributed it to temperature distortion.

[20] George Graham, 'A Contrivance to Avoid the Irregularities in a Clock's Motion', Royal Society Library, MS. *R.B.C. 12.739*. The paper is dated 28/4/1726.

[21] Edward Troughton, 'An Account of Dividing Astronomical Instruments by Ocular Inspection', *Phil. Trans.* **99** *(1809), p. 109.*

[22] William Ludlam, *Introduction* [6], p. iv. footnote. Also, C. Doris Hellman, 'John Bird, mathematical instrument maker in the Strand', *Isis* **50** 17 (Jan. 1932) p. 128.

[23] James Bradley, *Astronomical observations made at the Royal Observatory, Greenwich, ... MDCCL to MDCCLXII*, ii, edited by Thomas Hornsby (Oxford, 1798–1805), p. ii.

[24] Troughton, *Dividing* [21], p. 109.

[25] Bird, *Dividing* [12], p. 2, 3. On p. 2, Bird's scale of equal parts is described as 90 in. long. This must refer to the scale below the vernier, for a 96-in. scale was necessary to strike off the radius chord.

[26] *Ibid.*, pp. 3–4.

[27] *Ibid.*, p. II for Bird's discussion of temperature control. R. T. Gunther, *Early Science in Oxford* II (Oxford, 1923) p. 323.

[28] *Edinburgh Encyclopaedia*, x, p. 379, for the time taken by Bird to divide.

[29] Bird, *Dividing* [12], p. 5.

[30] *Edinburgh Encyclopaedia*, x, p. 367.

[31] Ludlam, *Introduction* [6], para. 16.

[32] *Ibid.*, para. 14.

[33] Bird, *Dividing* [12], p. 6; pp. 8–9.

[34] Bradley, *Works* [14], p. lv.

[35] Bradley, *Observations* [23], p. XIV.

[36] *Early Science in Oxford* [27], p. 319. Also James Ingram's *Memorials of Oxford*, ii (Oxford, 1837), section headed 'The Observatory', p. 7, states that 'Hornsby was the first person who could induce Bird to use achromatic glasses, against which he had taken up an extraordinary prejudice'.

[37] Troughton, *Dividing* [21], p. 10.

[38] Bradley, *Observations* [23], p. XIV.

[39] Troughton, *Dividing* [21], p. 138, For Troughton's examination of the Bird quadrant in 1808.

[40] Nevil Maskelyne, *Nautical Almanac* (London, 1767) p. 152. Bird, *Dividing* [12], p. 13.

[41] Rees, *Cyclopaedia* [18], xvi, Sig. 3, Y, r.

[42] Ludlam, *Introduction* [6], footnote, p. 4. Letter 20th May, 1766.

[43] *Ibid.*, para. 12.

[44] *Ibid.*, para. 23.

[45] *Ibid.*, para. 10. Smeaton, 'Graduation' [17], p. 9.

[46] Rees, *Cyclopaedia* [18], xvi, Sig. 3, Y, 2, recto.

[47] *Ibid.*, Troughton later replaced Sission's three index marks with three verniers, so that the angle could be cross-checked around the scale. See William Gardiner, *Practical Surveying Improved* (London, 1737). See plate and description of Sisson's theodolite.

[48] Bradley, *Works* [14], pp. lxxxiii, lxxxiv.

[49] E. G. R. Taylor, *The Mathematical Practitioners of Hanoverian England* (Cambridge, 1966) pp. 143 and 169.

[50] W. Ludlam, 'An Account of the Expense of several Mechanical and Philosophical Instruments &c' (1758). MS. volume in the Museum of the History of Science, Oxford, *Museum 221*. Also in the same collection, 'A Catalogue of the Engines Tools and Materials for Mechanical purposes in the Collection of WL.' (1758), *Museum 220*.

[51] Ludlam, *Account* [50], pp. 52 and 58.

[52] Z. Conrad von Uffenbach gave a good account of an 18th century pencil maker; see *London in 1710*, edited by W. H. Quarrell and M. Mare (London, 1934) pp. 144–145.

[53] Ludlam, *Account* [50], p. 54v.

[54] E. G. R. Taylor, [49], p. 218.

[55] A. W. Skempton and Joyce Brown, 'John and Edward Troughton, Mathematical Instrument Makers', *Notes and Records* **27**, 2 (Feb. 1973) pp. 237–242.

[56] Troughton, *Dividing* [21], p. 110.

[57] Rees, *Cyclopaedia*, under J. Troughton, *ibid*.

[58] J. Troughton attempted to combine division equality with a perfect quadrant; Troughton, *Dividing* [21], p. 111.

[59] Troughton, *Dividing* [21], p 106.

[60] Troughton, *Dividing* [21], p 111. Also, Smeaton 'Graduation' pp. 13, 16. Smeaton considered that division equality *and* a perfect quadrant to be geometrically unattainable.

[61] Smeaton, 'Graduation' [1], pp. 13–14. See p. 15, for Bird's division of Hadley quadrants.

[62] John Smeaton, 'Description of a New Pyrometer', *Phil. Trans.* **48** (1754) p. 598.

[63] *Ibid.*, p. 600. In Smeaton's day, this pyrometer was owned by James Short. On p. 607, the clockmaker John Ellicott is also said to have possessed a pyrometer.

[64] *Ibid.*, p. 605. Smeaton claimed this instrument to be accurate to 1/23145 in. In Smeaton's paper, the fraction 1/23145 is misprinted 1/2345, a mistake made clear by his numbers.

[65] Smeaton, 'Graduation' [1], pp. 12 and 17: On his rejecting the vernier and 96-part scale. Smeaton, *Pyrometer* [62], p. 605.

[66] Bird's experience as a graduator convinced him of the superiority of the faculty of touch, as expressed in the maxim 'Contact is more subtile than vision', Ludlam, *Introduction* [6], para. 14. In his researches on the expansion of metals, conducted with a pyrometer, Smeaton claimed that he could measure a variation of 1/23145 in with a manual micrometer, which he could not see visually; Smeaton, 'Graduation' [1] [64], p. 605. See also Troughton, *Dividing* [21], p. 112.

5   TECHNIQUES OF EIGHTEENTH-CENTURY ASTRONOMY

[1] James Bradley, 'A Letter to the Earl of Macclesfield Concerning an Apparent Motion . . . of the Fixed Stars', *Phil. Trans.* **45** (1748), 1.

[2] Peter Horrebow, *Basis Astronomiae, sive Astronomiae pars mechanica* (Copenhagen, 1735) p. 48.

[3] James Bradley, *Miscellaneous Works and Correspondence of the Rev. James Bradley, D.D.*, edited by S. P. Rigaud (Oxford, 1832) p. 1.

[4] S. P. Rigaud, 'Some particulars respecting the principal instruments at . . . Greenwich, in the time of Dr Halley', *M.R.A.S.* **9** (1836) pp. 205–207. Compiled from Bradley's notebooks, R.G.O. MS *121*; Derek Howse, *Greenwich Observatory*, iii, 'The Buildings and Instruments' (London, 1975) pp. 33–34. Robert Smith, *A Compleat System of Opticks* (Cambridge, 1738) para. 841.

[5] Decription of shadow scales, Thomas Digges, *Alea seu scalae mathematicae* (London, 1573), see 'Capitulum Septimum'. Nevil Maskelyne, *Nautical Almanac* (London, 1769) p. 33.

[6] William Derham, *The Artificial Clockmaker* (1696) and (London, 1759) pp. 149–150. *Nautical Almanac* (1769) pp. 18–19; 33.

[7] 'Greenwich in 1742' [4], p. 209.

[8] *Ibid.*, p. 210. Smith, *Opticks* [4], para. 838.

[9] *Ibid.*, p. 210. In July 1975, I carefully examined the park wall south of the Royal Observatory, attempting without success to locate the old meridian marks, but the wall has been rebuilt since 1750.

[10] Nevil Maskelyne, *Astronomical Observations made at the Royal Observatory, Greenwich, from MDCCLXV to MDCCLXXIV*, i (London, 1785) pp. iii–v, hereafter Maskelyne, *Observations*. In 1824, A Northern meridian mark

was set up at Chingford, Howse, *Greenwich Observatory* [4], iii, p. 39.

[11] Thomas Hornsby, *The Observations of the Rev. Thomas Hornsby, D. D. ... 1774–1798*, edited by H. Knox-Shaw, J. Jackson, and W. H. Robinson (London, 1932) p. 21.

[12] Römer devised an *Amphioptra*, or collimating telescope, *Basis Astronomiae* [2], p. 97. David Rittenhouse also devised one, 1785, 'On a New Method of Placing a Meridian Mark', *Transactions of the American Philosophical Society* **2** (Philadelphia, 1786) 181–183.

[13] James Bradley, *Astronomical Observations made at the Royal Observatory, Greenwich, from the year MDCCL to the year MDCCLXII*, i (1798) p. 2. Smith, *Opticks* [47], paras. 829–833.

[14] Sir George Shuckburgh, 'An Account of an Equatorial Instrument' [47], *Phil. Trans.* **83** (1793), footnote, p. 92.

[15] Smith, *Opticks* [4], p. 828.

[16] Hornsby, *Observations* [11], p. 20, Ref. 20. Thomas Bugge, of Copenhagen, left one of the earliest accounts of the Radcliffe Observatory and its instruments, 1777. See T. Bugge, 'Travel Diary, Aug/Dec, 1777' MS Kongelige Bibliotek, Copenhagen MS. *Ny Kgl, Saml. 377e* pp. 60–71.

[17] Shuckburgh, 'Description' [14], p. 92. On spirit levels, see Robert Hooke, *Some Animadversions on the First Part of Hevelius, his 'Machina Coelestis'* (London, 1674) p. 63.

[18] Bradley, *Observations* [13], p. ii.

[19] *Ibid.*, pp. iii–iv.

[20] Bradley, *Works* [3], p. 383.

[21] A. A. Rambaut, 'A note on the unpublished observations made at the Radcliffe Observatory, Oxford, between the years 1774 and 1838, with some results for the year 1774', *M.N.R.A.S.* **60**, 3 (Jan. 1900) 256–293.

[22] Smith, *Opticks* [4], p. 840. For the speed of the 'transit' method to take right ascensions, see Nicholas Bion, *Construction and Principal Uses of Mathematical Instruments*, translated by Edmund Stone (London, 1758) p. 278.

[23] For Maskelyne's techniques, see, T. H. Safford, 'Investigation of corrections to the Greenwich planetary observations, from 1762 to 1830', *Astronomical Papers Prepared for the Use of the American Ephemeris* **2** (1891) pp. 49–105.

[24] Bradley, *Works* [3], pp. 212, 222.

[25] Bradley, *Observations* [13], p. iii.

[26] Maskelyne, *Observations* [10], ii.

[27] Bradley, *Observations*, p. vi. Writing in 1898, shortly after the electric chronograph had rendered this 'eye and ear' method of observing transits obsolete, Simon Newcomb mentioned that an experienced observer could frequently estimate right ascension angles to within 1/10 s, S. Newcomb, *Popular astronomy* (London, 1898) p. 155.

[28] Thomas Hornsby, 'Notes and Instructions, Oxford, Dec. 1785', Manuscript in the Museum of the History of Science, Oxford, MS. *Radcliffe 16*. Also, Hornsby, *Observations* [11], p. 9. The effectiveness of Hornsby's technique was verified by Rambaut's reductions of the observations of 1774. Mean R.A. = 0s.0834.; Dec. = 1.62″. A. A. Rambaut, 'Notes on Observations' [21], pp. 277–278.

[29] Robert Hooke, *An Attempt to Prove the Motion of the Earth* (London, 1674) p. 7.

[30] *Ibid.*, p. 8.

[31] J. Picard (?), 'A Breviate of M. Picart's (sic.) ... Measure of the Earth', *Phil. Trans.* **10** (1675) 261–272.

[32] Hooke, *Motion of the Earth* [29]. p. 19. Hooke, *Animadversions* [17], pp. 13–15.

[33] Bradley, *Works* [3], pp. 100–101.

[34] Bradley, *Observations* [13], p. vii. Maskelyne, *Observations* [10], pp. viii–x, for collimating techniques. Howse, *Greenwich Observatory* [4], iii, pp. 63–64.

[35] Bradley, *Works* [3], pp. 194–195.

[36] James Bradley, 'A letter to Dr Halley giving account of a new discovered motion of the fixed stars', *Phil. Trans.* **35** (1728), p. 643.

[37] Bradley, *Works* [3], p. 98. viz 7 or 8″. The telescope field was 28″. Bradley, 'Aberration' [36], 642.

[38] Bradley, 'Aberration' [36], p. 643.

[39] Bradley, *Works* [3], p. 199.

[40] C. Huygens, *Horologium* (Hague, 1658). For an English translation by Ernest L. Edwards, see *Antiquarian Horology* **7** (Dec. 1970) 38–55. See also, Huygens, *Horologium Oscillatorium; sive de Motu Pendulorum ad Horologia* (Paris, 1673).

[41] N. Stephenson, *The Mathematical Compendium Collected out of the Notes and Papers of Sir Jonas Moore* (London, 1674) p. 110. Seconds pendulum of 39.2 in (Huygens); 39.45 (Brouncker and Rooke). *Artificial Clockmaker* [6], p. 81. Thomas Birch, *A History of the Royal Society of London*, i (London, 1756) pp. 500, 507, 509, 511.

[42] W. H. Gazeley, *Clock and watch escapements* (Princeton, 1956) p. 21.

[43] *Artificial Clockmaker* [6], p. 107. The Wadham College clock, Oxford, employed an anchor escapement, the original movement dating to c. 1670. C. F. C. Beeson, 'The Wadham College Clock', *Antiquarian Horology*, **2**, 3 (June, 1957) 47–50. Beeson discusses the provenance of the anchor, with special reference to the Wadham clock. Smith, *Horological Disquisitions on the Nature of Time* (London, 1694) p. 3.

[44] F. W. Britten, *Britten's Old Clocks and Watches*, edited by G.H. Baillie (London, 1955) p. 114.

[45] Howse, *Greenwich Observatory*, iii, p. 126.

[46] Derek Howse, 'The Tompion clocks at Greenwich and the dead beat escapement', Part 1, *Antiquarian Horology* **7**, 1 (Dec. 1970) 24–29.

[47] *Ibid.*, pp. 21–22. Birch, *Royal Society* [41], ii, pp. 340, 361, 388, 398.

[48] Britten, *Clocks and Watches* [44], pp. 114–116.

[49] H. T. Pledge, *Science since 1500* (London, 1939) reprinted (London, 1966), see p. 70 for the graph supplied by F. A. B. Ward.

[50] A. Cumming, *Elements of Clock and Watch Work* (London, 1766) paras. 332–346. Britten, *Clocks and Watches* [44], p. 116.

[51] George Graham, 'A Contrivance to Avoid the Irregularities in a Clock's Motion', Manuscript, Royal Society Library, MS. *R.B.C. 12. 739.*

[52] 'Greenwich in 1742' [4], 227.

[53] *Ibid.*, p. 227.

[54] P. A. Wayman, 'Notes on the history of the Dunsink Observatory, III; the Arnold Clocks', *The Irish Astronomical Journal* **10**, 8 (Dec. 1972).

[55] For an account of the ordering and transportation of a regulator and other instruments from London to Glasgow, see Correspondence between William Ruat and R. Simpson, Glasgow University Senate Archives, Faculty Minutes, 1754–1756.

[56] Maskelyne, *Observations* [10], p. vi.

[57] D. Howse, 'Tompion clocks at Greenwich' [46], i, pp. 24–25.

[58] Bradley, *Works* [3], p. 143. Hooke made a 'year clock' with a 14-ft pendulum, in 1669, see Birch, *Royal Society* [41], ii, p. 361.

[59] E. Beckett, (Lord Grimthorpe), *A Rudimentary Treatise on Clocks, Watches and Bells* (London, 1903) pp. 148–151.

[60] Maskelyne, *Observations* [10], p. vi.

[61] A slightly modified version of Ward's original graph, including recent developments in quartz crystal and caesium clocks, appears in F. A. B. Ward's *Time Measurement*, Science Museum (London, 1970) p. 8.

[62] John Flamsteed, *Historia Coelestis Britannica*, iii (London, 1725) pp. 138–140.

[63] Allan Chapman, 'Astronomia Practica; the principal instruments and their uses at the Royal Observatory, 1675–1775', *Vistas in Astronomy*, vol. 20, edited by A. and P. Beer (Oxford, 1976) pp. 141–156.

[64] Bradley, 'Nutation' [1], pp. 4–5.

[65] Bradley, *Works* [3], p. 382.

[66] 'Greenwich in 1742' [4], pp. 220–221.

[67] Maskelyne, *Observations* [10], p. viii.

[68] 'Greenwich in 1742' [4], p. 215.

[69] *Ibid.*, 217.

[70] *Ibid.*, 218.

[71] *Ibid.*, 219.

[72] *Ibid.*, 217.

[73] F. Baily, 'An Account of the Astronomical Observations made by Dr Halley at the Royal Observatory at Greenwich', *M.R.A.S.* **8** (1935) 169–190.

[74] Bradley, *Works* [3], p. 382.

[75] William Ludlam, 'Quadrantologia, or an Account of an Eighteen Inch Quadrant made by John Bird, 1771'. Manuscript in the Library of the Institute of Astronomy, University of Cambridge, para. 19.

[76] Bradley, *Works* [3], p. lv.

[77] *Ibid.*, pp. lv, lvi.

[78] *Ibid.*, p. liii.

[79] *Ibid.*, p. lv.

[80] Bradley, *Observations* [13], p. xiv.

[81] *Ibid.*, p. viii.

[82] Maskelyne, *Observations* [10], p. viii–x.

[83] John Bird, *The Method of Constructing Mural Quadrants* (London, 1768) pp. 16–18.

[84] Hornsby, *Observations* [11], pp. 68–69. For micrometer technique.

[85] Newton had suspected a pressure and temperature effect on refraction, and

advised Flamsteed to ascertain their quantities, but Flamsteed did not act upon the suggestion, E. W. Maunder, *A History of the Royal Observatory, Greenwich* (London, 1900), p. 57.

[86] See Bradley's post-1750 observation books at the R.G.O. Also, Bradley [13], *Observations*, p. iii. These strictures did not apply to the zenith sector observations, where the vertical disposition of the instrument eliminated refraction.

[87] J. Evans, *The Juvenile Tourist* (London, 1810) pp. 342–343.

[88] T. Bugge, 'Travel Diary' [16], p. 71. E. J. Stone, 'The Determination of the N.D.P., 1790, January 0, of Gamma Draconis from the Observations made at Oxford by Dr Hornsby', *M.N.R.AS.* **55**, 8 (June, 1895) 409. (See Appendix 3.) A. Chapman, 'Thomas Hornsby and the Radcliffe Observatory', in *Oxford Figures: 800 years of Oxford Mathematics*, J. Fauvel, R. Flood and R. Wilson (editors), Oxford University Press (Oxford, 1966 (forthcoming)).

[89] Bradley, *Observations* [11], p. 9.

[90] Bird, *Quadrants* [83], p. 27.

[91] John Bird, *The Method of Dividing Astronomical Instruments* (London, 1767) pp. 13–14.

[92] Hornsby, *Observations* [11], pp. 79–81.

[93] Stone, 'Determination of N.P.D.' [88], pp. 411–412.

[94] T. H. Safford, 'Investigations of Corrections to the Greenwich Planetary Observations from 1762–1830', *Astronomical Papers Prepared for the Use of the American Ephemeris* **2** (1891) 57.

[95] John Pond, 'On the Declination of the Principal Fixed Stars, together with a description of an Astronomical Circle . . .', *Phil. Trans.* **96** (1806) 424.

[96] Safford, 'Investigations', 62.

[97] *Ibid.*, p. 64.

[98] Rambaut, 'Note on Observations' [21], pp. 277–278. The reduced R.A. errors with the transit = 0.0834 s. See [28].

[99] *Ibid.*, pp. 277. Great tribute was paid to Bradley by F. W. Bessel, in *Fundamenta Astronomiae pro anno MDCCLV deducta ex Observationibus ... James Bradley* (Königsberg, 1818).

6   THE ACHIEVEMENTS OF EIGHTEENTH-CENTURY POSITIONAL ASTRONOMY

[1] James Bradley, 'A Letter to the Earl of Macclesfield, Concerning an Apparent Motion . . . of the Fixed Stars', *Phil. Trans.* **45** (1748) 1.

[2] James Bradley, 'A Letter to Dr Halley giving Account of a New Discovered Motion of the Fixed Stars', *Phil. Trans.* **35** (1728) 640.

[3] Isaac Newton, *Principia Mathematica* (London, 1687), Andrew Motte's translation (London, 1725), editor F. Cajori (Berkeley, 1962), Bk. 1, Prop. 66, Cor. 20. An original interpretation of Bradley's discovery of the Aberration is argued by John R. Fisher, 'James Bradley and the New Found Motion: The Origins, Development and Rectification of James Bradley's Hypothesis of the New Discovered Motion of the Fixed Stars', unpublished M.Sc dissertation, University of London, 1994.

[4] Bradley, 'Aberration' [2], pp. 646–647.

[5] Robert Hooke, *An Attempt to Prove the Motion of the Earth* (London, 1674) p. 7.

[6] Peter Horrebow, *Basis Astronomiae, sive Astronomiae pars Mechanica ...* (Copenhagen, 1735) p. 66.

[7] John Wallis, *Opera Mathematica*, iii (Oxford, 1699) p. 705.

[8] F. G. W. Struve, *Etudes d'astronomie stellaire* (St. Petersburg, 1847) p. 95. Peters' latest value for the aberration was 22″.481, p. 96.

[9] Bradley, 'Aberration' [2], p. 638.

[10] *Ibid.*, 660.

[11] Bradley, 'Nutation' [1], p. 9.

[12] *Ibid.*, pp. 10–23.

[13] *Ibid.* See tables pages 14, 27, for Nutation values for 1727–1745.

[14] *Ibid.*, pp. 13, 28.

[15] *Ibid.*, p. 26.

[16] *Ibid.*, p. 27.

[17] *Ibid.*, p. 4.

[18] *Ibid.*, p. 6.

[19] *Ibid.*, pp. 5–6.

[20] J. Richer, 'Observationes Astronomiques et Physiques faites en L'Isle de Caienne', (1672), *Mémoires de l'Académie Royale des Sciences depuis 1666, jusqu'à 1699*, 8, 1 (1729). Also, Edition 1736, p. 88. A ligne was $\frac{1}{12}$ Paris in., or 0.0888 English in.

[21] *Principia* [3], Bk. III, Prop. 20, Problem iv.

[22] J. Picard, and others, *The Measure of the Earth ... by Diverse Members of the Academy of Sciences at Paris*, translated by Richard Waller (London, 1687) p. 28.
N.B. This book was sold bound up as a supplement to Claude Perrault's *Memoir for a Natural History of Animals* (London, 1687).

[23] J. N. de L'Isle, 'A Proposal for the Measurement of the Earth in Russia, read at ... the Academy of Sciences of St Petersbourg, Jan. 21, 1737', translated by T. S., *Phil. Trans.* **40** (1737–1738) 33.

[24] J. Cassini, 'De la Grandeur de la Terre et de soi figure Par M. Cassini' *Mémoires de l'Académie Royale des Sciences* (Paris, 1718–1719) p. 245.

[25] *Principia*, Bk. III, Prop. 20, Problem IV, pp. 428–433.

[26] P. L. M. Maupertuis, 'La Figure de la terre determinée par Messieurs de l'Académie Royale de Sciences, Qui ont mesuré le Degré du Meridien au Cercle Polaire', *Histoire de l'Académie Royale des Sciences, Année MDCCXXXVII* (Paris, MDCCXL), pp. 389–461.

[27] *Ibid.*, p. 426

[28] *Ibid.*, pp. 408. 409. Mention of Graham's instruments. See also, J.A. Bennett, 'The English Quadrant in Europe: Instruments and the growth of consensus in Practical Astronomy', *J.H.A.* **xxiii** (1992) 1–14:5.

[29] *Ibid.*, p. 427. The exact dimensions of the Académiciens' surveyed triangle was 380 *toises*, 1 *pied*, 3 *pouces*, by 36 *toises*, 3 *pieds*, 6 *pouces*, 6½ *lignes*.

[30] *Ibid.*, p. 426.

[31] *Ibid.*, p. 457.

[32] *Ibid.*, p. 458.

[33] *Ibid.*, p. 408.

[34] *Ibid.*, p. 465. Table of pendulum lengths, p. 466.

[35] *Ibid.*, p. 426.

[36] *Ibid.*, p. 463..

[37] Bradley, 'Nutation' [1], pp. 11–12.

[38] Robert Grant, *A History of Physical Astronomy* (London, 1852) p. 158.

[39] Nevil Maskelyne, 'An Account of Obersvations made on Schehallion for Finding its Attraction', *Phil. Trans.* **65** (1775) 500.

[40] *Ibid.*, pp. 502, 509–511.

[41] *Ibid.*, pp. 515–517. For Maskelyne's reversing and adjusting of the sector, see p. 518.

[42] *Ibid.*, p. 531.

[43] *Ibid.*, pp. 529–530.

[44] *Ibid.*, p. 533.

[45] Charles Hutton, 'An Account of the Calculations made from the Survey and Measures of Schehallion', *Phil. Trans.* **68** (1778) 781–784. Also, John Playfair, 'An Account of a Lithological Survey of Schehallion', *Phil. Trans.* **101** (1811), see p. 376, for mean density.

[46] Henry Cavendish, 'Experiments to Prove the Density of the Earth', *Phil. Trans.* **88** (1798) 469–526. *vide*, 521–522. The modern density value is 5.517.

[47] Hutton, 'Account' [45], p. 784.

[48] Tycho's 1592 catalogue contained 777 stars, which were made up to 1000. J. L. E. Dreyer, *Tycho Brahe*, (1890) and (New York, 1963) p. 227. Flamsteed's catalogue was based on some 4500 stars; E. G. Forbes *Greenwich Observatory*, i, 'Origins and early history' (London, 1975) p. 49. For the estimated accuracy of Flamsteed's arc, see the present book, Chapter 11.

[49] D. H. Sadler, *Man is not lost* (London, 1968) pp. 7–8, 12.

[50] Edmund Halley, *Astronomical Tables, with Precepts in both English and Latin* (London, 1752), see 'Preface' and 'Lunae Meridianae'. for Halley's instruments and techniques in 1678, see; E. Halley, *Catalogus Stellarum Australium, sive Supplementum Catalogi Tychoni* (London, 1769), Introduction.

[51] Tobius Mayer, *Theoria Lunae juxta Systema Newtonianum* (London, 1767).

[52] Grant, *Physical Astronomy* [38], p. 46.

[53] H. Woolf, *The Transits of Venus* (Princeton, 1959) pp. 16–22.

[54] *Ibid.*, pp. 190–197, for reductions.

7   THE PRECISION GRADUATION OF FULL CIRCLES

[1] John Pond, 'On the Declinations of the Principal Fixed Stars, together with a Description of an Astronomical Circle ...' *Philosophical Transactions* **96** (1806) 423.

[2] Abraham Rees, *The Cyclopaedia, or Universal Dictionary of Arts Sciences and Literature*, xvi (London, 1819), see article 'Graduation' by W. Pearson. Considering the reduction values for Tycho's observations, discussed in Chapter II, one might regard the 4' accruacy for a Tychonic observation, cited

in H.T. Pledge, *Science since 1500* (1939) and London (1966) p. 291, to be over-cautious. See also Sir George Shuckburgh, 'An Account of an Equatorial Instrument', *Phil. Trans.* **83** (1793) 70.

[3] Shuckburgh, 'Account' [2], pp. 93–94.

[4] *Miscellanea Berolinensia ad Incrementum Scientiarum*, ii (1728) pp. 276–278. The *Miscellanea* was a seven-volume publication of the Histoire de l'Académie Royale des Sciences et des belles-lettres de Berlin, issued between 1710–1743.

[5] M. F. d'A, duc du Chaulnes, *Nouvelle Méthode pour Diviser les Instruments de Mathématique et d'Astronomie* (Paris, 1768) pp. 33–35.

[6] Rees, *Cyclopaedia*, xvi, article 'Graduation', [2] Sig. 3Y3v. Christopher Clavius, *Opera Mathematici . . .* , ii (Mainz, 1611) pp. 14 and 33.

[7] Du Chaulnes, *Nouvelle Méthode* [5], pp. 35–37.

[8] David Brewster, *The Edinburgh Encyclopaedia*, x (Edinburgh, 1830) article 'Graduation', p. 379.

[9] Rees, *Cyclopaedia*, xvi, article 'Graduation', [2] Sig. 3Y4r. Edward Troughton, 'An Account of a Method of Dividing Astronomical Instruments by Ocular Inspection . . .' *Phil. Trans.* **99** (1809) p. 113. *Edinburgh Encyclopaedia*, x, p. 370.

[10] *Edinburgh Encyclopaedia*, x, p. 370.

[11] Rees, *Cyclopaedia*, xvi, article 'Graduation', Sig. 3Y4r.

[12] Shuckburgh, 'Description' pp. 97 and 100, footnotes. Troughton's 'Dividing' p. 113. The equatorial was re-graduated by Messrs Troughton and Simms, 1860. Derek Howse, *Greenwich Observatory iii*, 'The buildings and instruments' (London, 1975), p. 86.

[13] Troughton, 'Dividing' [9], p. 114.

[14] Rees, *Cyclopaedia*, xvi, article 'Graduation', Sig. 3Y4r.

[15] Shuckburgh, 'Description' [2], pp. 95–102.

[16] William Lax, 'On a Method of Examining the Divisions of Astronomical Instruments', *Phil. Trans.* **99** (1808) p. 232.

[17] *Edinburgh Encyclopaedia*, x, p. 370.

[18] Troughton, 'Dividing' [9], p. 133.

[19] *Ibid.*, p. 115.

[20] *Ibid.*, p. 106.

[21] *Ibid.*, p. 116.

[22] *Ibid.*, p. 120. To divide the six-foot Greenwich circle, Troughton used four microscopes; two at 180° and two at 120° to check eccentricity. Rees, *Cyclopaedia*, xvi, article 'Graduation', Sig. 3Y4r. v.

[23] Troughton, 'Dividing' [9], p. 126.

[24] *Ibid.*, p. 128.

[25] *Ibid.*, p. 127.

[26] *Ibid.*, p. 114. See also, William Roy, 'An account of the Trigonometrical Operations whereby the Distance between the Meridians of the Royal Observatories of Greenwich and Paris has been Determined', *Phil. Trans.* **80** (1790) 148.

[27] Troughton, 'Dividing' [9], p. 133, footnote.

[28] *Ibid.*, pp. 141–142.

[29] *Ibid.*, pp. 133–134.
[30] E. W. Taylor, J. S. Wilson and P. D. Scott-Maxwell, *At the Sign of the Orrery; the origins of the firm of Cooke, Troughton and Simms Ltd.* (York, 1960) p. 29.
[31] Thomas Jones, letter to Edward Troughton, 15/7/1813, printed in *Edinburgh Encyclopaedia*, x, p. 382.
[32] Henry Cavendish, 'On an Improvement in the Manner of Dividing Astronomical Instruments', *Phil. Trans.* **99** (1809) p. 221. *Edinburgh Encyclopaedia*, x, p. 383.
[33] Rees, *Cyclopaedia*, xvi, article 'Graduation', on Lax's method.
[34] Henry Kater, 'An Improved Method of Dividing Astronomical Circles', *Phil. Trans.* **104** (1814) p. 419. *Edinburgh Encyclopaedia*, x, pp. 382–384. Rees, *Cyclopaedia*, xvi, article 'Graduation', Sig. 3 Y4.
[35] The fitting of a new counterpoise to Hornsby's quadrant at Oxford caused a new error in the readings. Thomas Hornsby *Observations of the Rev. Thomas Hornsby D.D.,* ... Edited by H. Knox-Shaw, J. Jackson and W. Robinson (London, 1935) p. 80.
[36] Bird disliked achromatic glasses in quadrants, believing their weight caused distortion. R. T. Gunther, *Early Science in Oxford*, ii (Oxford, 1923) p. 319. Achromatic glasses costing £4-4-0 per pair were fitted to the Oxford quadrants, *Ibid.*, p. 320. Their use in circular instruments was general by 1790; see Shuckburgh's 'Account'. *Phil. Trans.* **83** (1793) p. 103.
[37] Ramsden was also attributed with the introduction of the conical beam into chemical balance design; J. T. Stock, *Development of the Chemical Balance* (London, 1964) p. 13. Though Ramsden was the first to use conical supports systematically, he did not invent them. They were commonplace on transit instruments before 1750.
[38] Thomas Bugge, *Observationes Astronomicae* (Copenhagen 1784) pp. liii–lvi. Tobias Mayer, *Tabulae Motuum Solis et Lunae, Novae et Correctae* (London, 1770), see 'Methodus Longitudinum'. J. C. Borda, *Description et usage du cercle de réflexion*, 1787 (Paris, 1816) p. 7. Also, Edward Troughton, 'An Account of the Repeating Circle, and the Altitude and Azimuth Instrument', *M.R.A.S.* **1** (1822) p. 33.
[39] Both Wollaston and Troughton attributed the micrometer microscope to Ramsden; Francis Wollaston, 'Description of a Transit Circle', *Phil. Trans.* **83** (1793) 133. Troughton, 'Dividing' [9], p. 114. Ramsden fitted micrometer microscopes both to General Roy's theodolite (1787), and to Shuckburgh's equatorial (1793), now in the Science Museum, South Kensington.
[40] W. Roy, 'Trigonometrical Operations' [26], pp. 148–149.
[41] *Ibid.*, p. 219. Also, C. C. Close, *The Early Years of the Ordnance Survey* (1926) and (Newton Abbot, 1969) p. 22.
[42] *Ibid.*, p. 15.
[43] D. Howse, *Greenwich Observatory* [12], iii, p. 88.
[44] Nevil Maskelyne to the Royal Society, letter, 14/1/1781, Royal Society Library, MS. *GH. 120.*
[45] Howse, *Greenwich Observatory* [12], iii, p. 87.
[46] William Pearson, *Practical Astronomy*, ii (London, 1829) p. 518.

[47] George Biddell Airy, Address to the Board of Visitors, Greenwich, 18/10/1858.

[48] Pearson, *Practical Astronomy* [46], ii, pp. 413–423; account of the Palermo circle. See also, the *Penny Cyclopaedia*, vii (London, 1837), article 'Circle', p. 187.

[49] Pearson, *Practical Astronomy* [46], ii, p. 423.

[50] J. Piazzi, *Praecipuarum Stellarum Inerrantium Positiones Mediae Ineunte Seculo XIX* (Palermo, 1814) see engraving p. 1. Also J. Piazzi, *Resultati delle Osservazioni della Nuova Stella* (Palermo, 1801).

[51] Even by 1837, there was no full description; *Penny Cyclopaedia*, vii (London, 1837) article 'Circle', p. 194, but the circle's performance was known from Dr J. Brinkley's 'Observationes made at Trinity College, Dublin, with an Astronomical Circle Eight Feet in Diameter', *Transactions of the Royal Irish Academy*, **13** (1815) 36–41, from a mean of 20 observations, the error was $\frac{1}{2}''$. Also Anita McConnell, 'From Craft Workshops to Big Business — The London Scientific Instrument Trade's Response to Increasing Demand, 1750–1820', *The London Journal*, **19** I (1994) 36–53; 46.

[52] John Aiken, *General Biography*, **8** (London, 1813) 454. Ramsden is said to have employed 'near sixty' workmen. Much of the information in the 'Ramsden' biography was supplied by the Rev. L. Dutens, who claimed in the article to have known Ramsden personally.

[53] Pearson, *Practical Astronomy* [46], ii, p. 429. See the De Bruhl circle, and p. 518, for the Coimbra Equatorial.

[54] J. Pond, ' … Description of an Astronomical Circle' [1], p. 431. From his coordinates, Pond was observing from Westbury-sub-Mendip, near Wells. I am indebted to Mr Andrew Murray F.R.A.S. for this information.

[55] *Ibid.*, pp. 423–424. For Troughton's Armagh Equatorial: J. A. Bennett *Church, State, and Astronomy in Ireland: 200 Years of the Armagh Observatory* (Belfast, 1990) p. 42. Also, Anita McConnell, *Instrument Makers to the World. A History of Cooke, Troughton & Simms*, (York, 1992) p. 10.

[56] Howse, *Greenwich Observatory* [12], iii, p. 28.

[57] *Penny Cyclopaedia*, vii, article 'Circle' [48], pp. 188–189.

[58] Pearson, *Practical Astronomy* [46], ii, p. 474. Howse, *Greenwich Observatory* [12], iii, p. 26. John Pond, *Astronomical Observations made at the Royal Observatory, Greenwich, MDCCXI* (London, 1812) pp. 234–236, 240. Pond thoroughly examined the Bird quadrant with the new circle, finding most of its 8–10″ error to be within 20° of the zenith. Single observations showed 3–5″ elsewhere, though its mean sequence of observations corresponded well with the circle.

[59] R. Sheepshanks and G. B. Airy, 'On the Figure of the Mural Circle at the Observatory of the Cape of Good Hope', *M.R.A.S.* **5** (1833) 325–326.

[60] Pearson, *Practical Astronomy* [12], ii, p. 475.

[61] Howse, *Greenwich Observatory*, iii, p. 29. J. Sheepshanks, 'An Account of the Cape Mural Circle', *M.N.R.A.S.* **2** (1832) 94.

[62] Pearson, *Practical Astronomy* [12], ii, p. 423. See tables, p. 483.

[63] F. Wollaston, 'Transit Circle' [39], pp. 133–134, 136–140.

[64] F. Wollaston, *Fasciculus Astronomicus* (London, 1800) Chapter 1, (pt. 1), pp.

10–19; (pt. 2), pp. 65–68. Methods of meridian finding.

[65] Pearson, *Practical Astronomy* [12], ii, pp. 402–410.

[66] *Ibid.*, pp. 407–409.

[67] *Memoirs of the Royal Astronomical Society* **9** (1836) 287. Footnote.

[68] Pearson, *Practical Astronomy* [12], ii, pp. 475–476.

[69] Reichenbach's circles were 'not … to be met with in this country', *Penny Cyclopaedia*, vii (London, 1837) article 'Circle' [48], p. 194. A. Chapman, 'The Astronomical Revolution', in *Möbius and his band, Mathematics and Astronomy in Nineteenth-century Germany* (Oxford, 1993) pp. 34–77, p. 68.

[70] G. B. Airy, *Astronomical, Magnetical and Meteorological Observations made at the Royal Greenwich Observatory in the year 1852* (London, 1854), Appendix II, p. 16. W. M. Witchell, 'The story of the Greenwich Transit Circle', *Occasional Notices of the Royal Astronomical Society* **14**, 2 (Dec. 1952) pp. 21–40.

[71] Airy, *Astronomical Observations 1852* [70], p. 17, and p. 21 for error table.

[72] Howse, *Greenwich Observatory* [12], iii, p. 44.

[73] W. M. Witchell, 'Greenwich Transit Circle' [70], p. 25. Simon Schaffer, 'Astronomers Mark Time: discipline and the personal Equation', *Science in Context*, **2**, I (1988) 115–145.

8   DIVIDING BY MACHINE

[1] William Simms, 'On a Self-Acting Circular Dividing Engine', *M.R.A.S.* **15** (1846) 83.

[2] David Brewster (editor), *The Edinburgh Encyclopaedia*, x (Edinburgh, 1830) article 'Graduation', p. 349. John Flamsteed, letter, 26/9/1679, 'Foul Observations Book', R.G.O. Library MS. *Fl. 1/188*.

[3] Robert Hooke, *Some Animadversions on the First Part of Hevelius, his 'Machina Coelestis'* (London, 1674) p. 14.

[4] *Edinburgh Encyclopaedia*, x (1830) p. 349. Thomas Bugge saw a 6-in. dividing plate in Dr Demainbray's collection in 1777. See, T. Bugge, 'Travel Diary, Aug/Dec 1777', MS. Deposited in the Kongelige Bibliotek, Copenhagen, *MS. Ny Kg Saml. 377c*. p. 42 left.

[5] R. S. Woodbury, *History of the Gear-Cutting Engine* (Cambridge, Mass., 1958) pp. iii, 45–46. John Hadley, 'Description of a New Instrument for Taking Angles', *Phil. Trans.* **37** (1731) 147. See also *Phil. Trans.* **37** (1732) 341.

[6] Robert Hooke, *The Diary of Robert Hooke, 1672–1680*, edited by H. W. Robinson and W. Adams (London, 1935), p. 5, entry 16/8/1672; p. 34, 8/3/1673; p. 35, 20/3/1673; p. 100, 2/5/1675, etc. Also, Woodbury [5], p. 46. Thomas Reid, *A Treatise on Clock and Watchmaking, Theoretical and Practical* (Edinburgh, 1826) p. 284; says Hooke devised an engine in 1655, making the French jealous. William Derham, *The Artificial Clockmaker* (London, 1696); in his preface, Derham gives priority to Hooke.

[7] K. R. Gilbert, *The Machine Tool Collection* (London, 1966), Item 170, p. 74, plate 18. This machine, attributed to Humphrey Marsh de Highworth, was dated from a calendar scale engraved beneath its plate. It would

be interesting to construct a more exact pedigree for this engine, although the absence of alternative information makes this impossible. T.R. Crom, in his *Horological Wheel Cutting Engines, 1700–1900* (Gainsville, 1970) pp. 84–85, mentions the dating of the discarded Gunter's scale on the underside of the dividing plate, although he reserves his opinion as to whether the engine and scale were close contemporaries, or whether the scale was already old when it came to be incorporated into the engine. Yet as worked platten brass, in sheets over a foot in diameter, was expensive in the seventeenth century, it is unlikely that even a discarded piece would have been left unused for long. It is my opinion, therefore, that the engine was most probably constructed in the 1670s.

[8] Nicholas Bion, *Construction and Principal Uses of Mathematical Instruments*, translated by Edmund Stone (London, 1758) pp. 90–91.

[9] E. W. Taylor, 'The Evolution of the Dividing Engine', *Engineering*, Sept. 1 (1944) 164–166. Article reprinted from the *Empire Survey Review* (April, 1944). Taylor specifies nine requirements for a successful engine.

[10] Hooke, *Animadversions* [3], pp. 48–53.

[11] Richard Waller, *The Posthumous Works of Robert Hooke* (London, 1705).

[12] William Derham, *The Philosophical Experiments and Observations of Robert Hooke, published by W. Derham* (London, 1726).

[13] Reid, *Treatise* [6], pp. 284–285.

[14] John Smeaton, 'On the Graduation of Astronomical Instruments', *Phil. Trans.* **76** (1786) 19–20.

[15] A. Thiout, *Traité de horologerie* (Paris, 1741) pp. 53–55: Vol. II. plate 23.

[16] Smeaton, 'Graduation' [14], p. 26.

[17] Edward Troughton, 'An Acount of a Method of Dividing Astronomical Instruments by Ocular Inspection', *Phil. Trans.* **99** (1809) 112.

[18] Smeaton, 'Graduation' [14], pp. 29 Footnote, 81.

[19] J. R. M. Setchell, 'Henry Hindley and Son, Clockmakers of York', University of Oxford B.Litt. Thesis (1971), p. 96.

[20] Smeaton, 'Graduation' [14], p. 20.

[21] Setchell [19], p. 125. Troughton, 'Dividing' [17], p. 128.

[22] John Smeaton, 'Machine Letters', ii, Manuscript volume in the library of the Institution of Civil Engineers, *Accession No. 62 (o44)*. Letter, J. Smeaton to E. Nairne, 1/3/1785, pp. 114–115.

[23] Smeaton, 'Graduation' [14], p. 22. I have not been able to find any evidence to suggest that Hindley submitted his engine for an official reward. Smeaton does not mention it, nor does his name appear in Eric G. Forbes' 'Index of Board of Longitude Papers at the Royal Greenwich Observatory' part 1, *J.H.A.* **12** 2 (Aug. 1970) 169–179.

[24] Smeaton, 'Machine Letters' [22], ii, Letter, 1/3/1785.

[25] Smeaton, 'Graduation' [14], p. 30. Setchell [19], p. 130.

[26] Smeaton, 'Graduation' [14], p. 31. Smeaton recommended 1440 teeth.

[27] R. J. Law, 'Henry Hindley of York', *Antiquarian Horology*, vii (June, 1971)–(Sept. 1972), p. 206. R. Davies, *A Walk Through the City of York* (London, 1880) pp. 22–23.

[28] J. Browne, *Guide to York Minster* (York, 1864). Setchell [19], p. 35.

[29] J. R. M. Setchell, 'The Friendship of John Smeaton, F.R.S., with Henry Hindley, Instrument and Clockmaker of York, and the Development of Equatorial Mounting Telescopes', *Notes and Records* **25** (1970) 79.

[30] John Holmes, *A Short Narrative of the Genius, Life and Works of the Late Mr John Smeaton, Civil Engineer, F.R.S.* (London, 1793) pp 1–16.

[31] Samuel Smiles, *Lives of the Engineers*, ii (London, 1862) p. 9. See also, John Smeaton, in *D.S.B.*

[32] John Stancliffe is said to have built his own dividing engine in 1788, see *Edinburgh Encyclopaedia*, x (Edinburgh, 1830) article 'Graduation', p. 353. In 1809, a 'John Stancliffe' acted as referee for James Allan's new prizewinning dividing engine, submitted to the Society of Arts; *Transactions of the Society of Arts, 1810* (London, 1811) pp. 179–184. I have checked the spelling of the name 'Stancliffe' in the manuscripts of the Society. Whether this Stancliffe was the same Stancliffe who had worked for Hindley and Ramsden, cannot be proved at this stage, although the connection is plausible. If the referee was the original John Stancliffe, he must have been very advanced in years by 1809. It is possible that Stancliffe the referee was the son of the original mechanician. I have looked in vain for an obituary for John Stancliffe *Mechanician* in the *Gentleman's Magazine*, between 1809 and 1825, the only man of that name to be recorded being a Yorkshire clothier who died in 1814. In 1992, new material on Stancliffe was published by John Brooks, 'The Circular Dividing Engine: Development in England 1739–1843', *Annals of Science* **49** (1992) 101–135, see Appendix I, pp. 131–132. Mr Brooks provides an excellent and scholarly account of the history of the Dividing Engine in his paper.

[33] Hindley's method worked 'wholly by contact'; Smeaton, 'Graduation' [14], p. 24.

[34] M. F. d'A. duc du Chaulnes, *Novelle Méthode pour Diviser les Instruments de Mathématique et d'Astronomie* (Paris, 1768) p. 15. A form of 'micrometre' is mentioned, but as it was cranked by a handle, it was clearly not a precision device. A more explicit if somewhat rough 'micrometre' screw on the linear engine is shown pp. 19–20.

[35] *Ibid.*, p. 16.

[36] *Ibid.*, pp. 16–17. The 'Graduation' article in the *Edinburgh Encyclopaedia*, x [32], p. 352, says du Chaulnes did not use the endless screw.

[37] Jesse Ramsden, *Description of an Engine for Dividing Mathematical Instruments* (London, 1777), p. 11.

[38] *Nouvelle Méthode* [34], pp. 7–10, Fig. 46.

[39] *Ibid.*, pp. 16–17, Plate V.

[40] *Ibid.*, see scale Plate V. One Pouce or French inch equals 1.0658 English inches, *Encyclopaedia Britannica* 24, 9th Edition (London, 1888), article 'Weights and Measures', p. 489.

[41] *Edinburgh Encyclopaedia*, x [2] (1830) p. 352.

[42] *Ibid.*, p. 352.

[43] *Ibid.*, p. 353. Setchell [19], p. 124.

[44] *Edinburgh Encyclopaedia*, x [2] p. 353.

[45] Smeaton, 'Graduation' [14], p. 18. Also, J. E. Watkins, 'The Ramsden Dividing Engine', *Annual Report ... of the Board of Regents of the Smith-*

sonian Institution to July 1890 (Washington, 1891) pp. 721–739.

[46] J. Ramsden, *Description* [37]; see Maskelyne's Preface.

[47] H. Quill, *John Harrison, the Man Who Found Longitude* (London, 1966) p. 203.

[48] *Dictionary of National Biography*. The article on Ramsden says that his engine was used to divide over 1000 sextants. See also, A. Chapman, 'Scientific Instruments and Industrial Innovation: The Achievement of Jesse Ramsden', in, *Making Instruments Count*, R. G. W. Anderson, J. A. Bennett and W. F. Ryan (editors), Variorum (Cambridge, 1993) pp. 418–430.

[49] Ramsden, *Description* [37]; Preface. Although the reward is mentioned in 1777, I have been unable to discover whether it was paid in that year or earlier. It was probably paid in 1776, the date on Maskelyne's Preface. The Ramsden award is not mentioned in Dr Eric G. Forbes' 'Index to the Board of Longitude Papers' [23], nor in the *D.N.B.* or *D.S.B.* Prof. E.G.R. Taylor's *The Mathematical Practitioners of Hanoverian England* (Cambridge, 1966) p. 244, seems misleading on the matter. She states that Ramsden got his £615 in 1773, but as this is one year before Bird's approval of a sextant divided upon it, two years before his official apprentice, and four years before the publication of the *Description* I believe the statement to be incorrect. It is unlikely that the prizewinning engine was operational before 1774. In her article, moreover, Prof. Taylor dates the *Description* incorrectly as 1771, as opposed to 1777, per the title page.

[50] Ramsden, *Description* [37], p. 1.

[51] *Ibid.*, pp. 8–9.

[52] *Ibid.*, p. 9.

[53] *Ibid.*, pp. 9–10. Brooks, 'The Circular Dividing Engine' [32] pp. 108, 133–135.

[54] *Ibid.*, p. 13–14. C. Singer, E. J. Holmyard, A. R. Hall and T. I. Williams (editors), *A History of Technology*, iv (Oxford, 1958) p. 387. Charles Holtzapffel, *Turning and Mechanical Manipulation*, ii (London, 1846) p. 635, 640.

[55] Jesse Ramsden, *Description of an Engine for Dividing Straight Lines* (London, 1779) pp. 13–16.

[56] Singer and Holmyard, iv [54], p. 388.

[57] Ramsden, *Description* [37], p. 11.

[58] *Ibid.*, see account of the cutter. Also, *Edinburgh Encyclopaedia*, x (1830) [32], p. 353.

[59] Smeaton, 'Graduation' [14], p. 18.

[60] Ramsden, *Description* [37], see Preface.

[61] *Edinburgh Encyclopaedia*, x (1830) [2], p. 353.

[62] H. C. King, *History of the Telescope* (London, 1955) p. 169.

[63] E. W. Taylor, J. S. Wilson and P. D. Scott-Maxwell, *At the Sign of the Orrery* (York, 1960) pp. 25–27.

[64] Troughton, 'Dividing' [17], p. 106.

[65] *Edinburgh Encyclopaedia*, x (1830) [2], p. 353.

[66] *Ibid.*, p. 353. Anita McConnell, *Instrument Makers to the World, A History of Cooke, Troughton & Simms* (York, 1992) pp. 6–23.

[67] *Ibid.*, p. 353.

[68] It is possible that Ramsden played some part in the design of this machine, for he was related to the Dollonds by marriage. In 1765, he married Sarah Dollond, and as part of the dowry received a share in the achromatic lens patent; see *D.N.B.* under Ramsden.

[69] Thomas Bugge, 'Travel Diary' [4], p. 42 left.

[70] *Sign of the Orrery* [63], p. 25.

[71] A. W. Skempton and Joyce Brown, 'John and Edward Troughton, Mathematical Instrument Makers', *Notes and Records* **27** 2 (Feb. 1973) 240. Also, an instrument box label for 'J. and E. Troughton' exists, bearing the pencilled date '1808, 14 Feb. .'. Though this does not prove when the label was printed, its engraving style seems early nineteenth century; H. R. Calvert, *Scientific Trade Cards in the Science Museum* (London, 1971) plate 50, catalogue no. 404. McConnell, *Instrument Makers to the World* [66], pp. 6–7.

[72] Troughton to Brewster, letter, published in *Edinburgh Encyclopaedia*, x (1830) [2] p. 353.

[73] D. Baxandall, 'The Circular Dividing Engine of Edward Troughton, 1793', *Transactions of the Optical Society* **25** 3 (1923–1924) 138–139.

[74] *Edinburgh Encyclopaedia*, x (1830) [2] pp. 354–355.

[75] *Ibid.*, pp. 353, 355. Also Rees' *Cyclopaedia*, xvi (1819), article 'Graduation'.

[76] *Edinburgh Encyclopaedia*, x (1830) [32] pp. 355–357.

[77] *Ibid.*, p. 357.

[78] George Adams, *Instructions for the Use of Hadley's Quadrant, containing the Principles on which that Admirable Instrument is Constructed, with a Description and Use of the Nonius Divisions*; undated tract, *c.* 1760, included in the *Radcliffe Tracts* **77** 7, Museum of the History of Science, Oxford. Troughton, 'Dividing' [17], p. 133. M. A. Pictet, *Voyages de Trois Mois en Angleterre 1801* (Geneva, 1802) pp. 170–171. Pictet bought a Troughton 'snuff box' sextant of 1½-in radius.

[79] *Sign of the Orrery* [63] p. 35.

[80] *Ibid.*, p. 35.

[81] William Simms, 'On a Self Acting Circular Dividing Engine', *M.R.A.S.* **15** (1846) 83.

[82] *Ibid.*, pp. 86, 90.

[83] *Ibid.*, pp. 85–90.

[84] *Ibid.*, p. 86.

[85] See Baxandall's article [73].

[86] *Sign of the Orrery* [63], p. 35.

[87] Troughton, 'Dividing' [17], p. 133. Eleanor Menim's *Transit Circle, The Story of William Simms 1793–1760*, W. Sessions (York, undated, 1993?) provides useful new material about Simms's life, largely from family letters, though it is a somewhat sprawling biography which does *not* discuss the technical aspects of Simms's work.

[88] G. B. Airy, *Astronomical, Magnetical and Meteorological Observations made at the Royal Greenwich Observatory in the year 1852* (London, 1854), see Appendix II, p. 17.

[89] *Ibid.*, p. 19.

[90] The dividing machine, using microscopes and micrometers, was also used to

engrave fine test plates for microscopists, and F. A. Nobert perfected such a machine in the 1840s. See Gerard L'E. Turner and Savile Bradbury, 'An electron microscopical examination of Nobert's finest test-plate of twenty bands', *Journal of the Royal Microscopical Society* **85** 4 (Aug. 1966) 435–447. The Hungarian physicist Anyos Jedlik also devised a similar engine in *c.* 1853. See, Laszlo Opitz, 'Automatic dividing engine by Anyos Jedlik', (Jedlik Anyos automatagepe) *Technikatörteneti Szemle*, **VII** (1973) 125–140.

9 THE LONDON SCIENTIFIC INSTRUMENT-MAKING TRADE

[1] H. R. Calvert, *Scientific Trade Cards in the Science Museum* (London, 1971), Plate 9.

[2] Gerard L'E. Turner and T. H. Levere, *Van Marum's Scientific Instruments in Teyler's Museum* (being Vol IV in the series *Martinus Van Marum. Life and Work*, E. Lefebvre and J. G. de Bruijn (editors)), Noordhof International (Leyden, 1973) pp. 21–23. One of the best analyses of the structure and significance of the London trade is by Anita McConnell, 'From Craft Workshop to Big Business — The London Scientific Instrument Trade's Response to Increasing Demand, 1750–1820, *London Journal*, **19**, 1 (1994) pp. 36–53.

[3] For a study in the rise of the private patron, especially in the arts, see M. Foss, *The Age of Patronage: the Arts and Society 1660–1750* (London, 1971).

[4] Much of the vigour of the period is captured in its cheap literature, especially following the repeal of the Licensing Act, 1695; see Phillip Pinkus, *Grub Street Stripped Bare* (London, 1968).

[5] E. G. R. Taylor, *The Mathematical Practitioners of Tudor and Stuart England* (Cambridge, 1968), biography 361. Also, see *Dictionary of National Biography* for John Bird.

[6] Abraham Rees, *The Cyclopaedia, or Universal Dictionary of Arts, Sciences and Literature* xxxvii (London, 1819). See 'Watch-maker'.

[7] M. Mortimer, *The Universal Director* (London, 1763) p. 54.

[8] R. T. Gunther, *Early Science in Oxford*, ii (Oxford, 1923) pp. 320–322. Gunther does not give the location of the manuscript originals of these letters. They do not appear to have been catalogued amongst the Radcliffe Papers, neither in the Museum of the History of Science, nor in the Bodleian Library, Oxford.

[9] Worshipful Company of Clockmakers, 'Register of Freemen and Apprentices', Guildhall Library, London. *MS. 3939.*

[10] Grocer's Company, 'Register of Freemen and Apprentices', Guildhall Library, London. *MS. II. 598/I.*

[11] Grocer's Company 'Register', Entry 17/1/1734, for John Troughton, *MS. 11. 598/2.*

[12] Grocer's Company 'Register', Entry 2/12/1773, Edward Troughton, *MS. 11. 598 & TCMR.*

[13] J. Campbell, *The London Tradesman* (London, 1747) p. 336.

[14] John Burnett, *A History of the Cost of Living* (1969) p. 162.

[15] Joyce Brown, 'Guild Organisation and the Instrument-Making Trade, 1550–1830; The Grocers' and Clockmakers' Companies', *Annals of Science* **36** (1979) 1–34. Also, Joyce Brown, *Mathematical Instrument Makers in the Grocers' Company 1688–1800* (London, 1979).

[16] *The London Tradesman*, p. 254.

[17] *Ibid.*, p. 331, 339.

[18] 'Clockmaker's Workshop Notebook', late seventeenth century, and possibly the work of Samuel Watson. In the collection of the Worshipful Company of Clockmakers, Guildhall Library, London, *MS. 6619/1*, pp. 17–20 and p. 51 v.

[19] *Ibid.*, p. 20.

[20] David Brewster, *The Edinburgh Encyclopaedia*, x (Edinburgh, 1830), see article 'Graduation', p. 351.

[21] Joyce Brown, 'Guild Organisation and the Instrument-Making Trade' [15]. See also, H. C. King, *A History of the Telescope* (London, 1955) p. 144. The way in which E. Scarlett and J. Mann, master opticians, subcontracted the components of Chester Moor Hall's achromatic lens to be ground by the otherwise obscure G. Bass indicates the degree to which signed work must have been performed by anonymous artisans.

[22] G. L'E. Turner, 'James Short, F.R.S., and his contribution to the construction of reflecting telescopes', *Notes and Records* **24** (June, 1969) 91–108.

[23] Humphrey Quill, *John Harrison, the Man Who Found Longitude* (London, 1966) pp. 1–8.

[24] For an account of Harrison's struggle to extract his £20 000 prize, see Quill's *John Harrison*, pp. 187–224.

[25] Contracts amounting to £1000 were paid to re-equip the Royal Observatory between 1742 and 1748; James Bradley, *Miscellaneous Works of the Rev. James Bradley, D.D.*, edited by S. P. Rigaud (Oxford, 1832) p. lxxiv.

[26] Bradley, *Works* [25], p. lxxiv. R. T. Gunther, *Early Science in Oxford*, ii (Oxford, 1923) p. 320.

[27] Gunther [26], p. 320.

[28] Bird agreed to supply two quadrants of 8-ft radius; a transit of 8 ft; an equatorial sector of 5 ft; a zenith sector of 12 ft, all to be ready by January 1st 1776. See the 'Articles of Agreement' between Bird and the Vice Chancellor of Oxford, March 2nd 1771. Museum of the History of Science, Oxford, *Radcliffe MS. 29*. Ivor Guest, *Doctor John Radcliffe and his Trust* (Radcliffe Trust, 1993) 255 ff.

[29] Gerald L'E. Turner, 'Henry Baker, Founder of the Bakerian Lecture', *Notes and Records* **24** (1969) p. 64.

[30] C. C. Close, *The Early Years of the Ordnance Survey*, (1926) reprinted (Newton Abbott, 1969) p. 15. Anita McConnell, 'From Craft Workshop to Big Business' [2], p. 40ff; for Ramsden's workshop organization, p. 45.

[31] William Ruat to R. Simpson, Letter 25/3/1754. Correspondence between Ruat in London and Simpson in Glasgow. Glasgow University *Senate Archives*, Faculty Minutes, 1754–1755.

[32] *Ibid.*, R. to S., 4/5/1754.

[33] *Ibid.*, R. to S., 4/5/1754.

[34] *Ibid.*, R. to S., 7/2/1754 and 1/2/1755.

[35] *Ibid.*, R. to S., 25/3/1754 and 9/10/1754. The ordering of apparently 'routine' instruments for the British Transit of Venus expeditions, 1761 and 1769, indicates that the stock in hand must have been small: H. Woolf, *The Transits of Venus* (Princeton, 1959) pp. 80–81.

[36] *Ibid.*, R. to S., 8/4/1755.

[37] *Ibid.*, R. to S., 1/2/1755 and 14/8/1755.

[38] *Ibid.*, R. to S., 14/12/1754.

[39] *History of the Cost of Living* [14], p. 128.

[40] J. R. Millburn, *Benjamin Martin; Author, Instrument-Maker and 'Country Showman'* (Leiden, 1976), Chapters 4 and 6.

[41] Benjamin Martin, *General Magazine* (London, 1755) see plate. Also, B. Martin, *The Young Gentleman and Lady's Philosophy* (London, 1772), see frontispiece. Joseph Wright's paintings, *The Orrery* and *The Airpump* capture the same spirit. Benedict Nicholson, *Joseph Wright of Derby, Painter of Light*, ii (London, 1968) plates 53 and 58.

[42] C. R. Weld, *History of the Royal Society*, ii (London, 1848) pp. 187–188. Ramsden was much respected by George III, and on one occasion, according to legend, arrived one whole year late for a Royal appointment without arousing the Sovereign's displeasure.

[43] R. Symonds, *Thomas Tompion, his Life and Work* (London, 1951) p. 49.

[44] George Graham, 'A Contrivence to Avoid the Irregularities in a Clock's Motion', Royal Society Library, MS. *R.C.B 12. 739.* Dated 28/4/1726.

[45] David J. Bryden, *James Short and his Telescopes* (Edinburgh, 1968) p. 17.

[46] *Dictionary of National Biography*, see Ramsden.

[47] Maurice Daumas, *Scientific Instruments in the Seventeenth and Eighteenth Centuries*, translated by M. Holbrook (London, 1972) p. 103.

[48] *Ibid.*, p. 101.

[49] H. C. King, *A History of the Telescope* (London, 1955) p. 229.

[50] Daumas, *Scientific Instruments* [47], pp. 242–243.

10   THE TECHNICAL FRONTIER

[1] Tycho Brahe, *Astronomiae Instauratae Mechanica* (Wandesburgi, 1598), translated by H. Raeder, E. Strömgren and B. Strömgren (Copenhagen, 1946), p. 46.

[2] J. L. E. Dreyer, *Tycho Brahe, a Picture of Scientific Life and Work in the Sixteenth Century* (1890) and (New York, 1963) pp. 56–57.

[3] *Ibid.*, pp. 167–168.

[4] Isaac Newton, *The Mathematical Papers of Sir Isaac Newton*, v, edited by T. Whiteside (Cambridge, 1972) p. 525, 19/9/1685. Also, Isaac Newton, *The Correspondence of Sir Isaac Newton*, ii, edited by H. W. Turnbull, J. F. Scott, A. R. Hall and Laura Tilling (Cambridge, 1960) pp. 419–420.

[5] I. Newton, *Mathematical Papers*, vi (1974) p. xvii, also *Correspondence*, ii (1960) p. 430, 14/10/1685.

[6] I. Newton, *Correspondence*, iii (1961) p. 202, 24/2/1691–1692. *Correspon-*

dence, iv (1967) p. 87, 16/2/1694–1695; p. 103, 20/4/1695; p. 137, 2/7/1695.

[7] Francis Baily, *An Account of the Revd. John Flamsteed* (London, 1835) p. 62.

[8] Newton, *Correspondence*, iv, p. 159, 6/8/1696.

[9] Newton, *Correspondence*, iii, p. 200.

[10] Gerd Buchdahl, *The Image of Newton and Locke in the Age of Reason* (London, 1961).

[11] M. Grosser, *The Discovery of Neptune* (Cambridge, Mass., 1962) pp. 45–46.

[12] *Ibid.*, p. 81. Also, A. Chapman, 'Private research and Public Duty: George Biddell Airy and the search for Neptune', *J.H.A.* **xix** (1988) 121–139.

[13] J. G. Crowther, *Scientific Types* (London, 1968) pp. 382–386. See also Sir George Airy's correspondence with J. Challis on the 'Uranus disturbing planet', Cambridge Observatory Library, Boxfile '1846–1847, Discovery of Neptune', Letter 13.

[14] Simon Newcomb, *Popular Astronomy* (London, 1898) p. 207. Henderson at the Cape made his initial parallax observations in 1832–1833 with a mural circle; see Robert Grant, *A History of Physical Astronomy* (London, 1852) pp. 550–551.

[15] For a full description of Airy's chronograph, see J. N. Lockyer, *Stargazing*, (London, 1878) pp. 269–270. Also, Derek Howse, *Greenwich Observatory iii*; 'The buildings and instruments' (London, 1975) p. 47. In his *Popular Astronomy*, p. 155, Newcomb states that the chronograph developed from telegraphy. Though experienced 'eye and ear' transit observers could already work to 1/10 s in right ascension, the chronograph gave greater regularity, and compensated for personal errors.

[16] George Biddell Airy, *Autobiography* (Cambridge, 1896) p. 218. For a general treatment of Airy's early engineering interests, see T. J. N. Hilken, *Engineering at Cambridge, 1783–1965* (Cambridge, 1967) pp. 45–50. Allan Chapman, 'Sir George Airy (1801–1892) and the concept of international standards in science, timekeeping and navigation', *Vistas in Astronomy* **28** (1985) 321–328.

[17] W. H. M. Christie, *Astrographic Catalogue 1900: Greenwich Section* (London, 1904) pp. i–xx, also, pp. xix–xxiii, for micrometer technique. D. Howse, *Greenwich Observatory iii*, p. 95. A. J. Meadows, *Greenwich Observatory ii*, 'Recent history 1836–1975' (London, 1975) p. 49.

[18] H. C. King, *A History of the Telescope* (London, 1955) Chapters XIV–XV. Allan Chapman, 'William Herschel and the measurement of space', *Q.J.R.A.S.* **30** (1989) 399–418. Also, A. Chapman, 'William Lassell, Practitioner, patron and "Grand Amateur" of Victorian astronomy', *Vistas in Astronomy* **32** (1989) 341–370.

[19] G. B. Airy, *Astronomer Royal's Report* (London, 1859). In Airy's time, positional, not physical, astronomy dominated the work of the Royal Observatory. When Christie succeeded him in 1881, azimuth observations were cut by a half to release assistants. A. J. Meadows, *Greenwich Observatory ii* [17], p. 55.

[20] W. M. Smart, *The Riddle of the Universe* (London, 1968) pp. 196–197.

[21] For an account of the way in which graduated instruments, and the quality of their scales, imposed a research 'frontier', see Allan Chapman, 'The accuracy of angular measuring instruments used in astronomy between 1500 and 1850', *Journal for the History of Astronomy* **XIV** (1983) p. 133.

11   THE ARCHAEOLOGY OF THE GRADUATED SCALE

[1] A table of astrolabes and related circular instruments measured in this study. All are in the collection of the Museum of the History of Science, Oxford.

Number	Date	Maker or identification	Diameter (ins)	Scale error in minutes	Museum number
1	Late 16th C.	Habermel	14.31	2.37	57-84/19
2	c. 1570	Arsenius	8.28	1.25	57-84/21
3	1560	Aegidius Cuiniet	7.75	9.15	IC-224
4	1521	Anon.	5.97	8.72	IC-252
5	1585	Habermel	6.656	2.29	IC-278
6	1600	Fr. Morillard	5.78	3.14	57-84/178
7	1659	Henry Sutton	16.25	0.48	IC-313
8	1559	Thomas Gemini 'Queen Elizabeth astrolabe'	13.16	2.03	36-6
9	1565	'Nepos Gemma Frisius'	10.46	1.36	IC-229
10	c. 1450	Anon.	10.69	1.49	IC-163
11	c. 1570	Arsenius (?)	10.59	1.50	52-1
12	1558	'Io: Dom Feciolus Trident Faciebat'	5.81	7.06	73-11/2

[2] Instruments No. 1 and 10 in the above table.

[3] Instrument No. 4.

[4] Instruments No. 1, 3 and 6.

[5] Instrument No. 10. Instruments 2, 8 and 9 also bear scribing dots.

[6] Instrument No. 7.

[7] Instruments No. 3 and 4.

[8] This Equatorium, in the Liverpool City Museum, Astronomy Collection, William Brown Street, Liverpool, is described in detail, along with a full account of its astronomical functions by John D. North, 'A Post-Copernican Equatorium', *Physis* **XI** (1969) 418–457.

[9] Table of quadrants, sextants and other large-radius instruments measured in the above-mentioned study.

No.	Instrument	Date	Maker or identification	Radius (in)	Scale error in seconds	Location	Accession number
I	Equatorial	c. 1700	A. Sharp	9.31	288	N.M.M.	A73-10L/00/R22
II	Quadrant (Inner scale)	c. 1637	E. Allen (?)	24.125	239	M.H.S.	36-4/3
III	Quadrant (Constr. dots)	c. 1637	E. Allen (?)	25.00	297	M.H.S.	36-4/3
IV	Quadrant	c. 1700	Butterfield	24.90	91	Sc. Mus.	1876/1530
V	Quadrant	c. 1710	A. Sharp	59.03	55	N.M.M.	NA 5008/OM/ MI
VI	Sextant	c. 1637	E. Allen (?)	73.26	73	M.H.S.	36-4/2
VII	Quadrant	1637	E. Allen	78.05	137	M.H.S.	36-4/1

M.H.S. — Museum of the History of Science, Oxford; N.M.M. — National Maritime Museum, Greenwich, London; Sc. Mus. — Science Museum, South Kensington, London.

[10] Instruments VI and VII in the above table. Only No. VII is signed by Allen, No. VI being a companion piece in the same set.

[11] Instrument No. II.

[12] Instrument No. V.

[13] Because of the intendedly broad and thematic nature of this book, full discussion of the author's techniques and findings relating to the archaeology of the graduated scale would be out of place. Full details of his researches into both astrolabes and large radius instruments, are to be found in Allan Chapman, 'A study of the accuracy of scale graduations on a group of European astrolabes', *Annals of Science* **40** (1983) pp. 473–488, and Allan Chapman, 'The design and accuracy of some observatory instruments of the seventeenth century', *Annals* **40** (1983) 457–471.

APPENDIX 1

[1] This 'Ramsden-type' dividing engine, Accession No. *1952. 478*, was donated to the Science Museum by Mr. A. J. Bennett in 1925. Provenance unknown. Mr Bennett also donated an 'Allan engine' with a 22-in plate that may have been related to the 'self-racking' engine which won James Allen a Society of Arts medal in 1810. *Edinburgh Encyclopaedia*, x (1830) p. 353. Photostat of letter dated 6/12/1924 from A. J. Bennett to D. Baxandall, Keeper of Mathematics, Science Museum Archives; no reference given.

APPENDIX 3

[1] Allan Chapman, 'Out of the Meridian: John Bird's Equatorial Sector and the new Technology of Astronomical Measurement', *Annals of Science* **51** (1995) 431–461.

Select bibliography

Full documentation to sources is given in the notes to the chapters. The present bibliography is intended as a short guide to the principal works touching upon the field of astronomical instrumentation and accuracy. Short titles only are cited.

Nicholas Bion, *The Construction and Principal Uses of Mathematical Instruments,* Translated by Edmund Stone (London, 1758) Reprinted by the Holland Press, 1972.

John Bird, *The Method of Dividing Astronomical Instruments,* (London, 1767).

Tycho Brahe, *Astronomiae Instauratae Mechanica,* (Wandesburgi, 1598), Translated as *Tycho Brahe's description of his Instruments and Scientific Work,* by H. Raeder and E. & B. Strömgren (Copenhagen, 1946).

David Brewster, (Editor) *The Edinburgh Encyclopaedia,* (Edinburgh, 1830), See Vol. x, article 'Graduation'.

Maurice Daumas, *Scientific instruments of the seventeenth and eighteenth centuries and their makers,* translated by Dr Mary Holbrook, (London, 1972).

John Flamsteed, *The 'Preface' to John Flamsteed's 'Historia Coelestis Britannica', 1725,* Edited and introduced by Allan Chapman, (National Maritime Museum Monographs, No. 52, 1982).

Eric G. Forbes, *Greenwich Observatory,* i; 'Origins and Early History' (London, 1975).

Robert Grant, *A History of Physical Astronomy* (London, 1852).

Robert Hooke, *Some Animadversions on the First Part of Hevelius, his 'Machina Coelestis',* (London, 1674).

Derek Howse, *Greenwich Observatory,* iii; 'The Buildings and Instruments', (London, 1975).

Derek Howse, *Nevil Maskelyne, the seaman's astronomer,* (Cambridge, 1989).

E. R. Kiely, *Surveying Instruments; Their History and Classroom Use,* (New York, 1947).

H. C. King, *A History of the Telescope,* (London, 1955).

Anita McConnell, *Instrument Makers to the World. A History of Cooke, Troughton & Simms,* William Sessions (York, 1992).

A. Pannekoek, *A History of Astronomy,* (London, 1961).

Abraham Rees, *The Cyclopaedia*, (London, 1819), See articles 'Circle' 'Graduation', etc.

Robert Smith, *A Compleat System of Opticks*, (Cambridge, 1738).

E. G. R. Taylor, *The Mathematical Practitioners of Tudor and Stuart England*, and *The Mathematical Practitioners of Hanoverian England*, (Cambridge, 1954 and 1966).

David W. Waters, *The Art of Navigation in England in Elizabethan and Early Stuart Times*, (London, 1958, 1978).

Harriet Wynter & Anthony Turner, *Scientific Instruments*, (London, 1975).

Index

Abberation, 14, 98–100, 105, 166, 182, 183, 188
Académie, of Paris, 37, 38, 102–105, 111, 149
Académie, of St. Petersburg, 144, 149
Accuracy, 17, 79–81, 82ff, 100, 107
 Bird quadrant, 72–96, 92–96, 120
 Bird zenith sector, 80, 87, 88, 89, 95
 ceiling of, 98, 108, 120, 122, 146–152
 Copernicus triquetrum, 24
 circles, 108–109ff, 117–122
 eighteenth-century, 92–97, 98–107
 Flamsteed mural arc, 56–59, 96, 157, 176, 178–180
 Flamsteed sextant, 50–51, 55
 Gascoigne micrometer, 42–45
 Graham, 67–71, 92–96
 Hevelius, 32, 39–40
 Hindley engine, 125–128
 Hooke telescopic sights, 38
 horological, 89–92
 Horrox, 27
 improvements, 108–109, 113
 modern measures, 153–157
 Oxford quadrants, 96–97
 pyrometer, 78–80
 Ramsden's engine, 13ff
 Simms, 136–137
 Troughton's engine, 135, 158–159
 Tycho, 19
Adams, George, 140, 198
Adams, John Couch, 150
Admiralty, 142
Airpump, 11
Airy, George Biddell, 121, 122, 137, 151, 152, 192, 194, 195, 198, 201–202
Albetti, G., 174
Allan, James, 196, 204
Allen, Elias, 156, 203, *Plates 1 and 9*, 203
Altitude/azimuth instrument, 192
Anderson, Mr, 179
Anderson, R., 197

Anne, Queen of England, 61, 141
Animadversions on Hevelius, 37, 38, 45, 52, 124, 165, 167, 173, 175, 176, 177, 194, 195, 205
Antikythera device, 14–15, 167
Apian, Petrus, 25–26, 170, 171
Apprenticeship premiums, 140ff
Arc, Flamsteed's mural, 54–59, 139, 148, 178, *Plates*, 20–23
 accuracy, 157, 189
 collimation, 57, 86
 'sight', 54
Archaeology, of graduated scale, 153–157, 179, 203–204
Archangel, 109
Arcturus, 97
Aries, first point, 18, 19, 86, 101
Arietis α, 18
Aristotle, 147
Armagh, observatory, 120, 163, 193
Armillary sphere, 18, 19, 82, 168, *Plate 2*
Arnold, John, 91, 141
Arsenius, G.[W.], 21, 26, 171, 203
Aske, Henry, 181
Astrograph, 151
Astrolabe, 22, 91, 137, 153–157, 166–167, 203–204 *Plate 38*
Astronomer Royal, 12, 51
Astronomiae Instauratae Mechanica, 16, 18, 19, 23, 25, 167ff, 201
Astronomical Ephemeris, 176
Astronomical radius (*see also* cross-staff)
 accuracy, 28, 170–171
 by Arsenius, in Spain, 26, 171
 Horrox, 26–31
Astronomical unit, 107
Astronomy, physical, 152
Astronomy, radio, 152
Astrophysics, 12
Atmospheric conditions, 95, 187–188
Aubrey, John, 51, 177
Auzout, A., 44

Bacon, Francis, 16, 138
Baconianism, 11
Backstaff, or Davis staff, 25
Baily, Francis, 173, 175, 177, 178, 179, 180, 181, 202
Baker, Henry, 200
Baker, J. R., 175, 200
Basis Astronomiae, 64, 181, 184, 189
Bass, George, 200
Baxandall, D., 198, 204
Beam compasses, *see* Compasses
Beaver, Donald de, 168
Beckett, E. (Lord Grimthorpe), 187
Beeson, Cyril, F., 186
Bennett, A. J., 198
Bennett, J. A., 165, 167, 176, 193, 197
Bennett, John, 138
Berge, Matthew, 113, 119
Berlin, Académie, 181, 191
Berlin, Observatory, 150
Bernoulli, Johan, 138
Bessel, F. W., 88
'Big Bang' theory, 152
Bion, Nicholas, 166, 170, 185, 195, 205
Birch, Thomas, 186
Bird, John, 12, 14, 47, 70, 71–76, 77, 79, 80, 81, 84, 109, 110, 112, 116, 139, 141, 142, 143ff, 145, 149, 162–164, 166, 170, 181–184, 192, 197, 200, 204, 205
   errors, 120
   transit, 85
Bisection, 67ff, 71ff, 76, 77, 78, 79, 80, 110ff
Bode's law, 150
Borda, J. C., 118, 192
Bosmans, H., 168
Bouguer, P., 105
Bourne, William, 170
Boyle, Robert, 174
Bradbury, Savile, 199
Bradley, James, Astronomer Royal, 14, 16, 55, 57, 70, 75, 80, 82, 83, 84–87, 88, 89, 92–97, 98–100, 100–102, 142, 151, 163, 166, 177, 182–184, 188, 185–190, 200
Brahe, Tycho (*see also* Tychonic), 34, 51, 57, 58, 68, 82, 83, 95, 109, 138, 146, 147, 152, 167–173, 179, 190, 201, 205
   accuracy, 19, 52
   armillae, 18, 19
   nonius, 23
   quadrant, 17
   triquetrum, 23
Brass, lack of homogeneity, 51, 73, 76, 115
'Bread and butter', routine instrument trade, 77, 141, 143
Breakthroughs, technological, 98, 108, 120, 122, 146–152
   eras, in, 152
Breguet, Abraham Louis, 145
Breteuil, duc de, 144
Brewster, David, 129, 134, 141, 166, 181, 182, 194, 198, 199, 200, 205
Brinkley, John, 193

Britten, F. W., 186
Brooks, John, 196, 197
Brooks, Randall, C, 176
Brouncker, Viscount, 89, 186
Brown, Joyce, 141, 183, 198, 200
Browne, J., 195
Bryden, David, 201
Bugge, Thomas, 96, 118, 134, 185, 188, 192, 194, 198
Butterfield, M., 203
Burgi, Jost, 167
Burstow, 54

Calendars, 43, 58
Calvert, H. R., 198, 199
Camera obscura (foramen), 40–41
Campbell, John, 140, 199
Cantzlar (Chancellor), Richard, 17
Cape of Good Hope Observatory, 120, 150, 193
Capella, 84, 89, 99
Carte du Ciel, 151
Cary, William, 121
Cassini, J. (II), 104, 189
Cassini, J. D. (I), 103, 104
Cassini, J. D. (IV), 144
Catoptric, *see* Sights
Cavendish, Henry, 61, 106, 117, 190, 192
Cayenne, 101
Ceiling, *see* Accuracy
Challis, John, 202
Chancellor, Richard (misnamed; *see* Cantzlar)
Chapman, Allan, 166–167, 169, 170, 171, 175, 180, 187, 188, 194, 196, 197, 198, 202, 204
Charles II, King of England, 49
Chaucer, Geoffrey, 14, 21, 164, 166, 169
Chaulnes, M. F. d'A, duc du, 109–112, 113, 115, 118, 128–129, 130, 162, 170, 191, 196
Chimborazo, Mount, 105
Christie, W. H. M., Astronomer Royal, 202
Christmann, J., 174
Chronograph, galvanic (*see also* Micrometer), 151, 202
Chronometer, 141
Circle, astronomical, 64, 77, 81, 108–122, 146ff, 150–151, 152, 190–194
   Cape, 193
   repeating, 192
   reversing, 110, 114
Circle-dividing techniques, 117–122
   Römer, 62–65
   du Chaulnes, 108–112
   Ramsden, 112–114
   Troughton, 114–117
Circle, mural, 120
Circle, transit, 121, 122
Circular instruments, frameworks, conical bearings, 118, 122
City of London livery companies, 140, 144, 199, 200
Civil Engineers, Institution of, 195
Clavius, Christopher, 22, 110, 169, 181, 185
Clock, 11, 45, 57, 64, 82, 83, 85, 86, 88, 102, 105, 146ff, 172, 182, 201

cost, 142
degree, 90, 148
Flamsteed, Towneley, 49
'journeyman', 91
loud ticks, 91
winding, 49, 91
Clock-drive, 49, *Plate 17*
Clockmakers' Company, 77, 139–140ff, 181, 193, 199
Close, Charles C., 192, 194, 200
'Coaxing' technique, Ramsden, 116–117, 137
Cole, Benjamin, 134
Coimbra, equatorial, 193
Collimation, 64, 69, 74
 circle, 121
 Flamsteed arc, 57
 transits, 84–87
 zenith sectors, 87–89, 92–97, 103–104, 105–107
Comet
 1577, 20
 1681, 148
 measuring cometary positions, 162–164
Compasses,
 beam, 55, 62, 67ff, 71ff, 76ff, 78, 113–114, 131, *Plate 31*
 scribing, 68, 73, 74
 spring bow, 52, 67ff, 71ff
 'stepping', 62, 63, 76, 79, 80, 126
Conical spokes in circles, 118–119
Contarini, Jacomo, 169
Cooke, Thomas, 193, 197
Copernicus and Copernicanism, 14, 18, 20, 23, 24, 146, 147, 155–156
Copley Medal, 114, 117
Cortes, Martin, 25, 170
Cosmology and instruments, 146–152
Costs of instruments, 197
 achromatic, 192
 Bird quadrant, 142ff
 Hooke quadrant, 47
 Ramsden, 132
 Sharp, 54
Counterpoises, 117
Crabtree, William, 26, 27, 35–40, 41, 170, 172, 174–176
Craftsmen, relations between, 76, 77, 116–117, 149
De Crepulis, 22, 169
Crom, T. R., 195
Cross-checks, 48, 68ff, 70, 75, 76, 77, 79, 80, 82, 83, 108–109, 111, 112, 120
 surveyed angles, 50–51
 transits. 84–87
 zenith secotrs, 87–89, 103–105
Cross-staff (*see also* Astronomical radius), 24–26, 26–31, 170–172
 by Arsenius, in Spain, 26, 171
 Horrox, 26–28, 31
 Flamsteed, 57
Cross-wires, *see* Reticule
Crossthwait, Joseph, 59–62, 67, 157
Cudworth, William, 178
Cuff, John, 139, 142

Cumming, A., 186
Cunn, Samuel, 166
Cutlerian, lectures, 38, 39, 45
Cutter,
 dividing engine, 131ff
 'spiral', 135, 136
Cygni, 61, 150

Daumas, Maurice, 176, 201, 205
Davis, Betty M., 173
Davis, John, 171
Davis staff *or* Backstaff, 25
Dee, John, 25, 171
Delambre, J., 64, 173, 175, 181
Demainbray, Dr S. C. T., 134, 194
Denton, Cuthbert, 53
Derham, William, 37, 172, 174, 184, 195
Desagulier, J. T., 143
Diagonal scale *see* Scale, diagonal
Dickie, Mr, of Edinburgh, 142
Digges, Leonard, 169, 170
Digges, Thomas, 25, 29, 167, 172, 184
Divided instruments, obsolete, 150
Dividing (*see also under individual instruments*),
 apprenticeship, 13
 Hooke, 45–49, 52–53
 official interest in, 13, 141ff, 175
 Sharp (Flamsteed), 55–59
 time required,
  Troughton's engine, 135, 158–159
  Simms, 136–137
 value of studying, 13, 15
Dividing engine, 79, 116, 123–137, 149, 158–159, 194–199, *Plates, 34, 35, 39*
 Garret Master's, 160–161, *Plate 39*
 horological, 124, 195
 scribing tool, 126, 130, 135, 159
 self-acting, 129ff
 twentieth-century, 153ff
Dividing knife, 68, 69, 70, 73, 123
Dividing technique, *Plates 29, 30*
 du Chaulnes, 109–112
 Bird, 71–76
 Flamsteed, 55–59
 Graham, 66–71
 Hindley, 125–128
 Hooke, 45–49
 Ramsden, 112–114, 131ff
 Römer, 62–65
 Sharp, 55–59
 Sisson, 76–77
 Simms, 136
 Smeaton, 78–80
 Troughton, Edward, 114–117, 133–137
 Troughton, J., 133–135
Dividing trade, English, 111, 116–117, 138–145
Divini, E., 37, 174
Divisions, homogeneity, 80
Dollond, John, 12
 dividing engine, 134, 139
 Sarah D., wife of Ramsden, 198
Dorpat Observatory, 150

Draconis, α and δ, 103ff
Draconis, γ, 55, 57, 87, 99, 101
Drake, Stillman, 172, 173
Dreyer, J. L. E., 167, 170, 179, 190, 195, 201
Dudley, Robert, 169
Dunsink, Observatory, 91, 187

Earth,
  density, 105–106
  motion in space, 11, 20, 98, 100, 147, 148
  rotation, 17, 90, 148
  shape, 98, 102–105, 175, 184–185, 189–190
Eclipses, timed by clock, 50
Ecliptic, obliquity, 76
Eden, R., 170
Edinburgh Encyclopaedia, 134, 182, 191, 192, 194, 196, 197, 198, 200, 205
Edwards, Ernest L., 186
Ellicot, John, 184
Encyclopédie, 13, 181
Engine for ruling microsp. plates, 198–199
Equation of time, 50
Equatorial mount,
  English, 162–164, *Plate 40*
  Flamsteed, 52, *Plate 19*
  German, 164
  Hindley, 195–196
  Hook, 48–49, *Plate 17*
  Tycho, 18–19
Equatorial Sector, 119, 162–164, *Plate 40*
Equatorium, Copernican, 155–156, 203
Equinox, vernal, 18, 19, 50, 58, 86
Errors, *see* Accuracy
Ertel, E., 121
Escapement, clock, 89–92
  pin-wheel, 49
  recoil, 90
Euclid, dividing axioms, 22
  Billingsley's Ed., 169
Eye, resolution, 33, 38, 39, 40

Fale, Thomas, 21, 22, 169
Fardoils, Pierre, 125
Fisher, John R. [for J. Bradley], 188
Flamsteed, John, Astronomer Royal, 12, 14, 16, 26, 32, 34–39, 41, 42, 44, 49–62, 64, 67, 70, 74, 80, 82, 83, 86, 89–90, 91, 92, 95, 96, 100, 106, 107, 123, 139, 141, 148, 149, 157, 163, 166, 172, 173–181, 186, 187, 188, 194, 199, 201, 205
  ill-health, 52, 57
Foramen, *see* Camera obscura, 50–41
Forbes, Eric, 39, 173, 177, 190, 195, 196, 199
Fouchy, G. de, 168
France, instrument makers, 144–145
Fraunhofer, J., 164
Friction in screws, 47, 50
Frisius, Gemma, 26, 171
  'Nepos', 203
Frontier, technical, 7, 11, 12, 14–15, 34ff, 98, 108, 120, 122, 146–152
Fusee engine, *see* Dividing engine, 125–126

Galilei, Galileo, 14, 16, 34, 108, 147, 172, 173
Galle, J. G., 181
Gardiner, William, 183
Garret Master, *see under* Dividing Engine
Gascoigne, William, 27, 31, 35–40, 41–45, 46, 48, 172, 174–176
Gassendi, Pierre, 30, 170, 172
Gaythorpe, S. B., 35, 172, 173
Gazeley, W. H., 186
Gears, 167, 194–195
  Garret Master's 160–161
  Hevelius, 32, *Plate 12*
  Hooke, 46, 48, 51, 52, 57, 124, *Plate 16*
  Ramsden, 131ff
  Troughton, 134ff
Gentry and science, 138–145, 199
George III, King of England, 77, 201
German astronomy, 194
Gerson, Levi Ben, 24, 167, 169, 170
Gilbert, K. R., 194
Gimbals, 83ff, 88
Gimpel, Jean, 167
Glasgow Observatory , 91
  cost of instrument, 142–143, 200
Glorious Revolution, 138
Goldstein, Bernard R., 167, 169, 170
Göttingen Observatory, 71
Govi, D., 174
Graduation, *see* Dividing
Graham, George, 13, 22, 32, 33, 66–71, 74, 75, 76, 79–80, 81, 83ff, 88, 90, 92–97, 98, 99, 100, 101–105, 108, 109, 112, 140, 140, 142, 143, 144, 145, 163, 181, 182, 186, 189, 195, 201
'Graham School' of dividing, 70, 71, 76, 80, 88, 141
Grant, Robert, 181, 190, 202, 205
Gravitation (*see also* Newtonianism), 12, 13, 14, 58–62, 101, 102ff, 105–106
Greenwich, *see* Royal Observatory
Greenwich Park, 50
Gresham College, 12, 38, 39, 54, 87, 99, 173
Grocers' Company, 139–140ff, 199
Groombridge, S., 121
Grosser, Marton, 202
Guest, Ivor, 200
Guildhall Library, 140, 199
Gunter, Edward, 170–171
Gunter scale, 141
Gunther, Robert T., 166, 171, 182, 192, 194, 199, 200

Habermel, Erasmus, 21, 169, 197, 203
Hacking, John, 77
Hackman, W. D., 170
Hadley, John, 12, 124, 126, 127, 130, 194
Hadley octant, *see* Quadrant
Hainzel, Paul, 17
Hall, Chester Moor, 200
Halley, Edmund, 32, 33, 61, 83, 85, 86
  failure to adjust quadrant, 92ff, 101, 107, 166, 173, 175, 177, 180, 184, 185, 186, 187, 188, 190
Harriot, Thomas, 171

Harrison, John, 90, 130, 141, 200
Health, Thomas, 140
Heineken, N. S., 178
Helioscope, Scheiner's, 35
Henderson, Thomas, 150, 202
Herschel, William, 12, 150, 152, 163, 166
Hevelius, Johannes, 23, 26, 31–33, 38, 39–40, 43, 52, 56, 82, 152, 165, 170, 171, 173, 174, 177, *Plate 11*
Hilken, T. J. N., 202
Hill, Chistopher, 169
Hindley, Henry, 79, 109, 124–128, 129, 130, 136, 196
Historia Coelestis (Tycho), 21, 51
Historia Coelestis Britannica (Flamsteed), 42, 58, 59–62, 166, 172, 175, 177–182, 187, 199, 205
Historia Coelestis in Libri Duo (Halley), 61ff, 180
Hodgson, James, 59–62
Holmes, John, 127, 128, 196
Holtzapffel, Charles, 171, 197
Hooke, Robert, 11, 16, 17, 32–33, 37, 38, 39, 44, 51, 52, 54, 55, 56, 64, 65, 85, 87, 90, 99, 124–125, 127, 138, 165, 167, 173, 174, 176, 185, 189, 193, 194, 195, 199
  Flamsteed attack, 51–52
  quadrant, 45–49
Hornsby, Thomas, 84, 85, 88, 91
  daylight observations, 96, 139, 142, 162–164, 182, 183, 185, 188, 192
Horrebow, Petter, 62, 109, 181, 183, 184, 189
Horrox [Horrocks], Jeremiah, 108, 140, 148, 171, 172, 173, 174, 175, 176
  observation technique, 26–31
  transit of Venus, 29, 35–40, 48
Horsky, Z., 169
Howse, Derek, 166, 177, 185, 186, 191, 192, 193, 202, 205
Huggins, Willaim, 152
Human perception and instruments, 11
Hunter, M., 165
Hutton, Charles, 106, 190
Huygens, Christiaan, 37, 43, 44, 45, 89, 174, 176, 186

Industrial revolution, 81, 132, 136–137
Ingram, James, 183
Instrument frames,
  Bird, 71
  conical, 192
  Flamsteed, 55–70
  Graham, 70
  Ramsden, 18–19
  Tycho, 19
Instrument makers, 138–145, 193
Instruments (*see also* Accuracy), 19, 20
  study of, 14

Jedlik, Anyos, 198
Johnson, F. R., 172
Jones, Thomas, 118, 120, 192
Jupiter, 43, 44

Kamal (Arab cross-staff), 171
Kassel, Landgrave, *see* William, IV
Kater, Capt. Henry, 192
Kepler, Johannes, 16, 19, 20, 21, 27, 28, 29, 30, 146, 147, 168, 172
Kiely, E. R., 167, 169, 205
King, H. C., 166, 176, 197, 199, 201, 202, 205
Knox-Shaw, H., *et al.*, 96, 185, 192
Kopal, Z., 180
Koyre, Alexander, 172

Lansberg, Philip, 30
Law, J. R., 195
Lax, William, 114, 117, 191
Le Comte, Louis, 168
Lecturers in science, 143
Leibniz, G. W., 64
Lenoir, E., 144
Lenses (*see also* Optics and resolution), 12, 36, 74, 200
  achromatic, 12, 74–75, 117–118, 183, 192, 198,
Levere, T. 199
Le Verrier, Urbain, 19, 150, 168
Ligne, French measure, 102
Liverpool, City Museum, 155–156, 203
L'Isle, J. N de, 189
Locke, John, 149
Lockyer, Joseph N., 152, 202
London,
  Fire, 1666, 37
  Scientific Instrument Trade, 138–145
Longitude (*see also* Lunars), 49, 75, 90, 141
  Greenwich/Paris, 118–119, 193
Longitude Act, 1714, 107, 126
Longitude, Board of, 14, 112, 121, 141, 195, 197
Longomontanus, 30
Lovell, Sir Bernard, 152
Ludlam, William, 75, 76, 77, 181, 182, 183, 187
Lunar diameter, *see* Moon
Lunar theory, 98, 148, 190
  Horrox, 26, 36, 140
  Newton, 58, 60, 107
'Lunars' for longitude, 49, 107, 130, 132, 141
Lusuerg, Jacobus, 170

Macclesfield, Earl of, 77, 101–102, 142, 184
Machina Coelestis, 31ff, 38, 166, 170, 171, 173, 177
MacPike, E. F., 175
Maddison, Francis, R., 170, 171
Malvasia, Marquis, 44
Mann, J., 200
Manuel, Frank, 180
Mars, 20, 21, 25, 146
Marsh, Humphrey [de Highworth], 194
Martin, Benjamin, 143, 201
Marum, Martinus van, 138, 199
Maskelyne, Nevil, Astronomer Royal, 12, 14, 55, 61, 86, 88, 91, 93, 94, 96, 97, 105–107, 119, 130, 163, 166, 180, 184, 185, 186, 187, 190, 191, 197
  as an observer, 97
Mathematical instrument makers (*see also* 'Bread

and Butter' trade), 139–145
minor items sold by, 77
appendices, 140
premiums, 140
'dynasties', 141, 143
Maudsley and Field, 136
Maunder, E. W., 188
Maupertuis, P. L. M., 103, 107, 189
Mayer, Tobias, 88, 96, 107, 130, 190, 192
McConnell, Anita, 193, 197, 198, 199, 200, 205
McKeon, Robert, 174, 176
Meadows, A.J., 202
Measurement, 11–13, 34–35
 French units, 102–105, 183, 196
 Tychonic units, 167
Mechanica, Astronomiae Instauratae (Tycho), 16, 18, 19, 23, 25, 167ff, 201
Medina, P. de, 170
Menim, Eleanor, 198
Mercury, transit, 1630, 30–31
Mercury (metal) for pendulums, 90
Meridian *see* Collimation
Meridian, Greenwich, 122, 184, 191
Meridian mark, 83, 84ff, 105, 185
Meridional degree, 38, 47, 102–105
Micrometer, 12, 21, 31, 40–45, 52, 70, 74, 77, 79, 80, 106, 115, 128–129, 146ff, 147, 148, 150, 174–176, 177, 187, 192, 196
 chronograph, 122, 155
 duplex, 151
 engineers', 156, 157
 French, 44, 45–49
 object glass, 142
 Towneleian, 49
Micrometer,
 on quadrant, 70, 74, 93–95, *Plate 24*
 on zenith sector, 88, 89, 95ff, 104
Micrometer microscope, 62, 109–122, 128, 129, 134
Microscope,
 cost, 142
 for reading scales, 11, 63–65, 77, 110, 113, 115ff, 120, 121, 128, 129, 134, 153ff, 191
Millburn, John, 200
Möbius, A. 194
Molyneux, Samuel, 88, 89, 99
Molyneux, William, 47, 51, 174, 175, 176
Moon,
 attraction, 100
 diameter, 29, 42, 44
 node, 101, 148
Moore, Sir Jonas, 49, 51, 52, 53, 177, 178, 186
Moray, Sir Robert, 174
Morin, J.-B., 35, 37, 174
Morillard, Fr., 203
Mortimer, M., 199
Murray, C. A., 193, 202
Museum of the History of Science, Oxford, 153ff, 156–157, 162–164, 167, 169, 170, 183, 185, 198, 203–204

Nairne, Edward, 126

National Maritime Museum, London, 157, 178, 180, 197, 203
Nautical Almanac, 130, 183
Needham, Joseph, 168
Neptune, 150, 202
Newcomb, Simon, 180, 202
'New Star' 1572, *see* Supernova
Newton, SIr Isaac, 12, 30, 34, 36, 58, 59–62, 98, 99, 146, 148, 149, 171, 180, 187, 188, 195, 201, 202
 Earth, shape of, 101–104
 Royal Observatory instrument, 60
Newton's laws and Newtonianism (*see also* Gravitation), 12, 13, 14, 30, 98, 102, 105, 107, 112, 143, 147, 149
Nicholson, Benedict, 201
Nielsen, A. V., 180
Nobert, A., 199
Node, *see* Moon
Noius Scale (*see also* Nunez, Pedro), 22, *Plate 5*
North, John, 203
North polar distance, Oxford quadrant, 96, 188
Nunez, Pedro, 22, 169
Nutation, 14, 99, 100–102
 In Principia, 101, 104, 184ff, 188–189, 190

Observatories, *see under names*
Observing techniques,
 aberration, 98–100
 Bird's quadrant, 74
 circles, 108–122
 cosmology, 146–152
 eighteenth-century, 92–97
 Flamsteed arc, 54–59
 Flamsteed sextant, 50–51
 Gascoigne, 36
 Hevelius, 31–33
 Horrox, 26–31
 Maskelyne, 97
 micrometer, 40–45
 nutation, 100–102
 regulator clock, 89–92
 Römer, 62–65
 transit, 83–87
 Tycho, 20, 21
 zenith sector, 87–89
Occult circle, 71
Octagon room at Royal Observatory, 49, 90, 91
Olber's paradox, 152
Oldenburg, Henry, 39
Olmsted, J. W., 37, 175
Opera Omnia (Tycho), 18
Opitz, Laszlo, 199
Optical instrument makers, 139
Optics and eye resolution, 12, 36
Opticks, Compleat System of (Smith), 66–67, 166, 181–182, 185, 200, 206
Oughtred, William, 36
Oxford Observatory (Radcliffe), 71, 74, 84, 85, 91, 95–96, 139, 162–164, 185, 192
 instrument, 200
 sector, 162
 quadrants' cost, 142

Palermo Observatory, 119, 120
Pannekoek, A., 205
Pappus, of Alexandria, 46
Parallax, errors of instrument, 17, 27
 solar, 27, 107, 176
 stellar, 11, 12, 25, 38, 87, 99, 147, 149, 150, 180
 Ordnance Survey, 192
Paris Observatory, 102ff, 118
Patronage in instrument making, 138–145
Pearson, William, 77, 112, 113, 117, 120, 192–193
Peking Observatory, 19, 168
Pendulums (see also Temperature), 57, 82, 83, 89–92, 106, 146ff
 arc of swing, 49, 89, 90, 102, 186
 Earth, shape, 102–105, 149, 188–190
 royal, 89
Penny Cyclopaedia, 193
Perrault, Claude, 175
Peters, C. A. F., 19, 100, 189
Petit, Pierre, 44
Peuhler, 17
Philosophical Experiments (Hooke), 125
Philosophical instrument makers, 139
Philosophical Transactions of Royal Society, 13, 14, 39, 41, 44, 125, 174, 176, 179, 181
Photographic measurement, 151, 155–156
Piazzi, J., 119, 193
Picard, J., 38, 88, 103, 104, 175, 183, 186, 189
Piers of transit, 85ff, 121
Pinnacidia, see Sights, pinnule
Place, Francis, 53, 178
Planetary diameters, measuring, 29, 43, 45
Playfair, John, 106, 190
Pledge, H. T., 167, 186, 191
Pleiades, 29, 42, 43
Plumb-line wires, 86, 88, 92–97, 106
Polaris, 53–54, 55, 100, 180,
Pond, John, Astronomer Royal, 96, 120, 121, 185, 187, 188, 190, 193
Potter, Francis, 51, 177
Pound, James, 83, 157, 179ff
Prague, National Museum, 169
Precession, 18, 58, 100, 102, 104
Pressure, see Atmospheric
Price, Derek de Solla, 167, 169
Prince, C. L. 165–166, 168, 173
Principia (Newton), 60ff, 99, 101–102, 106, 148, 171, 183, 184, 188, 189
Progymnasmata (Tycho), 16, 167
Proper motions, 177
 Hooke's suspension, 47
Ptolemy and Ptolemaic system, 20, 172
Ptolemy's rulers (see also Triquetrum), 23–24
Purbach, G. von, 25
Pyrometer, 79, 184

Quadrant (see also Arc), 82, 83, 86, 87, 88, 101–102, 108ff, 123, 150, 168, 176–178, 181–184
 Bird, 71–76, 95–96, 142, 151, 200
 cost, 142
 errors, 94
 Flamsteed, 54–59

Gascoigne, 36, 42
Graham, 32, 66–71, 91–96, Plates, 27, 28, 29, 30
Hevelius, 31
Hooke,
 screws, 45–49, Plate 16
 10-foot, 52–53, Plate 18
Nonius, 22
rectification, 92–97
Römer, 64
Sisson, 76–77
Smeaton, 78–80
Troughton, 77–78
twentieth-century measures, 156–157, 203–204
Tycho, 17, 32
Quadrant, Hadley, 124, 126–127, 130, 132, 133, 135, 184, 194, 200
Quill, H., 191, 200

Radcliffe, John, 200
Radcliffe Observatory, Oxford, 162–164, 200, see also Hornsby, T.
Raistrick, A., 181
Rambaut, A. A., 185, 188
Ramsden, Jesse, 14, 71, 78, 81, 109, 116ff, 126, 128, 139, 141, 144, 145, 149, 160, 162, 190–192, 193, 196, 197, 198, 200, 201, 204
 circular division, 112–115
 dividing engine, 129–133, 136, 159, 160, 197, 198
 equatorial (Shuckburgh), 85, 109, 112, 114, 119, 132, 173, 179, 191, 192
 'Palermo' circle, 119, 120, Plate 37
 sharp practice, 119
 sixty workmen, 119, 142
Ransome and May, instruments, by, 122, 137
Rees, Abraham, 169, 182, 183, 190, 191, 192, 198, 199, 206
Regiomontanus, (Johannes Müller), 23, 25, 168
Reichenbach, G., 121, 194
Reid, Thomas, 125, 194
Reinhold, Erasmus, 40
Repsold, G. and A., 173
Reticules, in telescopic sights, 38, 39, 40, 41, 50, 74, 84, 86, 110
 candle illumination, 96
De Revolutionibus (Copernicus), 147
Richer, J., 102–103, 149, 189
Richey, M. W., 171
Rigaud, S. P. and S. J., 41, 148, 174, 176, 182, 184, 194, 200
Rittenhouse, David, 185
Rhee, Samuel, 132
Robinson, H. W., and Adams, W., 178
Roller, used in circle dividing, 115–117, 126, 135, 136
Römer, O., 32, 62–65, 83, 85, 100, 109, 118, 138, 179, 181, 184, 185
Rooke, Lawrence, 89, 186
Rose, L. P., 169
Roslund, Curt, 167
Rosse, Lord, 152
Roy, General William, 112, 116, 118, 119, 121, 191, 192

Royal Greenwich Observatory, Herstmonceux, 42, 60, 70
Royal Observatory, Greenwich, 12, 14, 16, 39, 45, 49–62, 60, 67, 71, 82, 83, 89, 90, 91, 92–97, 101, 120, 121, 122, 137, 141, 142, 148, 166, 176–181, 184–188, 190, 193, 194, 196, 200, 202
  importance to Newtonianism, 60
Royal Society, 11, 14, 32, 47, 49, 51, 54, 91, 100, 105, 114, 123, 138, 144, 175, 179
Ruat, William, 142, 143, 200
Rudolphine Tables (Kepler), 30
Rulers of parallax, *see* Triquetrum
Ryan, W., 197
Ryle, Sir Martin, 152

Sadler, D. H., 190
Safford, T. H., 96, 185, 188
St. Petersburg Académie, 144
St. Petersburg Observatory, 71, 112
St. Pierre, Sieur de, 49
Saturn, 25, 27
Scale,
  circular divisions, 21–22
  Clavius', 22
  diagonal, 17, 21, 22, 23, 31–33, 39
    Hooke's alternative, 45ff
    Flamsteed's, 51–52, 55–56
    Römer's, 63, 69, 156–157, 166
Scale,
  96-part, 66-71, 71-76, 77, 166, 182
  of parts, 71ff, 76, 77, 78, 80, 113, 182
  straight rod (*see also* Triquetrum and cross-staff), 23–32
  sub-division, 17, 21, 22, 23, 31–33, 39, 45, 51, 52, 55–56, 63, 69, 111
  sector, 115
  Vernier, 22, 23, 69ff, 74, 75, 94, 118, 169–170, 182, *Plates 11 and 28*
    Hevelius, 31–33
Scarlett, E., 200
Schaffer, S., 165, 194
Schahallion, Mount, 105–106, 180, 190
Scheiner, Christopher, 35, 174
Schöner, J., 162, 170
Science Museum, London, 158–159, 192, 194–195, 203–204
Scientific instruments,
  and social mobility, 138–145
  for cultured gentlemen, 138–145
Screw-cutting, 176
  Hindley, 124–130
  Hooke, 46–47
  Ramsden, 130–132
Screw-edged, quadrant (Hooke) (*see also* Quadrant and sextant), 45–52
Screw measurements (*see also* Micrometer), 21, 31, 40–45
  Hooke, 45–49, 50–52, 176
Screw, tangent (*see also* Wormwheel), 46
Senses, primacy of, 149
Setchell, J. R. M., 195, 196
Sextant, 57, 60, 82, 86, 88, 132, 168, 196–198

Flamsteed, 32, 50–52, 54, 55, 57, 148, 190, *Plate 19*
Gascoigne, 36–37
Hevelius, 31–32, *Plate 10*
screw-edge
Tycho's, 18, *Plate 3*
Sharp, Abraham, 33, 60, 67, 109, 139, 149, 157, 178, 179, 203
  arc, 54–59
Sheepshanks, Richard, 193
Shelton, John, 91, 105
  cost of clock, 143
Shirburn Observatory, 71, 77, 101–102
Shirley, J. W., 171
Shooter's Hill, 84
Short, James, 139, 142, 143, 144, 184, 200, 201
Shuckburgh, Sir George (*see also* Ramsden), 85, 109, 112, 114, 163, 173, 175, 185, 192, 193, *Plate 33*
Sights,
  catoptric, Hooke's 45–49
  'peg and slit', or pinnule,
    Hevelius, 32
    Tycho, 18, *Plate 6*
  telescopic (*see also* Lenses), 117, 118, 146ff, 150, 152, 174–175
    achromatic, 74–75
    French, 37
    Hevelius, 32–33, 35–40
    Morin, 35
    single-cell, 37, 38, 45–49, 50
Simms, William, 118, 122, 123, 136–137, 159, 160, 194, 197, 198
Singer, Charles, *et al.*, 176
Sirius telescope, 50
Sisson, Jeremiah, 71, 76–77, 81, 112, 140, 142, 163
Sisson, Jonathan, 70, 71, 140
Skempton, A. W., 183, 198
Skopova, O., 169
Smart, W. M., 202
Smeaton, John, 13, 23, 63, 69, 78–80, 81, 125–128, 170, 180, 183, 184, 195, 196, 197
Smiles, Samuel, 196
Smith, Adam, 139
Smith, J., 186
Smith, Robert, 13, 66–67, 166, 181, 182, 184ff, 206
Solar diameter, 27ff, 30, 40, 175–176
Solstices, 18, 58, 100
Spectacle Makers's Company, 139–140
Spectroscope, 12
Spirit level, 48, 85, 185
Stafford, J., 54
Stancliffe, John, 127, 128, 130, 159, 196
Steadman, Christopher, 140
Steady-state theory, 152
Stellar diameters, 28–29, 172
Stephenson, N., 186
Stock, J. T. 192
Stone, Edmund, 13, 96, 188
Streete, Thomas, 140
Struve, F. G. W., 150, 189
Supernova, 1572, 20, 25

Sutton, Henry, 203
Symonds, R., 201
Systema Saturni (Huygens), 37, 44, 176

Taylor, E. G. R., 171, 183, 197, 199, 206
Taylor, E. W., 192, 195, 196
Telescope, 12, 34, 35, 150, 166
  astrograph, 151
  Galilean, 35, 147
  Keplerian, 50
  reflecting, 139, 142
Telescopic sight, *see* Sights, telescopic
Temperature errors, 70, 73, 74, 79, 85, 88, 90, 112,
  114, 116, 162, 182
  pendulums, 90, 91, 102
  Sun's heat on instrument, 85
Theodolite, 105, 112, 116, 118ff, 192
Thiout, A., 195
Thoren, Victor, 168
Toise (*see also* Measures), 103ff
Tompion, Thomas, 47, 49–50, 51, 67, 91, 140, 149,
  177, 181, 186, 201
Tornea, Lapland, 103, 111
Torode, T, 167
Touch, best faculty in dividing (*see also* Vision),
  74, 79–80, 109–110, 184
Towneley, Richard, 37, 41, 42, 43, 44, 90, 174, 175
Tracking mechanisms, Hevelius, 32
Transit instrument, 64, 82, 83–87, 91, 105, 184,
  185, 192, *Plates 25, 26, 36*
  cost, 142
  Hornsby's, 200
  piers, 85, 121
  reversing, 95
Transversals, *see* Scales, diagonal
Triangulation, 50–51, 103–105, 107
  Greenwich/Paris, 118
Trinity College, Dublin (*see also* Armagh), 119,
  193
Triquetrum, 18, 146, *Plate 7*
  accuracy, 23–24
Trisection, 67, 71, 76ff, 78, 80, 110ff
Troughton, Edward, 12, 13, 77, 78, 81, 112, 113,
  114–117, 120, 121, 122, 126, 139, 145, 182, 183,
  184, 191, 192, 193, 195, 197, 198, 199
  dividing engine, 133–137, 158–159
  partnership, 134
Troughton, John, 71, 77, 78, 81, 115, 116, 140,
  158–159, 160, 198–199
  dividing engine, 133–135
  partnership, 134
Troughton and Simms, 122, 133–137, 191–192
Tupman, G. L., 19, 168
Turner, A. J., 170, 206
Turner, Gerald L'E., 198, 199, 200
Tychonic instrument, 16–33, 68, 146ff, 152, 167–
  173

Uffenbach, Z. C. von, 54, 138, 178–179, 183
Uraniborg, 17, 18, 21, 24, 82
Uranus, 12, 163, 202

Van Marum, Martinus, 199
Venus, 18, 27, 29, 179
  transit, 1639, 29–30, 107, 144, 172, 190, 200
Verbiest, Ferdianand, 19, 168
Vernier, P. (*see also* Scale, Vernier), 22
Vision, sensitivity in dividing (*see also* Touch), 80
Volkoff, Ivan, *et al.*, 173

Wadham College, Oxford, 186
Waghenaer, Lucas, 25, 170
Walker, Adam, 143
Waller, Richard, 176, 189, 195
Wallis, John, 171, 180, 189
Walther, Bernard, 25, 168
Wanstead, 83, 88, 89, 101
Ward, F. A. B., 92, 187
Watchmaking, 139
Water, density, 106
Waters, D. W., 171, 206
Watson, Samuel, 140–141, 199
Wayman, P. A., 187
Weld, Charles R., 201
Wesley, Walter, 19, 168
Westbury Observatory (see also Pond, J.), 120, 188
Westfall, R. S., 180
Whatton, A. B., 171, 173
Whiston, William, 140
Whitehead, Richard, 47
William IV, Landgrave of Kassel, 21, 57, 165, 167,
  170
Wing, Vincent, 140
Witchell, W. M., 194
Wittich, Paul, 21
Wollaston, Francis, 121, 192, 193
Woodbury, R. S., 194
Woolf, Harry, 190, 201
Worcester College, Oxford, 84
Wormwheel, 46, 52, 135, 159
  hourglass, 126, 128, 131
Wren, Christopher, 37, 44, 176
Wright, Edward, 27, 171
Wright, Joseph, 201
Wynter, Harriet, 206

Year, Flamsteed's determination of, 58

Zenith sector, 38, 57, 80, 82, 83, 87–89, 94–95,
  100–102, 105–107, 149, 188, 190, *Plate 32*
  Bradley's, 98–100
  costs, 142
  Graham's for Académie, 102–105
  Hornsby's, 200